Pure Mathematics and Statistics for Actuarial Studies

**Suitable to study for
CAA Global
Module 0 (Entry Test) Exam**

Our text is designed to provide an **effective** and **efficient** way of covering the M0 syllabus.

In this textbook we:

- Cover **all** the M0 syllabus through **focused learning objectives**

- **Explain fully** each learning objective

- Emphasise the **key skills** required to develop knowledge, comprehension and application of the subject

- Include **many worked examples** to help apply the skills developed

- Improve **understanding** using a wide range of **practice questions**

- **Provide summary solutions** to all practice questions

- **Reference all the important topics** in the **full index**

BPP
ACTUARIAL EDUCATION

Second edition November 2018

ISBN 978-0-9931718-2-6

e-ISBN 978-0-9931718-3-3

Published by

BPP Actuarial Education Limited
McTimoney House
1, Kimber Road
Abingdon OX14 1BZ

www.BPPActEd.com

BPP
ACTUARIAL
EDUCATION

Contents

Other Support for CAA Module 0 Exam

This textbook contains the essential information for students studying for the Certified Actuarial Analyst Module 0 (Entry Test) Exam. It is the main component in BPP's *Bronze Study Package for CAA students* and is also one of the key components of the *Silver and Gold Study Packages*:

	Textbook	Study Manual	Full solutions to textbook questions	Introductory and Progress Tests	Practice Exams	Online Tutorials	Tutor Support
Bronze	✓	✗	✗	✗	✗	✗	✗
Silver	✓	✓	✓	✓	✓	✗	✗
Gold	✓	✓	✓	✓	✓	✓	✓

Products explained

Textbook	This contains notes, worked examples with solutions, and practice questions with answers. The textbook covers all the published syllabus in one book, so there is no need to purchase other textbooks.
Study manual	The study manual gives you a step-by-step guide to studying each chapter of the textbook including shortcuts to help you study more efficiently. An online introductory test for each chapter helps you to focus on your key areas for learning and to make the most effective use of your study time. A progress test at the end of each chapter allows you to check regularly your understanding of the material.
Practice Exams	Realistic Practice Exams to check exam readiness.
Online Tutorials	This is a comprehensive, easily-searched collection of pre-recorded, online tutorial units. The teaching units really help you to understand the course material, and the worked examples improve your question answering skills.
Tutor Support	Expert tutor support is available through the Online Classroom's discussion forums.

1

Notation and terminology

Learning Objectives

The following learning objectives are covered in this chapter:

- Understand the meaning of standard mathematical notation and terminology.

- Understand the concept of a mathematical proof and the meaning of 'necessary', 'sufficient' and 'necessary and sufficient' as they are used in mathematical derivations.

- Know the representations and names of the letters of the Greek alphabet that are commonly used in mathematical, statistical and actuarial work.

- Understand the distinction between 'expression'/'equation'/'formula' and 'term'/'factor'.

- Understand dimensions and units of measurement.

- Understand the meaning of conventions commonly used in financial and actuarial mathematics.

- Be familiar with the concepts of quarters and tax years.

- Understanding the meaning of basic actuarial terminology.

- Understanding the meaning of Latin expressions and abbreviations that are used by actuaries.

1.1   Sets

A *set* is a collection of objects. Each object in a set is said to be an *element* of the set. We use the notation $\{a, b, c, d\}$ to denote the set that consists of the four elements a, b, c and d.

We are particularly interested in sets whose elements are numbers, *eg* the set of even numbers, $\{2, 4, 6, 8, ...\}$. The '...' notation means 'and so on'. However, we are not always able to write the elements in a set in the form of a list, even if we use the '...' notation. For example, we can't list all the values of x such that $a < x < b$. We solve this problem by using the notation (a, b) to represent the set of all numbers x such that $a < x < b$. A round bracket indicates that the endpoint of the interval is *not* included in the set. The round bracket is replaced by a square bracket if we want to include the endpoint in the set, *eg*:

• $[0, 10)$ is the set of values of x such that $0 \le x < 10$

• $[-2, 2]$ is the set of values of x such that $-2 \le x \le 2$.

In the table below, we describe some other commonly used set notation.

Symbol	Meaning
$\varnothing$	The empty set, *ie* the set that contains no elements
$\{\ \}$	Alternative notation for the empty set
$\in$	Is a member of the set *eg*, if S is the set of even numbers, then $2 \in S$
$\notin$	Is not a member of the set *eg*, if S is the set of even numbers, then $13 \notin S$
$\subset$	Is a subset of $C \subset D$ if every element of the set C is also an element of the set D
$\not\subset$	Is not a subset of $C \not\subset D$ means that the set C contains at least one element that is not an element of the set D
$\cup$	Union $C \cup D$ is the set of elements contained in set C or set D or both
$\cap$	Intersection $C \cap D$ is the set of elements in set C that are also elements of set D
$\bar{C}$	Complement of set C $\bar{C}$ is the set of elements that do not belong to set C
C'	Alternative notation for the complement of set C

Example 1.1

If P is the set of prime numbers and E is the set of even numbers, determine $P \cap E$.

Solution

A prime number is a natural number (not including 1) that can only be divided by 1 and itself. The only even prime number is 2. So:

$$P \cap E = \{2\}$$

◆◆

Some sets of numbers are used so often that they have special names and symbols associated with them and they are often written in a special font. In actuarial work, we use the following notation:

Symbol	Name	Description
$\mathbb{N}$	The set of natural numbers	$\mathbb{N} = \{1, 2, 3, 4, ...\}$
$\mathbb{Z}$	The set of integers	$\mathbb{Z} = \{..., -3, -2, -1, 0, 1, 2, 3, ...\}$
$\mathbb{Q}$	The set of rational numbers (fractions)	The set of numbers of the form $\frac{p}{q}$ where $p, q \in \mathbb{Z}$ and $q \neq 0$
$\mathbb{R}$	The set of real numbers	The set of all numbers between $-\infty$ (negative infinity) and ∞ (infinity)

Some mathematicians define the set of natural numbers to include 0 but we will use the convention that 0 is not a member of this set. A superscript '+' or '−' on symbols such as $\mathbb{R}$ refers to the positive or negative numbers within the set. So, for example:

$$\mathbb{Z}^{+} = \{1, 2, 3, 4, ...\} = \mathbb{N}$$

Example 1.2

Explain whether the following statements are true or false:

(i) $\dfrac{\sqrt{3}}{4} \in \mathbb{Q}$

(ii) $\dfrac{\sqrt{3}}{4} \in \mathbb{R}$

(iii) $\mathbb{Z} \subset \mathbb{R}$

Solution

(i)   This statement is false as $\sqrt{3}$ cannot be written in the form $\frac{p}{q}$ where p and q are integers.

$\sqrt{3}$ is an example of a *surd*, *ie* a square root that cannot be written as an integer. $\sqrt{4}$ is not a surd.

(ii)   This statement is true as $\dfrac{\sqrt{3}}{4}$ lies in the interval $(-\infty, \infty)$.

$\dfrac{\sqrt{3}}{4}$ is an example of an *irrational* number, *ie* it is a member of the set of real numbers but it is not a member of the set of rational numbers.

(iii)   This statement is true. Every integer is a real number, so $\mathbb{Z}$ is a subset of $\mathbb{R}$.   ♦♦

1.2   Logic and proofs

Instead of writing out words in full, mathematicians often use the following shorthand:

Symbol	Meaning	Example
$\forall$	For all	$x^2 > 1 \; \forall x > 1$
$\exists$	There exists	$\exists x \in \mathbb{R}$ such that $x + 1 = 5$
$\nexists$	There does not exist	$\nexists x \in \mathbb{N}$ such that $x^2 = 2$
:	Such that	$\mathbb{R}^- = \{x : -\infty < x < 0\}$
st	Such that	$\exists x \in \mathbb{R}$ st $x + 1 = 5$
$\Rightarrow$	Implies	$x = -2 \Rightarrow x^2 = 4$
$\Leftrightarrow$	Implies and is implied by (equivalent to)	$x = 0 \Leftrightarrow x^3 = 0$
iff	If and only if Same meaning as $\Leftrightarrow$	n is even iff $\dfrac{n}{2} \in \mathbb{Z}$
$\rightarrow$	Tends to (or approaches)	$\dfrac{1}{x} \rightarrow 0$ as $x \rightarrow \infty$

When the superscript '+' is used in situations such as $x \rightarrow 1^+$, it means that x is approaching 1 'from above', *ie* $x \rightarrow 1$ but is always slightly greater than 1. Similarly, $x \rightarrow 1^-$ means that x is approaching 1 'from below', *ie* $x \rightarrow 1$ but is always slightly less than 1. So, for example:

$$\frac{1}{x} \rightarrow 0^+ \text{ as } x \rightarrow \infty$$

$$\frac{1}{x} \rightarrow 0^- \text{ as } x \rightarrow -\infty$$

Writing $x \rightarrow 1$ (without a superscript of + or −) means that x is approaching 1 from either direction.

Since it is not possible to divide by 0, we say that the function $f(x) = \frac{1}{x}$ is *not defined* for $x = 0$. In practice, this usually means that the value is ∞ or $-\infty$.

When proving that a mathematical result is true, it is not enough to show that it works for a particular case. For example, when proving that:

$$a + ar + ar^2 + \cdots + ar^{n-1} = \frac{a(1 - r^n)}{1 - r}$$

it is not sufficient to choose particular values for a, r and n and show that the result holds for that choice of numbers. (This formula will be proved in Chapter 4.)

However we can prove that something is *not* true in general by showing that it doesn't work for a particular case. We call such a case a *counterexample*.

The following terminology is often used in mathematical proofs.

Necessary, sufficient, necessary and sufficient

If A is necessary for B, then $B \Rightarrow A$ (*ie* B implies A). In other words, B is true *only if* A is true.

If A is sufficient for B, then $A \Rightarrow B$ (*ie* A implies B). In other words, B is true *if* A is true.

If A is necessary and sufficient for B, then $A \Leftrightarrow B$ (*ie* A implies and is implied by B). In other words, A and B are equivalent statements, or A is true *if and only if* B is true.

Let's illustrate this with an example. Suppose that:

A is the statement 'the integer x ends in a 5'

B is the statement 'the number x is divisible by 5'

Then A is sufficient for B, as every integer ending in 5 is divisible by 5.

However, A is not necessary for B, since there are integers that don't end in 5 that are divisible by 5, *eg* 10.

So we can write $A \Rightarrow B$ but not $B \Rightarrow A$.

1.3   *Mathematical constants*

The number e is an important irrational number. To display its value on most calculators, we press $\boxed{e^{\square}}$ or $\boxed{e^x}$ or $\boxed{\text{exp}}$, then $\boxed{1}$ and $\boxed{=}$. However, on some calculators, $\boxed{1}$ must be pressed first.

The value of e is:

2.718281828...

Although a calculator shows only 10 or so figures, the decimal representation of e never ends and never settles into a repeating pattern.

As n increases, the quantity $\left(1+\dfrac{1}{n}\right)^n$ becomes closer and closer to e. We can write this mathematically as follows:

$$\left(1+\frac{1}{n}\right)^n \rightarrow e \text{ as } n \rightarrow \infty$$

An alternative way of expressing this result is:

$$\lim_{n\to\infty} \left(1+\frac{1}{n}\right)^n = e$$

We'll talk more about this notation in Chapter 3.

The number e is the base used in natural logarithms. We will study logarithms in Chapter 4.

Another important irrational number is π. To display its value on most calculators, we press $\boxed{\pi}$ then $\boxed{=}$. The value of π is:

3.141592654...

Like e, the decimal representation of π never ends and never settles into a repeating pattern.

Although the number π is defined to be equal to the ratio of the circumference of a circle to its diameter, it also appears frequently in formulae from statistics and other branches of mathematics.

1.4   *Greek letters*

Many Greek letters are used in actuarial work. The most frequently used letters, their symbols and common usage are given below:

Letter	Lower case	Common usage	Upper case	Common usage
alpha	α	parameter		
beta	β	parameter	B	beta function
gamma	γ	parameter	Γ	gamma function
delta	δ	small change	Δ	difference
epsilon	ε	small quantity		
theta	θ	parameter		
kappa	κ	parameter		
lambda	λ	parameter		
mu	μ	mean, mortality rate		
nu	ν	mortality rate when sick		
pi	π	= 3.141592654…	Π	product
rho	ρ	correlation coefficient, recovery rate		
sigma	σ	standard deviation, sickness rate	Σ	sum
tau	τ	parameter (usually pronounced as in first syllable of 'tower' but sometimes pronounced as in 'tall')		
phi	ϕ or φ	probability density function of standard normal distribution	Φ	cumulative distribution function of standard normal distribution
chi	χ	χ^2 distribution (pronounced as first syllable of 'Cairo')		
psi	ψ	probability of ultimate ruin		
omega	ω	limiting age in a life table		

1.5   *Expressions, equations, formulae, terms and factors*

It is important to understand the distinction between mathematical expressions, equations and formulae as well as the difference between terms and factors.

◆ *Expressions*

A mathematical *expression* is any combination of mathematical symbols, *eg*:

$$2+2, \quad 1.09^{25}, \quad x+2y, \quad a(b-c)$$

Usually expressions involve more than one symbol and many expressions include letters. Expressions may not contain the 'equal to' sign or any type of inequality.

◆ *Equations*

An *equation* is a statement concerning the equality of two expressions. Some examples of equations are given below:

$$2+2=4, \quad 1.09^{25}=8.6231, \quad x+2y=-5, \quad a(b-c)=ab-ac$$

In word processing packages the word 'equation' is often used more generally to mean anything containing mathematical symbols, which is not strictly correct.

◆ *Formulae*

A *formula* is a special type of equation that shows the relationship between different quantities. For example, the formula for area of a triangle is as follows:

$$area = \frac{1}{2} \times base \times height$$

A formula often uses letters to represent the variables. For example, the formula for the circumference of a circle is:

$$C = 2\pi r$$

In this formula, C denotes circumference and r denotes radius.

◆ *Terms and factors*

A *term* is an element in an expression that is *added* or *subtracted*. For example, the terms in the expression $ab-ac$ are ab and ac.

A *factor* is an element in an expression that is *multiplied* or *divided*. For example, the factors in the expression $a(b-c)$ are a and $b-c$. A numerical factor appearing in an expression, such as the 3 in $3x^2$, is also sometimes called a *coefficient*.

1.6   Dimensions and units of measurement

The units in which we measure a value, (*eg* pounds, metres, years, kilograms), affect the numerical value given, *eg* lengths of 2.7m and 270cm represent the same quantity. This creates problems when we wish to compare values, since we need to ensure that they are measured in the same units, and this conversion can be complicated (*eg* converting a speed in 'metres per second' into one in 'miles per hour').

Dimensions are used to show what a numerical value actually represents. For example, we would say that 2.7m and 270cm both have the dimension of length, and an area (measured in units m^2 or cm^2) has the dimension length squared. In actuarial work the dimensions usually involve currency and time. For example, if it was stated that the average annual salary in the UK was £20,000, the units of this would be pounds per year.

Numbers or coefficients (including constants such as π and e) have no dimension and they are referred to as *dimensionless*.

We can only add or subtract quantities if they have the same dimension. For example, we cannot add £2 and 5 years together. If the units are different, we will need to convert them to a consistent basis, *eg* when adding 2m and 500cm, or £2 and $5.

If two values that have the same dimension are divided, then the resulting value is dimensionless. This is true of percentages and proportionate errors. These will both be studied in Chapter 5. Other values that are used in actuarial work that are dimensionless include the coefficient of skewness. We will define coefficient of skewness in Chapter 15.

Dimensions can give us a convenient way of working out if a formula is correct.

Example 1.3

Determine the dimension of the average (or mean) length of life of a particular type of light bulb.

Solution

The mean is calculated by summing a set of lifetimes and dividing by the number of lifetimes considered, *ie* $\bar{x} = \dfrac{1}{n}\sum_{i=1}^{n} x_i$, where $\bar{x}$ represents the mean, n is the number of lifetimes considered and x_i is the lifetime of the i th light bulb. The dimension of the life of an individual bulb is time, and n is dimensionless (as it is just a number) so the dimension of the mean is time. Typically, the average lifetime of bulbs would be measured in hours.   ♦ ♦

We can also use dimensions to work out how the result of a formula will be affected if the values of the components are rescaled, *eg* multiplied by 10.

Example 1.4

A garden maintenance company charges for cutting lawns according to the area of the lawn cut. One of the grass cutters has said 'Two customers have doubled the length and width of their lawns, so we can double our charge for them'. Determine if the statement is true or not.

Solution

The charge is based on the area. The dimension of area is length squared. If the length and width of a lawn have each doubled, the area has been multiplied by 4 and not 2, so the statement is wrong.   ♦ ♦

1.7   Conventions used in financial and actuarial mathematics

There are many conventions and abbreviations used in financial and actuarial mathematics including those described below.

◆ Abbreviations used for large monetary amounts

Abbreviations are used for thousands and millions to save writing many zeros. For example, £9K means £9,000 (the 'K' comes from the 'kilo' prefix seen in words such as kilometre, meaning 1,000 metres) and $6.2m means $6,200,000. This is used in preference to using *scientific notation* (or *standard form*), where $6,200,000 would be written as 6.2×10^6.

◆ Interest rates

If interest rates were 6% in January, 8% in February and $7\frac{3}{4}$% in March, this might be described as an increase of 2 percentage points, followed by a reduction of 25 basis points (one basis point being one-hundredth of a percentage point). Basis points are sometimes abbreviated to bps. This terminology avoids confusion when we are talking about quantities expressed as percentages. If we said that the interest rate of 6% in January had increased by 2% in February, this could mean that the rate in February was $6 \times 1.02 = 6.12\%$.

◆ Negative amounts of money

In accounting, negative amounts of money are represented by placing them in brackets. For example, consider the following simple income statement for a company. This is sometimes called a *profit and loss account*. Tax and dividends represent negative cashflows from the company's point of view and hence they are shown in brackets.

	£
Pre-tax profit	9.6m
Tax	(2.4m)
Net profit	7.2m
Dividends	(1.7m)
Retained profit	5.5m

The instruction 'calculate the profit (loss) made last year' means we have to calculate the difference between the income received by the company and the payments it made, writing the answer as a positive number if there is a profit, or writing the answer in brackets if there is a loss.

Example 1.5

The cashflows for a retailer over the last month are as follows:

	£
Sales	2.7m
Wages	(0.9m)
Rent	(0.8m)
Bills (other than rent)	(0.4m)

Calculate the retailer's profit or loss for this month.

Solution

The profit is:

$$2.7 - 0.9 - 0.8 - 0.4 = £0.6\,m \text{ or } £600,000 \qquad \blacklozenge\blacklozenge$$

◆ Change in a quantity

Δ is used to denote a change in a quantity, for example Δ profit = £534K means that the profit has risen by £534,000 and Δ profit = £(534K) means that the profit has fallen by £534,000 .

1.8 Time intervals

◆ Quarters

Many organisations divide each calendar year into four quarters for budgeting and accounting purposes. The quarters are defined as follows:

> Quarter 1 (Q1) runs from 1 January until 31 March
>
> Q2 runs from 1 April until 30 June
>
> Q3 runs from 1 July to 30 September
>
> Q4 runs from 1 October until 31 December

In actuarial calculations where payments are made quarterly it is normally sufficiently accurate to assume that each quarter is exactly $\frac{1}{4}$ of a year long.

◆ Tax years

In the UK, the amount of tax payable by individuals is calculated based on the transactions during each *tax year* (or *fiscal year*), which runs from 6 April to 5 April. So, for example, the 2014/15 tax year is the period from 6 April 2014 to 5 April 2015 (both days inclusive).

Tax years differ between countries, *eg* the New Zealand tax year runs from 1 April to 31 March.

Here's an example involving time intervals that an actuary might need to calculate.

Example 1.6

(i)   Five payments are made at 9-month intervals with the first payment on 1 January 2014. On what date will the final payment be made?

(ii)   Calculate the length of the period from 1 March 2005 to 28 February 2015.

Solution

(i)   There are 4 periods of 9 months between the 5 payments. This is a total period of 36 months, or 3 years. So the final payment will be made on 1 January 2017.

(ii)   The length of this period is 10 years.   ♦ ♦

In actuarial notation, a fixed period of time is represented by using a right-angle symbol, so that '5 years', for example, is represented by $\overline{5|}$. This may be used as a shorthand notation. For example, writing 'the pension incorporates a $\overline{5|}$ guarantee' means 'the pension includes a 5-year guarantee'.

Any dates shown in abbreviated form in this course will use the European date format DD/MM/YYYY, not the American format MM/DD/YYYY. So 06/04/2014 refers to 6th April 2014, not 4th June 2014.

1.9   Glossary

In this glossary, we list some terminology and Latin abbreviations that are widely used in actuarial work.

◆❯ Basic actuarial terminology

The BASIS for an actuarial calculation is used to mean the set of assumptions (*eg* mortality rates, interest rates) used in the calculation.

A LIFE just means a person.

A FIRST-CLASS LIFE is a person in perfect health. Otherwise, they are IMPAIRED.

IMMEDIATE is the opposite of 'deferred'. It doesn't necessarily mean 'straight away'. A 'deferred pension' would normally start making payments a number of years in the future. An 'immediate pension' would make the first payment at some time during the coming year, but not necessarily at the start of that year.

LEVEL means constant, *eg* 'level payments' are for the same amount each time.

A NET payment is one where something has been deducted. Net monthly pay generally refers to the amount of your 'take home' pay after your employer has deducted any amounts due in tax, pension contributions *etc*. Your GROSS monthly pay ignores these deductions. In actuarial contexts the words 'net' and 'gross' are used a lot and need not refer to tax. On seeing the word 'net', the question to ask is 'net of <u>what</u>?', *ie* what is it that has been deducted?

An OFFICE (short for LIFE OFFICE) just means an insurance company.

OUTGO is (very logically) the opposite of INCOME.

The word PAYABLE means '*must* be paid' rather than '*may* be paid'. For example: '£1,000 tax is payable on 31 January' doesn't mean there is an option; it means the tax must be paid on that date.

The word SECULAR is used to mean, 'in relation to time measured by reference to the calendar'. It clarifies the meaning when time could be measured relative to some other reference point, *eg* the time since you were born or since you took out your life insurance policy (which is called the DURATION). So, for example, the statement 'Mortality can be expected to improve over an individual's lifetime because of secular effects', means that in the future people are likely to live longer than in previous generations, as over time, there are likely to be medical advances.

STOCHASTIC means allowing for random variation over time. It is the opposite of DETERMINISTIC.

◆ *Latin expressions and abbreviations*

PER ANNUM is a common phrase meaning 'each year', *eg* 'Some actuaries are paid more than £100,000 *per annum'*. The abbreviation *pa* is universally recognised. We also use *pm* (for 'each month'), *pcm* (for 'each calendar month') and *pq* (for 'each quarter'), but these are not so well known.

PRO RATA means in proportion. For example, 'Your pension will be calculated as 1/60th of your salary for each year of service, with months counting *pro rata'* means that, if an individual worked for 5 years and 5 months (say), this would be counted as $5\frac{5}{12}$ years of service in the calculation. It is also used as a verb, *eg* 'We can *pro rata* the payments to allow for holidays'.

VICE VERSA means 'the other way round'.

eg. This means 'for example' and is used when giving an example that could have been one of several.

ie. This means 'that is' and is used to clarify exactly what is meant.

cf. This means 'compare'. For example, 'Using the approximation, I got £73.98 (*cf* £74.02 when calculated accurately).'

Chapter 1 Practice Questions

◆ Sets, logic and proofs

Question 1.1

List the elements in the set $\{x \in \mathbb{N} : -1 \le x < 5\}$.

Question 1.2

Consider the following subsets of the set $\{1, 2, 3, 4, 5, 6, 7, 8, 9, 10\}$:

$$A = \{2, 4, 6, 8\}$$

$$B = \{1, 2, 3, 4\}$$

$$C = \{1, 3, 6, 10\}$$

List the elements of $\{1, 2, 3, 4, 5, 6, 7, 8, 9, 10\}$ in the set $(A \cap \bar{B}) \cup C$.

Question 1.3

Decide whether each of the following statements is true or false.

(i)   Ending in 5 is a necessary condition for an integer to be a multiple of 5.

(ii) $\{x : x \in \mathbb{Z}, x^2 = 4, x \ne 2\} = \varnothing$

(iii) $x^2 - 5x + 7 > 0, \forall x \in \mathbb{R}$

Question 1.4

X is the statement "the integer x is odd", Y is the statement "the integer x is divisible by 3". Which one of the following statements is true?

A   X is necessary for Y

B   X is sufficient for Y

C   X is necessary and sufficient for Y

D   none of the above

◆ Greek letters

Question 1.5

Which Greek letters are used to represent sums and products?

◆ Dimensions and units of measurement

Question 1.6

The variance of a set of values $x_1, x_2, ..., x_n$ is defined to be $\dfrac{1}{n-1}\sum_{i=1}^{n}(x_i - \bar{x})^2$, where

$\bar{x} = \dfrac{\sum_{i=1}^{n} x_i}{n}$. If x represents the length of life of a light bulb, determine the dimension of variance.

Question 1.7

Given the definition of the variance in Question 1.6, decide which of the following could be other possible equivalent formulae for variance by considering dimensions.

(i) $\dfrac{1}{n-1}\left(\sum_{i=1}^{n} x_i^2 - \bar{x}^2\right)$

(ii) $\sum_{i=1}^{n} x_i^2 - (n-1)\bar{x}$

(iii) $\dfrac{1}{n-1}\sum_{i=1}^{n} x_i^2 - \dfrac{1}{n-1}\bar{x}\sum_{i=1}^{n} x_i$

Question 1.8

In the following equations, k is measured in £, α is a dimensionless quantity and λ is a quantity of unknown dimension:

$$\kappa_1 = \frac{\alpha}{\lambda} + k, \quad \kappa_2 = \frac{\alpha}{\lambda^2}, \quad \kappa_3 = \frac{2\alpha}{\lambda^3}$$

(i)   Determine the dimensions of λ to make κ_1 meaningful.

(ii)   Hence, determine the units of measurement of κ_1, κ_2 and κ_3.

(iii)   Determine the value of the constant c that would make the quantity $\dfrac{\kappa_3}{\kappa_2{}^c}$

        dimensionless.

◆ Conventions used in financial and actuarial mathematics

Question 1.9

In June, interest rates were 2%. They rose by 40 basis points in July. What was the interest rate after this change?

◆ *Time intervals*

Question 1.10

Ten payments of $100 are made at half-yearly intervals. The first payment is made on 1 September 2013. Determine the date of the last payment.

2

Numerical Methods I

Learning Objectives

The following learning objectives are covered in this chapter:

- accurately rounding numbers
- the use of an electronic calculator
- estimation
- monetary abbreviations.

2.1   Rounding

In this chapter we consider conventions about rounding and accuracy, in particular rounding a number to a fixed amount of *decimal places* or *significant figures*. Obtaining an accurate answer is very important to an actuary, so rounding is more important in actuarial studies than it is in, say, undergraduate university mathematics courses. However, we should not use accuracy that is not valid, for example quoting the price of something as £2.78643 is not appropriate.

One of the first things we need to make clear is the use of commas and full stops in numbers. In some countries (continental Europe in particular) commas and full stops in numbers are used with the opposite meaning from in the UK and the US, ie in Europe the decimal point is written as a comma and full stops (or spaces) are used to separate a large number. For example, a German person would write $\pi = 3,142$ and the population of Germany is approximately 82.000.000. We will use the UK notation, as that will be used in UK actuarial exams.

◆ *Decimal places*

We may have to round a numerical answer to a given number of *decimal places* (DP).

We start counting the decimal places *immediately after the decimal point*, so that the second decimal place for the number 34.576 is 7. We have to truncate the number after the required number of decimal places and decide if we have to round the last digit up or keep it the same. We follow the rule 'if the *next* digit is at least 5, round up, otherwise keep it the same'. So the number 34.576 rounded to two decimal places is 34.58 – the third digit after the decimal point is 6 so we round the 7 up to 8.

When we write a number as 6.00, it implies that we believe it is correct to 2DP, ie the exact value lies somewhere in the range [5.995, 6.005) (the square bracket meaning that the number can be exactly equal to 5.995).

Example 2.1

Round the following numbers to two decimal places: 3.784, 15.239, 6.028, 6, 2002, –0.399 .

Solution

The answers are 3.78, 15.24, 6.03, 6.00, 2002.00, –0.40.   ◆◆

In all of these answers there are two figures (digits) after the decimal point.

◆ *Significant figures*

Instead of rounding to a certain number of decimal places, we may have to round a number to a given number of *significant figures* (SF).

We start counting the significant figures at the *first non-zero digit*, so that the second significant figure for the number 34.576 is 4 and the second significant figure for the number 0.002587 is 5. We have to truncate the number after the required number of significant figures and decide if we have to round the last digit up or keep it the same. We follow the same rule as we had for decimal places: 'if the *next* digit is at least 5, round up, otherwise keep it the same'. So the number 34.576 rounded to two significant figures is 35 – the third significant figure is 5 so we round the 4 up to 5. The number 0.002587 rounded to two significant figures is 0.0026 – the next digit after the second significant figure is 8 so we round the last digit (5) up to 6.

Example 2.2

Round the following numbers to two significant figures: 3.784, 15.239, 6.028, 6, 2002, −0.399 .

Solution

The answers are 3.8, 15, 6.0, 6.0, 2000, −0.40.   ♦♦

2.2   Use of a calculator

It is important to be able to use a calculator accurately and efficiently. In this section we will give many examples of different types of calculations encountered in actuarial exams. It is important to study these examples actively, inputting the values into your own calculator and making sure you can reproduce our results, rather than just reading the examples through passively.

We are not going to cover how to use a particular calculator as there are several different calculators allowed in the exams. Please choose a permitted calculator and practise using that model. If you have lost your instruction book, many can be downloaded from the internet.

We need to keep accurate values for intermediate stages of any calculations so that no accuracy is lost.

Example 2.3

Calculate $6.23^{1.4} + 5.8^{3.6}$ to 4DP.

Solution

The answer is 573.1474.

Hints: Use the power key, $\boxed{x^y}$ or $\boxed{y^x}$. Brackets may be needed to arrive at the correct answer depending on the calculator being used.   ♦♦

Example 2.4

Calculate $\left(1 + \sqrt[4]{1.723}\right)^{5.1}$.

Solution

The answer to 3DP is 49.091.

Hints: Use the root key, $\boxed{\sqrt[x]{}}$ or $\boxed{x^{1/y}}$, and the power key, $\boxed{x^y}$ or $\boxed{y^x}$. On many calculators we need to enter 4 followed by $\boxed{\sqrt[x]{}}$ followed by 1.723 to get $\sqrt[4]{1.723}$. If your calculator doesn't have the root key, treat the expression as $(1 + 1.723^{\frac{1}{4}})^{5.1}$ and use the $\boxed{x^y}$ or $\boxed{y^x}$ key.   ♦♦

Example 2.5

Calculate $\left(1+\dfrac{2}{3}\right)^2$.

Solution

The answer is $2\dfrac{7}{9}$ or to 3DP 2.778.

Hints: Most calculators have a fraction key $\boxed{a\,{}^b\!/_c}$, which can be helpful in evaluating expressions such as this one. However, be aware that different models of calculator perform calculations in different orders when fractions are involved.   ♦♦

Example 2.6

Calculate $\left(\dfrac{4}{7}+\ln 5.2\right)^2$.

Solution

The answer to 3DP is 4.929.

Hints: Most calculators have a squared key $\boxed{x^2}$ to avoid having to use the power key. Some calculators might have a key labelled $\boxed{\log_e}$ rather than $\boxed{\ln}$. This is called the natural logarithm and we will look at this function again later in this textbook.   ♦♦

Example 2.7

Calculate $\sqrt[4]{\dfrac{2}{3}e^{3.1}}$.

Solution

The answer to 3DP is 1.961.

Hints: Some calculators have e^x and ln on the same key. Press $\boxed{\text{SHIFT}}$ to get the function written above the key (on some calculators the $\boxed{\text{SHIFT}}$ key is called '2nd function' or is marked in a different colour). On most calculators, to get $e^{3.1}$, we need to type $\boxed{e^x}$ followed by 3.1 followed by = or Ans.   ♦♦

Example 2.8

Calculate 4!

Solution

The answer is 24.

Hints: 4! is read as 'four factorial'. There should be a factorial key $\boxed{n!}$ on your calculator. Be aware that $n!$ means $n\times(n-1)\times(n-2)\times\cdots\times1$. So $4!=4\times3\times2\times1=24$.   ♦♦

Example 2.9

Calculate $\tanh 2$ and $\tanh^{-1} 0.4$.

Solution

The answers to 3DP are $\tanh 2 = 0.964$ and $\tanh^{-1} 0.4 = 0.424$.

Hints: These are hyperbolic tangents and inverse hyperbolic tangents respectively. Type $\boxed{\text{hyp}}$ first. Some calculators give options at this stage so select the correct function. ♦♦

Example 2.10

Calculate $\dfrac{15.2 - 3.74}{2.7 + 19.86} \pm \sqrt{\dfrac{4^2 - 1.68 \times 2.49}{3}}$.

Solution

The answers to 3DP are 2.493 and −1.477.

Hints: We can use brackets for the first part of the expression and the memory function for the second, or the memory for both parts. ♦♦

When substituting a value for a variable that occurs several times within an expression, it can be helpful to use a shortcut called 'nested multiplication'. The following example shows what this shortcut involves.

Example 2.11

Calculate $v + 3v^2 + 7v^3$ when $v = 0.9259 \left(= \dfrac{1}{1.08} \right)$.

Solution

We can do this as a nested multiplication:

$$v + 3v^2 + 7v^3 = v + v^2(3 + 7v)$$
$$= v[1 + v(3 + 7v)]$$

Start by multiplying v by 7, then add 3, then multiply by v, then add 1, and finally multiply by v. The answer to 3DP is 9.055. ♦♦

2.3   Estimation

We have looked at how to use a calculator efficiently and accurately, but it is always possible to make a mistake. So it is important to have a rough idea of what the numerical answer to a calculation is likely to be. To do this, we round the numbers in the question to a sensible level of accuracy and then carry out the calculation **without** using a calculator.

Example 2.12

Estimate the value of $\dfrac{2.7^2 + 3.1^4}{5.2 - 7.8}$.

Solution

$\dfrac{2.7^2 + 3.1^4}{5.2 - 7.8}$ is roughly $\dfrac{3^2 + 3^4}{5 - 8} = \dfrac{9 + 81}{-3} = -30$.

The actual answer to 1DP is –38.3.   ◆◆

We need to be careful estimating values when the calculation involves:

- subtracting two numbers of a similar size

- dividing by a small number

- raising a number to a high power

since the estimated values and accurate values may not be very close together.

Example 2.13

Estimate the value of the following calculations, then calculate the accurate answers correct to 3DP:

(i) $\dfrac{1 - 1.004^{-25}}{0.004}$

(ii) $\left(\dfrac{4.378}{2.293}\right)^{10}$

Comment on the numerical values obtained.

Solution

(i)   Rounding the numbers to 1 SF we get $\dfrac{1 - 1^{-25}}{0.004} = 0$. The accurate value is 23.746.

(ii)   Rounding the numbers to 1 SF we get $\left(\dfrac{4}{2}\right)^{10} = 1{,}024$. The accurate value is 643.750.

The estimated values are not very close to the accurate answers, so the estimates are not very useful.   ◆◆

When numbers have been rounded, and are subsequently used in a calculation, the final answer is affected by the rounding. Therefore, when answering questions, it is essential to realise how accurately to quote your final answer. For example, if all the figures in the question are given to three significant figures, do not give your final answer to five significant figures.

2.4   Convenient abbreviations

When we have to deal with very large numbers, we can end up writing out several zeros. For example, 45.3 million pounds is written as £45,300,000. We will often find it more convenient to work in thousands or millions. We can write £000s to mean thousands of pounds, and £m to mean millions of pounds.

Example 2.14

Calculate the value of $T = Pv^9 + \dfrac{R(1-v^8)}{i}$ when $P = £14,000$, $R = £700$, $v = \dfrac{1}{1+i}$, and $i = 0.05$. Work in £000s.

Solution

Working in £000s, $P = 14$ and $R = 0.7$. Then $T = \dfrac{14}{1.05^9} + \dfrac{0.7\left(1 - \dfrac{1}{1.05^8}\right)}{0.05} = 13.549$ or in other words T is £13,549 to the nearest pound.   ◆◆

Example 2.15

If $A = 4,000$, calculate $\sqrt{A^2 + 2,000A + 1,000^2}$

(i)   directly

(ii)   working in units of 1,000.

Solution

(i) $\sqrt{25,000,000} = 5,000$

(ii)   In units of 1,000:

$1,000^2$ becomes $1^2 = 1$, $2,000$ becomes 2 and A becomes 4

The calculation is then done as follows:

$$\sqrt{4^2 + 2 \times 4 + 1} = \sqrt{25} = 5$$

ie the 'real' answer is 5,000.   ◆◆

Chapter 2 Practice Questions

◆ *Decimal places and significant figures*

Question 2.1

Round these numbers to 3 decimal places:

       0.0678, 15.3489, 9.9999

Question 2.2

What is 2.89951 rounded to 3 decimal places?

Question 2.3

Round these numbers to 3 significant figures:

       14.3678, 5.9879, 0.08006

Question 2.4

What is 4,716 rounded to 3 significant figures?

Question 2.5

What is £1,495,000,000 rounded to 2 significant figures?

Question 2.6

What is 0.020581 rounded to 2 significant figures?

◆ *Use of a calculator*

Question 2.7

Calculate $\dfrac{1-(1.04)^{-3.5/12}}{0.04/1.04}$, giving the answer to 6DP.

Question 2.8

Calculate $\dfrac{1}{2}\ln\left(\dfrac{1+0.1}{1-0.1}\right)$, giving the answer to 3DP.

Question 2.9

Calculate $\tanh^{-1}0.6$, giving the answer to 3DP.

Question 2.10

Calculate $\dfrac{1-(1+i)^{-n}}{i/(1+i)}$ where $i = 0.062$ and $n = 10$, giving the answer to 3DP.

Question 2.11

Calculate $\dfrac{100}{(1.035)^{10}} + \dfrac{17\left(1 - \dfrac{1}{1.035^{10}}\right)}{\ln 1.035}$, giving the answer to 3DP.

Question 2.12

Calculate $\dfrac{6!}{3} + 4^{5/12} + \sqrt[4]{20}$, giving the answer to 4SF.

Question 2.13

Calculate $\dfrac{10!}{7!2!}$.

Question 2.14

Calculate the value of $\dfrac{1}{0.8\sqrt{2\pi}}\exp\left[-\dfrac{1}{2}\left(\dfrac{\ln 5 - 1.02}{0.8}\right)^2\right]$ giving the answer to 3DP.

Question 2.15

Evaluate $\dfrac{\dfrac{1-v^n}{d} - nv^n}{i}$, given that $i = 0.10$, $n = 10$, $v = (1+i)^{-1}$ and $d = iv$, giving the answer to 2DP.

Question 2.16

Calculate $v + 2v^2 + 5v^3 + 6v^4$, when $v = 0.9091 \left(= \dfrac{1}{1.1}\right)$, giving the answer to 4SF.

Question 2.17

Calculate $6v + 8v^2 + 10v^3 + 12v^4$ where $v = \dfrac{1}{1.08}$, giving the answer to 3SF.

◆ *Estimation*

Question 2.18

Estimate the value of $\dfrac{2+\sqrt{(3.789^2+2.5)^{4.5}}}{5.5-2.1^3}$ and then calculate the accurate value, giving the answer to 3DP.

Question 2.19

Estimate the values of $\dfrac{3\pm\sqrt{(-3)^2-4\times2\times-4}}{2\times2}$ and then calculate the accurate values, giving the answers to 3DP.

Question 2.20

The rules of a pension scheme state that employees who leave the company before retirement age are entitled to receive an annual pension payable monthly from retirement age. The amount of each payment is calculated using the formula:

Pension payment = Pension entitlement at date of leaving $\times1.05^t$

where t is the number of complete calendar years between the date of leaving and the date of payment. Pension payments are made on the first day of each month, starting in the month following the member's 60th birthday.

One member's details are as follows:

Sex = Male   Date of birth = 14.04.1956   Date of leaving = 23.07.2003

Pension entitlement at date of leaving = £3,620 per annum

(i)   Calculate the amount of the first pension payment this member will receive and write down the date on which this will be paid. (Assume that all months are of equal length.)

(ii)   Calculate the total amount of pension this member will receive during the first ten years of retirement assuming that he is alive throughout that period. Apply a reasonableness check to your answer.

◆ *Convenient abbreviations*

Question 2.21

The interest rate i charged for a financial arrangement satisfies the following equation:

$$43,600,000(1+i)^{10} = 12\times10\times366,000(1+i)^5 + 60,192,000$$

By working in units of 1 million, or otherwise, calculate the value of i, expressing your answer as a percentage to 3SF.

3

Mathematical constants and standard functions

Learning Objectives

The following learning objectives are covered in this chapter:

- The definitions and basic properties of the functions x^n, c^x, $\exp(x)$ and $\ln x$.

- The functions $|x|$, $[x]$, $\max(...)$ and $\min(...)$.

- The concept of a limit and the notation used for limits.

3.1   *Exponential function*

The *exponential function* is used extensively throughout mathematics. In actuarial science we will use it in statistical distributions and in evaluating the present and accumulated values of cashflows, amongst other things.

Definition of the exponential function

The exponential function, e^x, can be defined by:

$$e^x = \lim_{n \to \infty} \left(1 + \frac{x}{n}\right)^n$$

or by the series expansion $e^x = 1 + x + \dfrac{x^2}{2!} + \dfrac{x^3}{3!} + \cdots$.

These formal definitions are not needed most of the time, since e is just a number which we can determine from a calculator.

Example 3.1

Calculate the value of the following:

(i) e^1

(ii) $e^{4.3}$

Solution

(i)   Using a calculator, $e^1 = 2.718$.

(ii)   Using a calculator, $e^{4.3} = 73.700$.   ♦♦

We can use a convenient alternative notation, $e^x = \exp(x)$, if the power is a long expression.

For example, $e^{-\frac{1}{2}\left(\frac{x-\mu}{\sigma}\right)^2} \equiv \exp\left[-\frac{1}{2}\left(\frac{x-\mu}{\sigma}\right)^2\right]$. This makes the expression clearer to read.

However, we cannot mix up these two notations by writing something like $\exp^x$, as this is meaningless.

The graph of $y = e^x$ is shown below:

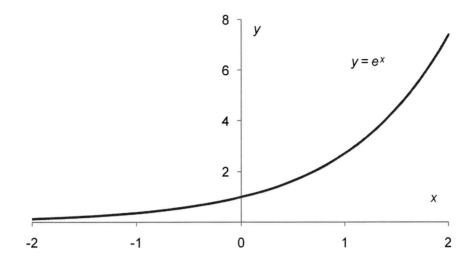

By looking at the graph, we can see that e^x can never be negative. This is because we can never get a negative answer if we raise a positive number to any power.

Key properties of the exponential function

From the graph, we can see that:

- e^0 is 1

- as x becomes large and positive, $e^x \to \infty$

- as x becomes large and negative, $e^x \to 0$.

3.2   *Other functions where x is the power*

Since e^x is just 'a number to the power of x', then the shape of the graph of e^x is also the basic shape of the graph of $y = c^x$, where c is any positive number greater than 1. However, we might also want to sketch the graph of $y = c^x$ where c is a positive number less than 1, which will look different from the graph of the exponential function.

The diagram overleaf shows the graphs of $y = 2^x$ and $y = 0.5^x$. The two numbers 2 and 0.5 have been deliberately chosen to be the reciprocal of each other (*eg* $\dfrac{1}{0.5} = 2$).

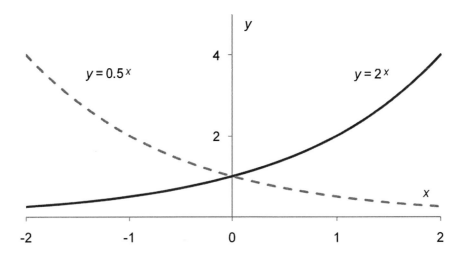

From the graphs, we can see several key features. Firstly, the graph of $y = 0.5^x$ is the mirror image (*reflection*) in the y-axis of the graph of $y = 2^x$. Secondly, both graphs have an intercept of 1, *ie* they cross the y-axis at 1. Lastly, as x becomes large and positive, $2^x \to \infty$, and as x becomes large and negative, $2^x \to 0$ (and the opposite is true for 0.5^x).

Key features of the graphs of functions with x in the power

If c is a positive number greater than 1:

- the graph of $y = \left(\dfrac{1}{c}\right)^x$ is the mirror image in the y-axis of the graph of $y = c^x$

- the graphs of $y = \left(\dfrac{1}{c}\right)^x$ and $y = c^x$ have an intercept of 1, *ie* they cross the y-axis at 1

- as x gets large and positive, $c^x \to \infty$ and as x gets large and negative, $c^x \to 0$

- as x gets large and positive, $\left(\dfrac{1}{c}\right)^x \to 0$ and as x gets large and negative, $\left(\dfrac{1}{c}\right)^x \to \infty$.

Remember that $\left(\dfrac{1}{c}\right)^x$ is the same as $\dfrac{1}{c^x}$ or c^{-x}. Similarly, $\left(\dfrac{1}{e}\right)^x = \dfrac{1}{e^x} = e^{-x} = \exp(-x)$.

3.3   *Log function*

The *logarithm* (or *log*) of a number is the power to which another fixed value (called the *base*) must be raised to produce that number. For example, log base 10 of 1,000 is 3, because 1,000 is the value of 10 raised to the power 3. This can be written as $\log_{10} 1,000 = 3$. If a log has a base of e, then it is referred to as the *natural log* and is written as $\ln$. In fact in actuarial work we will always use log base e (in other words ln) so if you see 'log' without a base indicated, you can assume that this also means the natural log. However, on most calculators the $\boxed{\text{log}}$ key means log base 10 and you must use the $\boxed{\text{ln}}$ key if you want a log base e. We will be looking further at bases of logarithms in Chapter 4. Here we will just concentrate on the graphs of log functions and some key properties that can be seen from them.

The graph of the natural logarithm function, $y = \ln x$, looks like this:

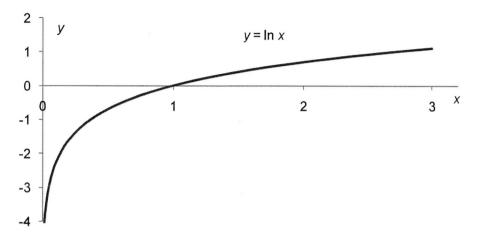

Key properties of the logarithm function

From the graph, we can see that:

- $\ln 1 = 0$

- $\ln a$ where $a \leq 0$ is not defined

- It is an increasing function

- $\ln x \rightarrow \infty$ as $x \rightarrow \infty$

- $\ln x \rightarrow -\infty$ as $x \rightarrow 0$.

These properties apply to logarithms of any base, so even though we have used 'ln' we could equally well have used the notation 'log'.

3.4   Inverse functions

An inverse function is a function that reverses the original function. For example, if the function is 'add 2 to a number' then the inverse must be 'subtract 2 from the number'. A function is written as $f(x)$ and the inverse of $f(x)$ is written as $f^{-1}(x)$. Because the inverse function reverses the original function we must have $f^{-1}(f(x)) = x$

Example 3.2

If $f(x) = x^2 + 3$:

(i)   Determine $f^{-1}(x)$.

(ii)   Show directly that $f^{-1}(f(4)) = 4$.

Solution

(i)   The function is 'square the value of x then add 3', so the inverse function is 'subtract 3 from the number and square root':

$$f^{-1}(x) = \sqrt{x-3}$$

For more complicated functions, we can find the inverse by letting the function equal, say, y, and then making x the subject of the resulting equation. Here we would have $y = x^2 + 3$. So $x = \sqrt{y-3}$, giving $f^{-1}(y) = \sqrt{y-3}$ or $f^{-1}(x) = \sqrt{x-3}$.

(ii)   We first need to calculate $f(4)$:

$$f(4) = 4^2 + 3 = 19$$

Then we need $f^{-1}(19)$:

$$f^{-1}(19) = \sqrt{19-3} = \sqrt{16} = 4$$ ♦♦

Recall the earlier sections on the exponential and natural logarithm functions. The exponential function is the inverse of the natural logarithmic function so that $e^{\ln x} = x$.

3.5   Powers of x

We have so far only looked at graphs of a number raised to the power of x. Now we will look at graphs of x raised to the power of a number. The shape of the graph will depend on whether the number is an odd or even number, a positive integer, a negative integer, zero or a fraction.

◆ *The power is an even positive integer*

Consider, for example, the graph of $y = x^4$ shown below:

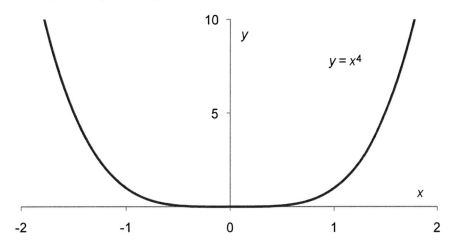

The graph of $y = x^4$ is symmetrical about the y-axis, since $(-x)^4 = x^4$ for all values of x.

The graph of $y = x^n$, where n is *any* even positive integer has the same general shape as this graph. The values of y for such functions can never be less than zero because negative numbers raised to a positive power are always positive.

The graph of $y = x^n$, where n is *any* even positive integer goes through the origin.

◆ *The power is an odd positive integer*

Now consider, for example, the graph of $y = x^3$ shown below:

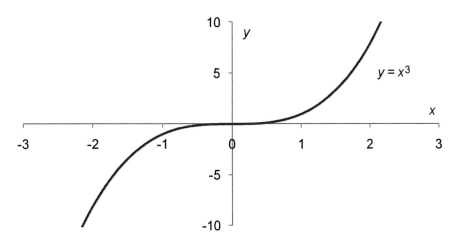

The graph of $y = x^3$ is not symmetrical about the y-axis. In this case $(-x)^3 = -\left(x^3\right)$ for all values of x. However, we can obtain the graph for the negative values of x by *rotating* the graph for the positive values of x by $180°$ around the origin.

The graph of $y = x^n$, where n is *any* odd positive integer has the same general shape as this graph and also goes through the origin.

◆ *Odd and even functions*

A function $f(x)$ which has the property $f(-x) = f(x)$ is called an *even function*. An example of an even function is $f(x) = x^4$, since $f(-2) = (-2)^4 = 16 = 2^4 = f(2)$. Graphs of even functions are symmetrical about the y-axis.

A function $f(x)$ which has the property $f(-x) = -f(x)$ is called an *odd function*. An example of an odd function is $f(x) = x^3$, since $f(-2) = (-2)^3 = -8 = -(2)^3 = -f(2)$. Graphs of odd functions are *not* symmetrical about the y-axis.

Odd and even functions

$f(x)$ is an even function if $f(-x) = f(x)$ for all values of x.
$f(x)$ is an odd function if $f(-x) = -f(x)$ for all values of x.

However, most functions are neither even nor odd.

Example 3.3

Is $f(x) = x^5$ an odd or even function?

Solution

We will calculate $f(-2)$ and $f(2)$ to work out the answer:

$$f(-2) = (-2)^5 = -32 \qquad\qquad f(2) = 2^5 = 32$$

Since $f(-x) = -f(x)$, $f(x)$ is an odd function.   ◆◆

◆ *The power is an odd negative integer*

We will now consider negative powers, so we will be using the fact that $x^{-n} = \dfrac{1}{x^n}$. It is important to understand how this function behaves as x gets close to zero.

Example 3.4

Calculate the value of $f(x) = x^{-3}$ for the following values of x:

(i)   0.5   (ii)   0.1   (iii)   0.01

Solution

(i) $f(0.5) = 0.5^{-3} = \dfrac{1}{0.5^3} = 8$

(ii) $f(0.1) = 0.1^{-3} = \dfrac{1}{0.1^3} = 1{,}000$

(iii) $f(0.01) = 0.01^{-3} = \dfrac{1}{0.01^3} = 1,000,000$ ♦♦

So we can see from Example 3.4 that, as x gets closer to zero from above, *ie* from the positive side, the function $y = x^{-3}$ tends towards infinity. Similarly, we could put in negative values for x and find that, as x gets closer to zero from *below*, *ie* from the *negative* side, the function $y = x^{-3}$ tends towards minus infinity.   So we say that the graph of this function has a *discontinuity* at $x = 0$. The graph of $y = x^{-3}$ is shown below. The discontinuity (where the two halves of the graph do not join up) is clear:

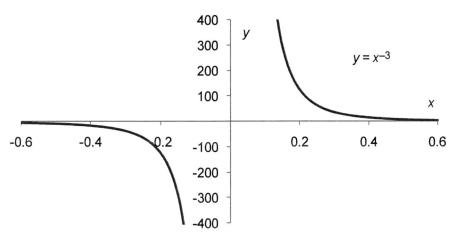

◆ *The power is an even negative integer*

Example 3.5

Plot a graph of $y = x^{-4}$.

Solution

This graph will also have a discontinuity at $x = 0$. However, the graph of this function will be symmetrical about the y-axis as it is an even function. The graph is shown below:

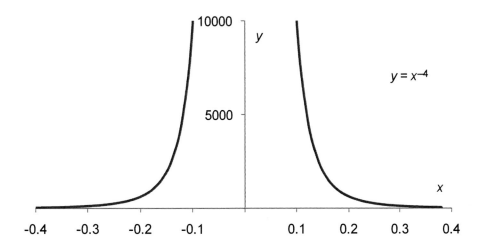

◆ *The power is a fraction*

We will now consider fractional powers, so we will be using the facts that $x^{\frac{m}{n}} = \sqrt[n]{x^m}$ and $x^{-\frac{m}{n}} = \dfrac{1}{\sqrt[n]{x^m}}$. Graphs with fractional powers have to be considered individually. Usually the values for these are not defined for negative values of x. The most important of these functions is the square root function $y = x^{0.5}$ (or $y = \sqrt{x}$) which is shown below.

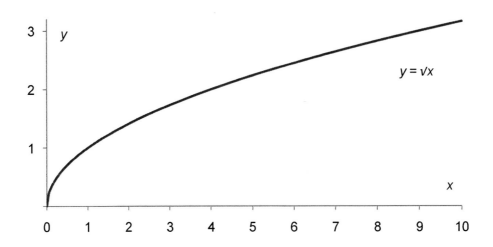

This graph does not exist for negative values of x since a real value of the square root of a negative number cannot be found.

Note that $y = \sqrt{x}$ is the inverse function of $y = x^2$. If we plot $y = x^2$ we will see that it is the reflection of the graph of $y = \sqrt{x}$ in the line $y = x$, as shown in the following graph.

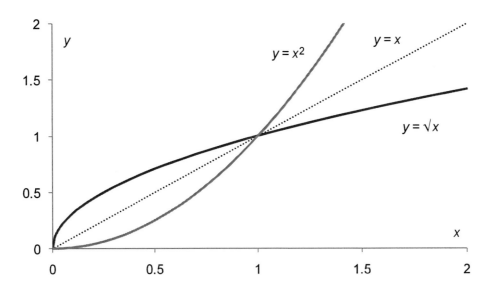

The same relationship applies to the graphs of any inverse functions. Look back at the graphs of $\ln x$ and e^x to see another example of this.

Graphs of inverse functions

The graph of the inverse of a function is always the reflection of the graph of the function in the line $y = x$.

Now let's look at where the power is a negative fraction. For example, the graph of $y = x^{-0.5}$ is shown below:

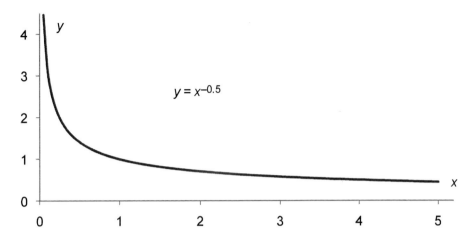

The value of $y = x^{-0.5}$ tends to infinity as x tends towards 0.

Summary of graphs of power functions

We can sketch the shape of the graphs of power functions by considering several key factors.

- If the power function is of the form $f(x) = c^x$ (where x is the power) consider if c is greater than 1 or not and whether it is positive or negative.

- If the power function is of the form $f(x) = x^n$ (where x is being raised to a power) consider if n is an even positive/negative integer, an odd positive/negative integer or a positive/negative fraction.

3.6   Limits

In the last section we looked at how some functions behave as x gets close to zero, for example, $f(x) = x^{-3}$. We face a problem because the function cannot be directly calculated at the value $x = 0$. It doesn't always have to be $x = 0$ that causes a problem, for example, $f(x) = \dfrac{1}{x-1}$ cannot be directly calculated at the value $x = 1$.

To investigate what happens at these problem values of x, we need to consider what happens as we get closer to, or *approach*, that value of x. The behaviour may be different depending which side we approach from, so we must consider separately approaching from above or below.

Considering the function $f(x) = \dfrac{1}{x-1}$, mentioned above, when x is slightly bigger than 1, say

$x = 1+\varepsilon$, where ε is a small positive number, then $f(x) = \dfrac{1}{\varepsilon}$. As ε gets smaller, in other words

when x gets closer to 1, $f(x)$ will get larger and larger. This is a long-winded way of saying what happens, so we use a shorthand notation, called the *limit notation*. To specify which direction we are approaching from, we use $x \to 1^+$, which means that x is approaching 1 from above. So here we can write:

$$\lim_{x \to 1^+} \frac{1}{x-1} = \infty$$

In words, we can say $\displaystyle\lim_{x \to 1^+} \frac{1}{x-1} = \infty$ as 'the limit as x tends to 1 from above of $\dfrac{1}{x-1}$ is ∞' or

alternatively we can say '$\dfrac{1}{x-1}$ tends towards ∞ as x tends to 1 from above'.

Example 3.6

(i)   Explain what the notation $\displaystyle\lim_{x \to 1^-} \frac{1}{x-1}$ means.

(ii)   Evaluate $\displaystyle\lim_{x \to 1^-} \frac{1}{x-1}$.

Solution

(i) $\displaystyle\lim_{x \to 1^-} \frac{1}{x-1}$ means the limit of the function $\dfrac{1}{x-1}$ as we approach $x = 1$ from below.

(ii)   When x is slightly smaller than 1, say $x = 1-\varepsilon$, where ε is a small positive number,

then $\dfrac{1}{x-1} = \dfrac{1}{-\varepsilon}$. As ε gets smaller, in other words when x gets closer to 1, $\dfrac{1}{x-1}$ will

get more and more negative.

So $\displaystyle\lim_{x \to 1^-} \frac{1}{x-1} = -\infty$.   ♦♦

In order to find limits, we can consider the numerical value of the function close to the limit. For instance, in the last example we could substitute in, say, 0.9, 0.99, 0.999 and so on. This will often give us some idea of whether the limit is finite or not (and if so, what its value is). Look back at Example 3.4 to see an example of this.

If the function we are considering has the same limit from both sides, we can just write $\displaystyle\lim_{x \to 1}$,

without a '+' or a '−'. Also, if the limit involves x (or another letter or parameter) tending to ∞ or $-\infty$ then it will not be possible to consider approaching from above and below because, for example, we cannot have a value of x greater than ∞. In such cases we just have one limit to consider.

Example 3.7

Evaluate $\lim\limits_{x\to\infty} e^{-x}$.

Solution

As x gets larger, e^{-x} gets smaller, so $\lim\limits_{x\to\infty} e^{-x} = 0$, which ties in with what we saw in Section 3.1, where e^x tends to 0 as x becomes large and negative.   ♦♦

Sometimes we might have a complicated function which we can manipulate so that it becomes easier to determine the limit.

Example 3.8

(i)   Evaluate $\lim\limits_{\sigma\to\infty} \dfrac{\frac{n}{\sigma^2}}{\frac{n}{\sigma^2}+\frac{1}{\sigma_1^2}}$.

(ii)   Evaluate $\lim\limits_{n\to\infty} \dfrac{\frac{n}{\sigma^2}}{\frac{n}{\sigma^2}+\frac{1}{\sigma_1^2}}$.

Solution

(i)   As σ increases, $\dfrac{n}{\sigma^2}$ gets smaller, so $\dfrac{n}{\sigma^2}$ tends towards 0. This means that $\dfrac{\frac{n}{\sigma^2}}{\frac{n}{\sigma^2}+\frac{1}{\sigma_1^2}}$ tends to $\dfrac{0}{0+\frac{1}{\sigma_1^2}}$ which is 0.

Alternatively, we can manipulate the function first as it can make the limit easier to determine. We are going to multiply the numerator and the denominator of the fraction $\dfrac{\frac{n}{\sigma^2}}{\frac{n}{\sigma^2}+\frac{1}{\sigma_1^2}}$ by $\sigma^2\sigma_1^2$ so that we can eliminate the fractions:

$$\frac{\frac{n}{\sigma^2}}{\frac{n}{\sigma^2}+\frac{1}{\sigma_1^2}}\times\frac{\sigma^2\sigma_1^2}{\sigma^2\sigma_1^2}=\frac{n\sigma_1^2}{n\sigma_1^2+\sigma^2}$$

As σ increases, the denominator $n\sigma_1^2+\sigma^2$ increases with no upper bound, which means that the value of $\dfrac{n\sigma_1^2}{n\sigma_1^2+\sigma^2}$ decreases to zero. So we have:

$$\lim\limits_{\sigma\to\infty}\frac{\frac{n}{\sigma^2}}{\frac{n}{\sigma^2}+\frac{1}{\sigma_1^2}}=0$$

(ii)   As n increases, $\dfrac{n}{\sigma^2}$ gets bigger, so $\dfrac{n}{\sigma^2}$ tends towards ∞. This means that $\dfrac{\frac{n}{\sigma^2}}{\frac{n}{\sigma^2}+\frac{1}{\sigma_1^2}}$

tends to $\dfrac{\infty}{\infty+\frac{1}{\sigma_1^2}}$ which is difficult to evaluate.

However, we can manipulate the function by multiplying the numerator and the

denominator of the fraction $\dfrac{\frac{n}{\sigma^2}}{\frac{n}{\sigma^2}+\frac{1}{\sigma_1^2}}$ by $\dfrac{\sigma^2\sigma_1^2}{n}$ to give:

$$\frac{\frac{n}{\sigma^2}}{\frac{n}{\sigma^2}+\frac{1}{\sigma_1^2}} \times \frac{\sigma^2\sigma_1^2/n}{\sigma^2\sigma_1^2/n} = \frac{\sigma_1^2}{\sigma_1^2+\frac{\sigma^2}{n}}$$

As n increases, $\dfrac{\sigma^2}{n}$ tends to 0, so that $\dfrac{\sigma_1^2}{\sigma_1^2+\frac{\sigma^2}{n}}$ tends to $\dfrac{\sigma_1^2}{\sigma_1^2+0}=\dfrac{\sigma_1^2}{\sigma_1^2}=1$. So we

have:

$$\lim_{n\to\infty}\frac{\frac{n}{\sigma^2}}{\frac{n}{\sigma^2}+\frac{1}{\sigma_1^2}}=1$$ ◆◆

3.7   Transformations

A *transformation* occurs when we adjust the x-values or the y-values on the graph of a function, for example by multiplying them by 2 or adding 5. We are now going to consider how to sketch graphs of transformed functions using standard results. We will consider transformations of the function $y = x^2$, which has the graph shown below. On each subsequent graph we will show the graph of the original function $y = x^2$ (as a dotted curve) so that we can easily see the effect of the transformation.

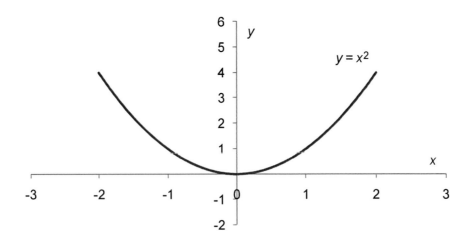

◆ *Add a constant to the function*

The graph of $y = x^2 + 1$ is shown below:

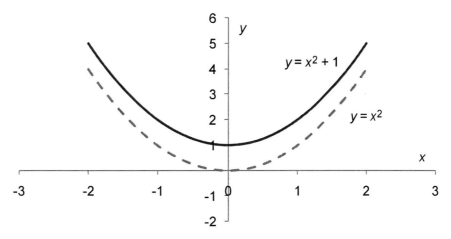

The graph of $y = x^2 - 1$ is shown below:

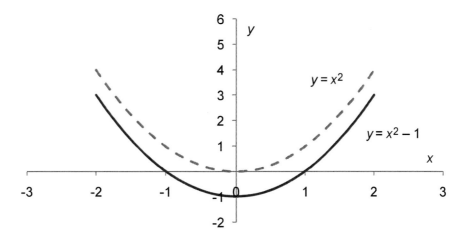

So, adding a value to or subtracting a value from the function causes a *vertical translation* (*ie* slide) either up or down in the y direction.

◆ *Add a value to x*

The graph of $y = (x+1)^2$ is shown below:

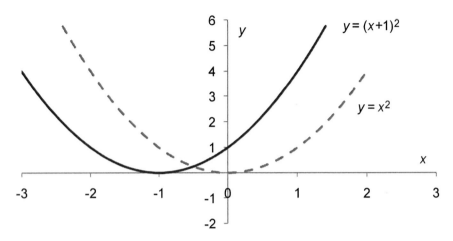

The graph of $y = (x-1)^2$ is shown below:

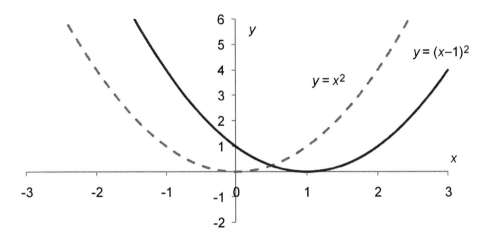

So, adding a value to x or subtracting a value from x causes a horizontal translation (*ie* slide) either to the left or right in the x direction. Be careful about which direction the graph moves here. Adding to the value of x causes the graph to move to the *left* (in the negative direction), whereas subtracting from it causes the graph to move to the *right* (in the positive direction).

◆ *Multiply the function by a constant*

The graph of $y = 1.5x^2$ is shown below:

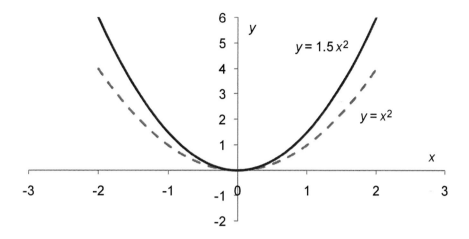

We can see that multiplying the function by 1.5 has 'stretched' the original graph vertically, *ie* in the y direction.

The graph of $y = 0.5x^2$ is shown below:

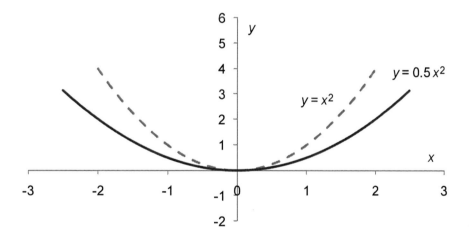

Here we can see that multiplying the function by 0.5 has 'squashed' the original graph vertically, *ie* in the y direction.

So, multiplying the function by a constant a causes a stretch in the y direction by a factor of a.

◈ *Multiply x by a value*

The graph of $y = (1.5x)^2$ is shown below:

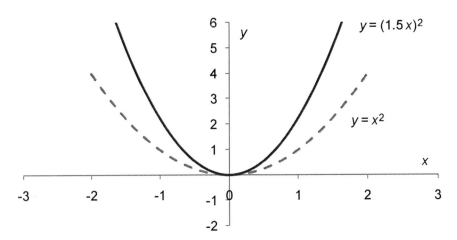

We can see that multiplying x by 1.5 has 'squashed' the original graph horizontally (*ie* in the x direction).

The graph of $y = (0.5x)^2$ is shown below:

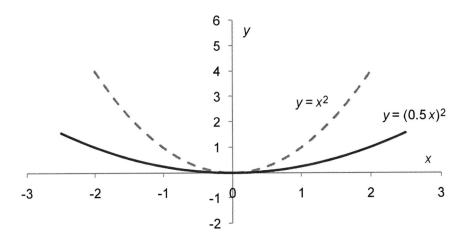

We can see that multiplying x by 0.5 has 'stretched' the original graph in the x direction.

So, multiplying x by a constant b causes a stretch in the x direction by a factor of $\dfrac{1}{b}$.

We need to be careful about which way this works: multiplying the x-values by a number smaller than 1 *reduces* the y-values, whereas multiplying by a number greater than 1 *increases* them.

Summary of transformations

The standard graph of $y = f(x)$ can be transformed as follows:

- $y = f(x) + d$ causes a vertical translation (*ie* slide), of amount d

- $y = f(x + c)$ causes a horizontal translation left, of amount c

- $y = af(x)$ causes a vertical stretch by a factor of a

- $y = f(bx)$ causes a horizontal stretch by a factor of $1/b$ (*ie* the graph is squashed by a factor of b).

In general, constants *outside* the function affect the function vertically (*ie* in the y direction), whereas constants inside the function affect it horizontally *ie* in the x direction).

Example 3.9

Describe what the graphs of $y = 2f(x)$ and $y = f(2x)$ look like in relation to the graph of $y = f(x)$.

Solution

The graph of $2f(x)$ will have all vertical distances doubled.

The graph of $f(2x)$ will have all horizontal distances halved.   ◆◆

3.8   Modulus function

$|x|$ is defined as the *modulus* of x (it is also called the absolute value of x). This means that we ignore any negative sign, for example, $|-4| = |4| = 4$.

Example 3.10

Sketch the graph of $y = |x|$.

Solution

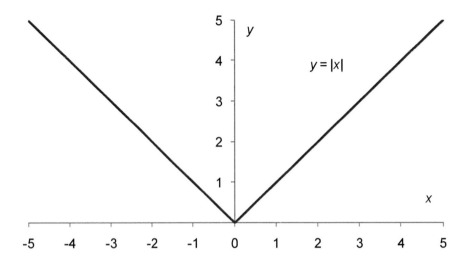

Note that $|x| < c$ is the same as saying $-c < x < c$ because x can only be: a positive number in the range $(0,c)$, a negative number in the range $(-c,0)$, or 0.

Example 3.11

Write the inequality $|2x - 1| < 3$ without the use of the modulus sign.

Solution

$|2x - 1| < 3 \quad \Rightarrow \quad -3 < 2x - 1 < 3$

This can be further simplified as follows:

$$-3 < 2x - 1 < 3 \quad \Rightarrow \quad -2 < 2x < 4 \quad \Rightarrow \quad -1 < x < 2$$ ♦♦

We will cover inequalities more fully in the next chapter.

3.9   Integer part

$[x]$ is defined as the *integer part* of x, for example $[2.89]$ is 2. Actuaries might use this to give the complete number of years that someone has lived.

When dealing with the integer part of *negative* numbers we need to check whether $[x]$ really means the integer *part*, so that $[-\pi] = -3$, or whether it means the *greatest integer not exceeding x*, so that $[-\pi] = -4$. The second definition is the more common.

Example 3.12

A baby boy was born on 26 November 1979. If x is defined to be his exact age, what is $[x]$ on 11 February 2012?

Solution

On 11 February 2012 his exact age is between 32 and 33 years, because his 32nd birthday was on 26 November 2011. So $\lceil x \rceil$ is 32.   ♦♦

3.10   Max and min

The notation max(…) or min(…) is used to denote the largest or smallest of a set of values. In insurance these functions can be used to define the amount of a claim paid out by an insurer.

Example 3.13

An insurer will pay out a maximum of 100 on any individual claim. This means that for any individual claim of less than 100 the insurer pays out the whole amount, and for any individual claim greater than 100 the insurer pays out 100. Write the amount that the insurer pays in terms of the max(…) or min(…) notation.

Solution

Let X be the amount of an individual claim. The insurer will pay out:

$$\begin{cases} X & \text{if } 0 \le X < 100 \\ 100 & \text{if } \quad X \ge 100 \end{cases}$$

that is, the *smaller* of the two quantities X and 100. We can write this as $\min(X,100)$.   ♦♦

Example 3.14

What values does the function $\max(x+2,10)$ take for values of x in the region $0 \le x \le 20$?

Solution

We could write $\max(x+2,10)$ as:

$$\begin{cases} 10 & \text{if } \quad 0 \le x < 8 \\ x+2 & \text{if } \quad 8 \le x \le 20 \end{cases}$$

♦♦

We can also use the abbreviation $(x-100)^+$, for example, to represent $\max(x-100,0)$. This notation can be useful in the context of reinsurance or insurance policies where an 'excess' is applied.

Chapter 3 Practice Questions

◆ *Exponential and log functions*

Question 3.1

Which of these is the graph of $y = e^{-x}$?

A

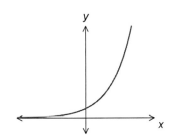

B

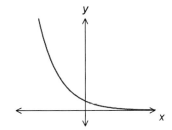

C

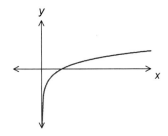

D

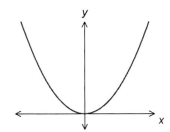

Question 3.2

Evaluate each of the following:

(i) $e\sqrt{e}$

(ii) $\ln 0.00001$

◆ Powers of x

Question 3.3

Which of these is the graph of $y = \dfrac{1}{x^n}$ where n is an odd positive integer?

A

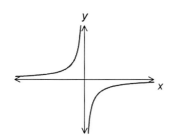

B

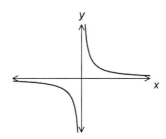

C

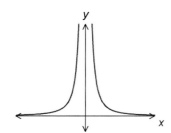

D

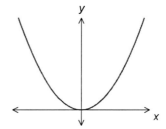

Question 3.4

State whether each of the functions below is an odd function, an even function or neither.

(i) $f(x) = 4x^5$

(ii) $f(x) = (x + 1)^2$

(iii) $f(x) = 3x^4 + 1$

Question 3.5

Sketch the graph of $y = x^{\frac{1}{3}}$ for $x \geq 0$.

◆ Limits

Question 3.6

Determine the value of $\displaystyle\lim_{x \to \infty} \frac{x^2 - 3x + 2}{3x^2 - 4x}$.

Transformations

Question 3.7

Sketch the graphs of the following functions:

(i) $y = x^{-1}$

(ii) $y = 3x^5$

(iii) $y = e^{4x} + 1$

(iv) $y = \ln(1 + x)$

(v) $y = (x - 3)^4$

Question 3.8

If the dotted line represents the graph of $y = f(x)$, which of these is the graph of $y = f(2x - 1)$?

A   B

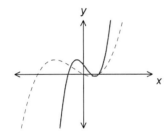   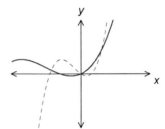

C   D

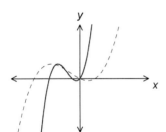   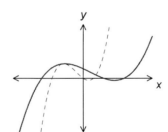

Modulus function, integer part and max and min

Question 3.9

Write the following inequalities without the use of the modulus sign:

(i) $|4x + 1| < 5$

(ii) $|\mu - 3x| > 2$

Question 3.10

A person was born on 15 June 1955. If x is defined to be his exact age, what is [x] on 21 March 2011?

Question 3.11

What are the values of the function $\min(x^2, 15)$ for values of x in the range $0 \le x \le 6$?

Question 3.12

Calculate V, where $x = 0.8$ and $V = \min(e^{-x}, \sqrt{\pi}/4)$.

Question 3.13

An insurer pays out an amount $\min(X, 450)$ on individual claims. What will the insurer pay if the individual claim is:

(i)   250

(ii)   700

4

Algebra

Learning Objectives

The following learning objectives are covered in this chapter:

- Manipulate algebraic expressions involving powers, logs, polynomials and fractions.

- Solve simple equations, including simultaneous equations.

- Solve quadratic equations.

- Solve strict and weak inequalities in simple cases.

- Understand and apply the Σ and Π notation for sums and products.

- Calculate the sum of a finite number of terms in an arithmetic or geometric series. Understand the condition required for the sum of an infinite geometric series to exist and be able to calculate this sum.

- Apply the formulae $\displaystyle\sum_{k=1}^{n} k = \frac{1}{2}n(n+1)$ and $\displaystyle\sum_{k=1}^{n} k^2 = \frac{1}{6}n(n+1)(2n+1)$.

- Recognise and apply the binomial expansion of expressions of the form $(a+b)^n$ where n is a positive integer, and $(1+x)^p$ for any real value of p. In the latter case, determine when the series converges.

4.1   Algebraic expressions

We begin this chapter by considering algebraic expressions that involve powers and logs, and fractions that involve polynomials rather than numbers.

◇ Powers

The expression 2^5 is read as '2 to the power of 5'. It means that the number 2 is multiplied by itself 5 times. So:

$$2^5 = 2 \times 2 \times 2 \times 2 \times 2 = 32$$

We define x^0 to be equal to 1 for all x. So, for example, $2^0 = 1$.

The power function has some important properties, which we will demonstrate with some examples. First of all, if we multiply 2^5 by 2^3, we see that we are able to add the powers (or *indices*) as follows:

$$2^5 \times 2^3 = (2 \times 2 \times 2 \times 2 \times 2) \times (2 \times 2 \times 2) = 2^{5+3} = 2^8$$

Secondly, if we divide 2^5 by 2^3, we see that we are able to subtract the power in the denominator from the power in the numerator:

$$\frac{2^5}{2^3} = \frac{2 \times 2 \times 2 \times 2 \times 2}{2 \times 2 \times 2} = 2 \times 2 = 2^{5-3} = 2^2$$

An alternative way of writing $\dfrac{1}{2^3}$ is 2^{-3}. So:

$$\frac{2^5}{2^3} = 2^5 \times \frac{1}{2^3} = 2^5 \times 2^{-3}$$

Again, we can add the powers in the final term in the equation above to simplify the expression, and doing this we obtain 2^2 as before.

More generally, the symbol x^{-n} can be used as an alternative to $\dfrac{1}{x^n}$.

A third important property is demonstrated by the following equation:

$$(2^5)^3 = 2^5 \times 2^5 \times 2^5 = (2 \times 2 \times 2 \times 2 \times 2) \times (2 \times 2 \times 2 \times 2 \times 2) \times (2 \times 2 \times 2 \times 2 \times 2) = 2^{15}$$

In this equation we can combine the powers by multiplying them together.

Below is a summary of these important *power laws* (or *rules of indices*).

Power laws

$x^a x^b = x^{a+b}$ $\qquad\qquad\qquad\qquad$ $x^0 = 1$

$\dfrac{x^a}{x^b} = x^{a-b}$ $\qquad\qquad\qquad\qquad$ $\dfrac{1}{x^b} = x^{-b}$

$(x^a)^b = x^{ab}$

Example 4.1

Simplify the following:

(i) $5x^3 \times 2x^5$

(ii) $\dfrac{16y^2}{6y^7}$

(iii) $(5b^3)^2$

Solution

(i) $5x^3 \times 2x^5 = 10x^{3+5} = 10x^8$

(ii) $\dfrac{16y^2}{6y^7} = \dfrac{8}{3}y^{2-7} = \dfrac{8}{3}y^{-5} = \dfrac{8}{3y^5}$

(ii) $(5b^3)^2 = 5^2(b^3)^2 = 5^2 b^{3\times2} = 25b^6$ ◆◆

 Logarithms

The logarithm (or log) function is the inverse of the power function. The expression $\log_a x$ is read as "log to the base a of x" or "log of x to the base a". To find a log, we have to work out the power the base must be raised to in order to get the number whose log we are trying to find. The base a can be any positive real number except 1 (as 1 raised to any power is still 1).

Definition of the log function

$y = \log_a x \Leftrightarrow a^y = x$

Example 4.2

Calculate:

(i) $\log_2 64$

(ii) $\log_{10} 0.001$

Solution

(i)   Since $2^6 = 64$, it follows that $\log_2 64 = 6$.

(ii)   Since $10^{-3} = 0.001$, it follows that $\log_{10} 0.001 = -3$ ◆◆

Observe that $\log_{10} 0.001 < 0$. In the usual case where $a > 1$, we have $\log_a x < 0$ for all $0 < x < 1$. $\log_a x$ is not defined for $x \leq 0$. On a graph, $\log_a 0$ corresponds to $-\infty$.

Example 4.3

Simplify the expression:

$$\log_a 1$$

Solution

Using the definition of logs:

$$y = \log_a 1 \Leftrightarrow a^y = 1$$

This is true when $y = 0$, so $\log_a 1 = 0$.   ♦♦

The most commonly used base is base e. e is a special number whose value is 2.7182... . The function $\log_e$ is often written as ln. It is called the natural log. Scientific calculators have two log functions, $\boxed{\log}$ (which gives $\log_{10}$) and $\boxed{\text{ln}}$.

The log function has some important properties, all of which can be derived from the power laws.

Log laws

$$\log_a x + \log_a y = \log_a xy \qquad\qquad \log_a 1 = 0$$

$$\log_a x - \log_a y = \log_a \tfrac{x}{y} \qquad\qquad \log_a \tfrac{1}{y} = -\log_a y$$

$$\log_a x^n = n \log_a x$$

The first of these can be demonstrated as follows. Suppose that:

$$m = \log_a x \ \text{ and } \ n = \log_a y$$

Then:

$$a^m = x \ \text{ and } \ a^n = y$$

Now using a power law, we have:

$$a^m a^n = a^{m+n} = xy$$

and from the definition of logs, it follows that:

$$\log_a xy = m + n = \log_a x + \log_a y$$

Example 4.4

Simplify the expression:

$$\log_a 2x + \log_a 4x - \log_a 5x$$

Solution

The expression simplifies to:

$$\log_a\left(\frac{2x \times 4x}{5x}\right)$$

which equals:

$$\log_a\left(\frac{8x}{5}\right)$$ ♦♦

The third log law can be used to help us solve equations and inequalities where the unknown term appears in a power.

Example 4.5

Solve the equation $1.1^{2n+1} = 2$.

Solution

Taking the natural log of both sides of this equation gives:

$$\ln 1.1^{2n+1} = \ln 2$$

Now using the third log law we have:

$$(2n + 1)\ln 1.1 = \ln 2$$

So:

$$2n + 1 = \frac{\ln 2}{\ln 1.1}$$

and hence:

$$n = 0.5\left(\frac{\ln 2}{\ln 1.1} - 1\right) = 3.13627$$ ♦♦

In fact, we could have used a log with any base to solve the equation in Example 4.5 and still get the same answer. When it is clear what base we are using, or if the base isn't important, we usually write $\log_a x$ as $\log x$.

 ## Fractions

Algebraic fractions can be manipulated using the same rules that are used for numerical fractions. Here are some examples.

Example 4.6

Simplify the expression:

$$\frac{2x + 3}{x + 1} - \frac{3x + 2}{6x - 1}$$

Solution

The first step is to put both terms over a common denominator. In this case the common denominator is the product of the two original denominators as they have no terms in common. This gives:

$$\frac{(2x+3)(6x-1)-(3x+2)(x+1)}{(x+1)(6x-1)}$$

Now multiplying out the bracketed terms in the numerator, we find that:

$$(2x+3)(6x-1)-(3x+2)(x+1) = (12x^2+18x-2x-3)-(3x^2+2x+3x+2)$$
$$= (12x^2+16x-3)-(3x^2+5x+2)$$
$$= 9x^2+11x-5$$

So:

$$\frac{2x+3}{x+1} - \frac{3x+2}{6x-1} = \frac{9x^2+11x-5}{(x+1)(6x-1)} \qquad \blacklozenge\blacklozenge$$

 ## Example 4.7

Simplify the expression:

$$\frac{\frac{1}{a}+\frac{1}{b}}{\frac{a}{b}+\frac{b}{a}}$$

Solution

Multiplying the numerator and a denominator of a fraction by the same amount does not change its value. Here the expression will be simplified if we multiply the numerator and the denominator by ab:

$$\frac{\frac{1}{a}+\frac{1}{b}}{\frac{a}{b}+\frac{b}{a}} \times \frac{ab}{ab} = \frac{\frac{ab}{a}+\frac{ab}{b}}{\frac{a^2b}{b}+\frac{ab^2}{a}} = \frac{b+a}{a^2+b^2} = \frac{a+b}{a^2+b^2} \qquad \blacklozenge\blacklozenge$$

4.2 Quadratic polynomials

A quadratic polynomial is an expression of the form ax^2+bx+c for some constants a, b and c. In actuarial work, we sometimes have to solve equations involving quadratics. There are three techniques that we can use to help us do this. They are:

- factorisation
- completing the square
- the quadratic formula.

We will look at each of these below.

◆◇ *Factorisation*

Expressions of the form $ax^2 + bx + c$ can sometimes be written in the form $(dx + e)(fx + g)$, where d, e, f and g are whole numbers. The process of writing a quadratic in this way is known as factorisation. The terms $dx + e$ and $fx + g$ are called *factors*. More generally, a factor is any term that divides a polynomial exactly, *ie* with no remainder.

Example 4.8

Factorise the expression $x^2 - 7x + 12$.

Solution

Since the coefficient of the x^2 term is 1, we want to write $x^2 - 7x + 12$ in the form $(x + e)(x + g)$.

We know that $e \times g = 12$. Since this is positive, e and g must have the same sign, *ie* they must both be positive or they must both be negative.

Furthermore, since the coefficient of the x term is −7, e and g must sum to −7. The only two values with a product of 12 and a sum of −7 are −3 and −4. So:

$$x^2 - 7x + 12 = (x - 3)(x - 4)$$
◆◆

You may recall the following result, which we use in our next example.

Difference of two squares

$$a^2 - b^2 = (a + b)(a - b)$$

Example 4.9

Factorise the expression $16x^2 - 1$.

Solution

Setting $a = 4x$ and $b = 1$ in the formula $a^2 - b^2 = (a + b)(a - b)$, we see that:

$$16x^2 - 1 = (4x - 1)(4x + 1)$$
◆◆

If we are able to factorise $ax^2 + bx + c$, it is then very easy to find the values of x for which:

$$ax^2 + bx + c = 0$$

These values are called the *roots* of the equation. If α and β are the roots of a quadratic equation, then $x = \alpha$ and $x = \beta$ are solutions of the equation. This is equivalent to saying that $(x - \alpha)$ and $(x - \beta)$ are factors of the quadratic expression.

Example 4.10

Factorise the expression $2x^2 + x - 3$ and hence find the roots of the equation:

$$2x^2 + x - 3 = 0$$

Solution

By comparing the terms, we can see that:

$$2x^2 + x - 3 = (2x + 3)(x - 1)$$

For this quadratic to be equal to 0, one of its factors must be equal to 0, *ie*:

$$2x + 3 = 0 \text{ or } x - 1 = 0$$

So $2x^2 + x - 3 = 0$ when $x = -1.5$ or $x = 1$.   ◆◆

Completing the square

To see how this works, let's return to the quadratic $x^2 - 7x + 12$ from Example 4.8. Our aim now is to write this in the form $(x + p)^2 - q$ for some p and q. We know that:

$$(x + p)^2 = x^2 + 2px + p^2$$

Here we set $2p = -7$ since -7 is the coefficient of the x term in the quadratic $x^2 - 7x + 12$. Since:

$$\left(x - \frac{7}{2}\right)^2 = x^2 - 7x + \frac{49}{4}$$

it follows that:

$$x^2 - 7x + 12 = \left(x^2 - 7x + \frac{49}{4}\right) - \frac{49}{4} + 12 = \left(x - \frac{7}{2}\right)^2 - \frac{1}{4}$$

This is of the form $(x + p)^2 - q$ as required.

It is now straightforward to solve the equation $x^2 - 7x + 12 = 0$:

$$x^2 - 7x + 12 = 0$$

$$\Rightarrow \left(x - \frac{7}{2}\right)^2 - \frac{1}{4} = 0$$

$$\Rightarrow \left(x - \frac{7}{2}\right)^2 = \frac{1}{4}$$

$$\Rightarrow x - \frac{7}{2} = \pm\sqrt{\frac{1}{4}} = \pm\frac{1}{2}$$

$$\Rightarrow x = \frac{7}{2} \pm \frac{1}{2}$$

$$\Rightarrow x = 3 \text{ or } 4$$

The $\pm$ symbol indicates that there are two answers, one obtained by using a plus sign and one obtained by using a minus sign.

Example 4.11

Solve the following equation by completing the square:

$$-3x^2 + 13x - 1 = 0$$

Solution

Let's start by dividing both sides of the equation by -3. The equation then becomes:

$$x^2 - \frac{13}{3}x + \frac{1}{3} = 0$$

Now:

$$\left(x - \frac{13}{6}\right)^2 = x^2 - \frac{13}{3}x + \frac{169}{36}$$

(Here we are setting $2p = -\frac{13}{3}$.)

Since:

$$x^2 - \frac{13}{3}x + \frac{1}{3} = \left(x^2 - \frac{13}{3}x + \frac{169}{36}\right) - \frac{169}{36} + \frac{1}{3}$$

it follows that:

$$x^2 - \frac{13}{3}x + \frac{1}{3} = \left(x - \frac{13}{6}\right)^2 - \frac{169}{36} + \frac{1}{3} = \left(x - \frac{13}{6}\right)^2 - \frac{157}{36}$$

So:

$$x^2 - \frac{13}{3}x + \frac{1}{3} = 0$$

$$\Rightarrow \left(x - \frac{13}{6}\right)^2 - \frac{157}{36} = 0$$

$$\Rightarrow \left(x - \frac{13}{6}\right)^2 = \frac{157}{36}$$

$$\Rightarrow x - \frac{13}{6} = \pm\sqrt{\frac{157}{36}}$$

$$\Rightarrow x = \frac{13}{6} \pm \sqrt{\frac{157}{36}}$$

$$\Rightarrow x = 0.07834 \text{ or } 4.25499$$

♦♦

◆ *Quadratic formula*

A third method of solving an equation of the form $ax^2 + bx + c = 0$ is to use the quadratic formula. This method is generally quicker than factorisation (which isn't always possible) and completing the square.

Quadratic formula

The roots of the equation $ax^2 + bx + c = 0$ are:

$$x = \frac{-b \pm \sqrt{b^2 - 4ac}}{2a}$$

If $b^2 - 4ac$ is negative, then the equation as no (real) roots.

This can be proved by applying the method of completing the square to the expression $ax^2 + bx + c$. We start by writing:

$$ax^2 + bx + c = a\left(x^2 + \frac{b}{a}x + \frac{c}{a}\right)$$

Now:

$$\left(x + \frac{b}{2a}\right)^2 = x^2 + \frac{b}{a}x + \frac{b^2}{4a^2}$$

and:

$$x^2 + \frac{b}{a}x + \frac{c}{a} = \left(x^2 + \frac{b}{a}x + \frac{b^2}{4a^2}\right) - \frac{b^2}{4a^2} + \frac{c}{a} = \left(x + \frac{b}{2a}\right)^2 - \frac{b^2}{4a^2} + \frac{c}{a}$$

So we can complete the square in the original equation as follows:

$$ax^2 + bx + c = 0$$

$$\Rightarrow x^2 + \frac{b}{a}x + \frac{c}{a} = 0$$

$$\Rightarrow \left(x + \frac{b}{2a}\right)^2 - \frac{b^2}{4a^2} + \frac{c}{a} = 0$$

$$\Rightarrow \left(x + \frac{b}{2a}\right)^2 = \frac{b^2}{4a^2} - \frac{c}{a} = \frac{b^2 - 4ac}{4a^2}$$

$$\Rightarrow x + \frac{b}{2a} = \pm\sqrt{\frac{b^2 - 4ac}{4a^2}} = \frac{\pm\sqrt{b^2 - 4ac}}{2a}$$

$$\Rightarrow x = \frac{-b \pm \sqrt{b^2 - 4ac}}{2a}$$

We'll now look at two examples that use the quadratic formula.

Example 4.12

Use the quadratic formula to solve the equation $3x^2 + 8x + 2 = 0$.

Solution

Here we have:

$$a = 3, \ b = 8, \ c = 2$$

So:

$$x = \frac{-8 \pm \sqrt{64 - 24}}{6} = \frac{-8 \pm \sqrt{40}}{6} = -2.38743 \ \text{or} \ -0.27924$$

♦♦

Example 4.13

Solve the equation:

$$3^{2x+1} + 4 \times 3^x - 4 = 0$$

Solution

This equation does not appear to be a quadratic. However, if we let $y = 3^x$, then $y^2 = 3^{2x}$ and:

$$3^{2x+1} + 4 \times 3^x - 4 = 3(3^x)^2 + 4(3^x) - 4 = 3y^2 + 4y - 4$$

So the equation becomes:

$$3y^2 + 4y - 4 = 0$$

Using the quadratic formula, we obtain:

$$y = \frac{-4 \pm \sqrt{4^2 - 4 \times 3 \times (-4)}}{6} = \frac{-4 \pm \sqrt{64}}{6} = \frac{-4 \pm 8}{6} = -2 \ \text{or} \ \frac{2}{3}$$

We now need to find the corresponding values of x. We know that 3^x must be positive for all values of x, so we can discard the value $y = -2$. Setting $3^x = \frac{2}{3}$ and taking logs gives:

$$x \ln 3 = \ln\left(\frac{2}{3}\right)$$

So:

$$x = \frac{\ln\left(\frac{2}{3}\right)}{\ln 3} = -0.36907$$

♦♦

Whenever we are solving equations, including quadratics, we should check that our answers are reasonable. In the above example, y has to take a positive value, so we reject the value of -2. There may also be situations when the value we require lies between particular limits, eg a probability must lie between 0 and 1. In such situations, we should reject any values that lie outside the limits and state why we are rejecting them.

◆ *Fractions involving quadratics*

Earlier in this chapter, we looked at some fractions that involve polynomials. Now let's consider an example involving quadratics.

Example 4.14

Simplify the expression:

$$\frac{x^2 - x - 2}{2x^2 - 5x - 12} \div \frac{x^2 + 3x + 2}{2x^2 + 5x + 3}$$

Solution

Dividing by a fraction is the same as multiplying by the reciprocal (or inverse) of the fraction. So:

$$\frac{x^2 - x - 2}{2x^2 - 5x - 12} \div \frac{x^2 + 3x + 2}{2x^2 + 5x + 3} = \frac{x^2 - x - 2}{2x^2 - 5x - 12} \times \frac{2x^2 + 5x + 3}{x^2 + 3x + 2}$$

To simplify further, we need to factorise the quadratics and look for any terms that cancel. We have:

$$x^2 - x - 2 = (x + 1)(x - 2)$$

$$2x^2 - 5x - 12 = (2x + 3)(x - 4)$$

$$2x^2 + 5x + 3 = (2x + 3)(x + 1)$$

and:

$$x^2 + 3x + 2 = (x + 2)(x + 1)$$

So:

$$\frac{x^2 - x - 2}{2x^2 - 5x - 12} \div \frac{x^2 + 3x + 2}{2x^2 + 5x + 3} = \frac{(x - 2)(x + 1)}{(2x + 3)(x - 4)} \times \frac{(2x + 3)(x + 1)}{(x + 2)(x + 1)}$$

The $(2x + 3)$ terms cancel from the numerator and the denominator. In addition, one of the $(x + 1)$ terms in the numerator cancels with the $(x + 1)$ term in the denominator. So the expression simplifies to:

$$\frac{(x - 2)(x + 1)}{(x - 4)(x + 2)} \qquad\qquad\qquad ◆◆$$

4.3   *Simultaneous equations*

Suppose we have two equations involving two variables (or unknowns), x and y. If both equations hold at the same time, then the equations are called *simultaneous* equations.

The example below involves two linear equations, *ie* equations that can be written in the form $y = mx + c$.

Example 4.15

Solve the following equations simultaneously:

$$2x + 5y - 4 = 0$$

$$7y = 2 - 4x$$

Solution

We will start by rewriting the equations and labelling them as follows:

$$2x + 5y = 4 \quad (1)$$

$$4x + 7y = 2 \quad (2)$$

Multiplying both sides of equation (1) by 2, it becomes:

$$4x + 10y = 8 \quad (3)$$

If we then subtract equation (2) from equation (3), the x terms cancel and we are left with:

$$3y = 6$$

So $y = 2$. We can now substitute this value into any of equations (1) to (3) above to find the value of x. Using equation (1), we see that:

$$2x = 4 - 5y = 4 - 10 = -6$$

So $x = -3$.   ♦♦

As demonstrated by the example above, we can solve two linear equations simultaneously by rearranging them into a suitable form, and then adding or subtracting a multiple of one of the equations to eliminate one of the variables.

In our next example, one of the equations is non-linear.

Example 4.16

Solve the following equations simultaneously:

$$x^2 + y^2 = 20$$

$$2x - 3y = 14$$

Solution

We can solve these equations simultaneously by writing one of the unknowns in terms of the other. We'll use the second equation to do this as it is simpler than the first. The second equation can be rearranged to give:

$$x = \frac{1}{2}(14 + 3y)$$

Substituting this into the first equation gives:

$$\tfrac{1}{4}(14 + 3y)^2 + y^2 = 20$$

Now let's remove the fraction by multiplying both sides of the equation by 4. Doing this we obtain:

$$(14 + 3y)^2 + 4y^2 = 80$$

Then expanding the squared term gives:

$$(196 + 84y + 9y^2) + 4y^2 = 80$$

Next, we'll put all the terms on the left-hand side. The equation now becomes:

$$13y^2 + 84y + 116 = 0$$

Using the quadratic formula (as it is the quickest method), we find that:

$$y = \frac{-84 \pm \sqrt{84^2 - 4 \times 13 \times 116}}{26} = \frac{-84 \pm \sqrt{1,024}}{26} = \frac{-84 \pm 32}{26} = -\frac{58}{13} \text{ or } -2$$

If $y = -\dfrac{58}{13}$, then $x = \dfrac{1}{2}(14 + 3y) = \dfrac{1}{2}(14 - 3 \times \dfrac{58}{13}) = \dfrac{4}{13}$.

If $y = -2$, then $x = \dfrac{1}{2}(14 - 3 \times 2) = 4$.   ♦♦

In the next example, both of the equations are non-linear. Once again we can solve them simultaneously by expressing one of the variables in terms of the other (using the simpler equation), and then substituting this expression into the other equation.

Example 4.17

Solve the following equations simultaneously:

$$ar^2 = 8$$
$$ar^3 + ar^4 = 30$$

Solution

From the first equation, we know that:

$$a = \frac{8}{r^2}$$

Substituting this into the second equation, we obtain:

$$8r + 8r^2 = 30$$

This can also be written as:

$$8r^2 + 8r - 30 = 0$$

or:

$$4r^2 + 4r - 15 = 0$$

Now, using the quadratic formula, we find that:

$$r = \frac{-4 \pm \sqrt{4^2 - 4 \times 4 \times (-15)}}{8} = \frac{-4 \pm \sqrt{256}}{8} = \frac{-4 \pm 16}{8} = -\frac{5}{2} \text{ or } \frac{3}{2}$$

If $r = -\dfrac{5}{2}$, then $a = 8 \times \left(-\dfrac{2}{5}\right)^2 = \dfrac{32}{25}$.

If $r = \dfrac{3}{2}$, then $a = 8 \times \left(\dfrac{2}{3}\right)^2 = \dfrac{32}{9}$.

Alternatively, the term a can be removed by dividing the second equation by the first. This gives:

$$\frac{ar^3 + ar^4}{ar^2} = \frac{30}{8}$$

This simplifies to:

$$r + r^2 = \frac{15}{4}$$

Again this can be solved using the quadratic formula.   ♦♦

Here is a final example involving simultaneous equations. This time both equations involve quadratics.

Example 4.18

Solve the following equations simultaneously:

$$2p^2 - pq - 3q^2 = -50$$
$$3p^2 + 4pq + q^2 = 35$$

Solution

The left-hand side of the first equation can be written as:

$$(p + q)(2p - 3q)$$

and the left-hand side of the second equation can be written as:

$$(p + q)(3p + q)$$

Dividing the first equation by the second, we obtain:

$$\frac{(p + q)(2p - 3q)}{(p + q)(3p + q)} = \frac{-50}{35}$$

This simplifies to:

$$\frac{2p - 3q}{3p + q} = \frac{-10}{7}$$

Now cross-multiplying (which is equivalent to multiplying both sides of the equation by $7(3p + q)$), we obtain:

$$7(2p - 3q) = -10(3p + q)$$
$$\Rightarrow 14p - 21q = -30p - 10q$$
$$\Rightarrow 44p = 11q$$
$$\Rightarrow 4p = q$$

Finally, replacing q by $4p$ in the second simultaneous equation gives:

$$3p^2 + 16p^2 + 16p^2 = 35$$

So $p^2 = 1$, *ie* $p = \pm 1$.

If $p = 1$, then $q = 4p = 4$. If $p = -1$, then $q = -4$.   ♦ ♦

4.4   Inequalities

Inequalities are relationships that include one or more of the following symbols:

Symbol	Meaning
$\leq$	Less than or equal to
$<$	(Strictly) less than
$\geq$	Greater than or equal to
$>$	(Strictly) greater than

Inequalities involving $<$ or $>$ are called *strict* inequalities, whereas inequalities involving $\leq$ or $\geq$ are called *weak* inequalities.

As an example, consider the weak inequality:

$$7x + 4 \geq 2x - 7$$

The solution to inequalities such as this one is a set of values rather than a single point. Subtracting $2x + 4$ from both sides of the inequality, we obtain:

$$5x \geq -11$$

or equivalently:

$$x \geq -2.2$$

Similarly, the solution to the strict inequality $7x + 4 > 2x - 7$ is $x > -2.2$.

We can manipulate inequalities in much the same way as we can manipulate equations, but special rules apply when we multiply or divide inequalities.

Manipulating inequalities

We can:

- add a constant to both sides (or subtract a constant from both sides)

- multiply or divide both sides by a **positive** constant

- multiply or divide both sides by a **negative** constant, provided we reverse the inequality sign

- take logs of both sides (provided both sides are positive).

The first example below is relatively straightforward but the second is more complicated.

Example 4.19

Determine the values of x that satisfy the inequality:

$$|x-1| < 3$$

Solution

Writing the inequality without the absolute value notation it becomes:

$$-3 < x - 1 < 3$$

Now adding 1 to each of the three elements, we see that the solution is:

$$-2 < x < 4$$ ♦♦

Example 4.20

Determine the values of x that satisfy the inequality:

$$(2x + 11)(x - 7) < -57$$

Solution

To start with, let's manipulate the inequality so that it is in the form $ax^2 + bx + c < 0$:

$$(2x + 11)(x - 7) < -57$$
$$\Rightarrow 2x^2 + 11x - 14x - 77 < -57$$
$$\Rightarrow 2x^2 - 3x - 20 < 0$$

Now we can factorise $2x^2 - 3x - 20$ as $(2x + 5)(x - 4)$. The expression $(2x + 5)(x - 4)$ changes sign when $x = -2.5$ and when $x = 4$. We can solve the inequality by considering the signs of the factors $2x + 5$ and $x - 4$ in each of the intervals $x < -2.5$, $-2.5 < x < 4$ and $x > 4$. This is illustrated in the table below:

	$x < -2.5$	$-2.5 < x < 4$	$x > 4$
$2x + 5$	–	+	+
$x - 4$	–	–	+
$(2x + 5)(x - 4)$	+	–	+

This is positive because the product of two negative numbers is positive.

This is negative because the product of a positive number and a negative number is negative.

From the table we see that $(2x + 5)(x - 4) < 0$ when $-2.5 < x < 4$.   ♦♦

Our final example in this section involves logs.

Example 4.21

Determine the values of y that satisfy the inequality:

$$0.25^y \le 0.001$$

Solution

Taking the natural log of both sides of the inequality and using the fact that $\ln 0.25^y = y \ln 0.25$, we obtain:

$$y \ln 0.25 \le \ln 0.001$$

To solve the inequality, we have to divide by $\ln 0.25$. However, this is a negative number (since $0.25 < 1$), so we have to reverse the sign of the inequality when we divide. This gives:

$$y \ge \frac{\ln 0.001}{\ln 0.25}$$

So the inequality is satisfied if $y \ge 4.98289$.   ◆◆

4.5   Sums and products

In this section we will introduce some shorthand notation for sums and products.

◆ Sigma notation

The Greek letter Σ (capital sigma) is used by mathematicians to denote a sum. For example:

$$\sum_{i=1}^{n} x_i = x_1 + x_2 + \cdots + x_n$$

$\sum_{i=1}^{n} x_i$ is read as 'the sum from $i = 1$ to n of x_i'. Using sigma notation removes the need for writing '$\cdots$' within a summation. It also makes it clear exactly which terms are represented by '$\cdots$' and how many of them there are. For example, $2 + 4 + \cdots + 32$ is unclear because it could mean that we are summing the first 16 even numbers or the first 5 powers of 2.

The letter i in the expression $\sum_{i=1}^{n} x_i$ is called a *dummy variable*. It can be replaced by any letter that isn't used elsewhere in the expression. $\sum_{j=1}^{n} x_j$ is exactly the same as $\sum_{i=1}^{n} x_i$.

Alternatively, we can use the notation from set theory to show the values over which the variable is being summed. For example, we could write $\sum_{i=1}^{\infty}$ as $\sum_{i \in \mathbb{Z}^+}$ where $\mathbb{Z}^+$ denotes the set of positive integers.

If it turns out that there are no terms in the sum (*ie* we have an *empty sum*), its value is taken to be 0.

Example 4.22

Write the following sums using sigma notation:

(i) $1^2 + 2^2 + 3^2 + \cdots + n^2$

(ii) $3 + 5 + 7 + \cdots + 71$

(iii) $1 + \dfrac{1}{2^2} + \dfrac{1}{4^2} + \dfrac{1}{8^2} + \cdots$

Solution

(i) $1^2 + 2^2 + 3^2 + \cdots + n^2 = \displaystyle\sum_{i=1}^{n} i^2$

(ii) $3 + 5 + 7 + \cdots + 71 = \displaystyle\sum_{j=1}^{35} (2j + 1)$

(iii) $1 + \dfrac{1}{2^2} + \dfrac{1}{4^2} + \dfrac{1}{8^2} + \cdots = \displaystyle\sum_{k=0}^{\infty} \dfrac{1}{2^{2k}} = \displaystyle\sum_{k=0}^{\infty} \dfrac{1}{4^k}$ ♦♦

◆ Pi notation

The Greek letter Π (capital pi) is used by mathematicians to denote a product. This notation works in a similar way to sigma notation. For example:

$$\prod_{i=0}^{n} y_i = y_0 \times y_1 \times \cdots \times y_n$$

$\displaystyle\prod_{i=0}^{n} y_i$ is read as 'the product from $i = 0$ to n of y_i'. Using pi notation removes the need for writing '$\cdots$' within a product. The value of a product with no terms (ie an empty product) is taken to be 1.

Example 4.23

Write the following products using pi notation:

(i) $3 \times 5 \times 7 \times \cdots \times (2n + 1)$

(ii) $e \times e^2 \times e^3 \times \cdots \times e^{2n+3}$

(iii) $\dfrac{1}{4\alpha} \times \dfrac{1}{9\alpha^2} \times \dfrac{1}{16\alpha^3} \times \cdots \times \dfrac{1}{256\alpha^{15}}$

Solution

(i) $3 \times 5 \times 7 \times \cdots \times (2n + 1) = \displaystyle\prod_{i=1}^{n} (2i + 1)$

(ii) $e \times e^2 \times e^3 \times \cdots \times e^{2n+3} = \displaystyle\prod_{j=1}^{2n+3} e^j$

(iii) $\dfrac{1}{4\alpha} \times \dfrac{1}{9\alpha^2} \times \dfrac{1}{16\alpha^3} \times \cdots \times \dfrac{1}{256\alpha^{15}} = \displaystyle\prod_{k=1}^{15} \dfrac{1}{(k+1)^2 \alpha^k}$

Alternatively, we could give the answer as $\displaystyle\prod_{k=2}^{16} \dfrac{1}{k^2 \alpha^{k-1}}$ ◆◆

4.6   *Arithmetic and geometric progressions*

A *progression* or *sequence* is a list of numbers written in a particular order, *eg* $1, \frac{1}{2}, \frac{1}{4}, \frac{1}{8}, \ldots$
A *series* is obtained by summing the terms in a sequence. In the remainder of this chapter, we will study several types of sequences and series that are of interest to actuaries.

◆ *Arithmetic progressions*

An *arithmetic progression* (AP) or *arithmetic sequence* is a list of numbers in which the *difference* between each two successive numbers is a constant. An example of an AP is:

    $3, 7, 11, 15, \ldots$

In this sequence, the difference between successive terms is 4. We call this the *common difference* and denote it by the letter d. The first term in the sequence is generally denoted by the letter a. Each term in the sequence can now be expressed in terms of a and d. In our example, we have:

    First term $= 3 = a$

    Second term $= 7 = a + d$

    Third term $= 11 = a + 2d$

    Fourth term $= 15 = a + 3d$

and so on. Following this pattern, we obtain the following formula for the n th term of an AP.

---

n th term of an arithmetic progression

The n th term of an AP with first term a and common difference d is:

    $a + (n - 1)d$

If the terms in the sequence are decreasing, then d will be negative but the formulae in this section will still work.

We may also have to calculate the sum of a given number of terms in an AP. Using S_n to denote the sum of the first n terms, we have:

$$S_n = a + [a+d] + [a+2d] + \cdots + [a+(n-2)d] + [a+(n-1)d] \qquad (4)$$

Reversing the terms on the right-hand side, we can also say:

$$S_n = [a + (n-1)d] + [a + (n-2)d] + \cdots + [a+d] + a \qquad (5)$$

Now adding the first term on the right-hand side of equation (4) to the first term on the right-hand side of equation (5), we obtain:

$$2a + (n-1)d$$

Similarly, adding the second term on the right-hand side of equation (4) to the second term on the right-hand side of equation (5), gives:

$$2a + (n-1)d$$

In fact, each pair of terms sums to $2a + (n-1)d$, and there are n pairs altogether. $2a + (n-1)d$ is the total of the first and last terms in the sum S_n. Using the letter l to denote the last term, we have:

$$2a + (n-1)d = a + l$$

Now summing equations (4) and (5) gives:

$$2S_n = n[2a + (n-1)d] = n[a + l]$$

Dividing both sides of this equation by 2, we obtain the following formulae.

Sum of the first n terms of an arithmetic progression

The sum of the first n terms of an AP with first term a and common difference d is given by:

$$S_n = \sum_{i=1}^{n} [a + (i-1)d] = \frac{n}{2}[2a + (n-1)d] = n\left[\frac{a+l}{2}\right]$$

The last term in this equation can be interpreted as the number of terms multiplied by the average term.

Here are some examples involving sums of APs.

Example 4.24

A student borrows some money from his parents and agrees to pay it back without interest according to the following schedule:

- the first monthly payment is £298
- payments decrease by £28 per month
- the last payment is £18.

Calculate:

(i)   the number of payments made

(ii)   the total amount borrowed.

Solution

(i)   Here we have:

$$a = 298 \text{ (the amount of the first payment)}$$

$$d = -28 \text{ (as each payment is £28 less than the previous one)}$$

If the last payment is the n th one, then:

$$a + (n-1)d = 298 - 28(n-1) = 18$$

Rearranging the equation:

$$28(n-1) = 280$$
$$\Rightarrow n - 1 = 10$$
$$\Rightarrow n = 11$$

So there are 11 payments altogether.

(ii)   The total amount borrowed is the sum of all 11 payments:

$$S_{11} = \frac{11}{2}\big[2a + 10d\big] = \frac{11}{2}\big[2 \times 298 - 10 \times 28\big] = \pounds1,738$$

Alternatively, we could say that S_{11} is 11 times the average payments, ie:

$$S_{11} = 11\left[\frac{298 + 18}{2}\right] = \pounds1,738 \qquad\qquad \blacklozenge\blacklozenge$$

Example 4.25

Simplify the expression $1 + 2 + 3 + \cdots + n$.

Solution

The sequence 1, 2, 3, ... is an AP with $a = 1$ and $d = 1$. So the sum of the first n terms in this sequence is:

$$S_n = \frac{n}{2}[2a + (n-1)d] = \frac{n}{2}[2 + n - 1] = \frac{n(n+1)}{2}$$

Alternatively, we could say that:

$$S_n = n\left[\frac{a+l}{2}\right] = n\left[\frac{n+1}{2}\right] = \frac{n(n+1)}{2} \qquad\qquad \blacklozenge\blacklozenge$$

◆ Geometric progressions

A *geometric progression* (GP) or *geometric sequence* is a list of numbers in which the *ratio* of each two successive numbers is a constant. An example of a GP is:

        3, 6, 12, 24, ...

In this sequence, each term is obtained from the previous one by multiplying it by 2. We call this multiplier the *common ratio* and denote it by the letter r. Again if we use the letter a to denote the first term, then each term in the sequence can be expressed in terms of a and r.

In our example, we have:

        First term $= 3 = a$

        Second term $= 6 = ar$

        Third term $= 12 = ar^2$

        Fourth term $= 24 = ar^3$

and so on. Following this pattern, we obtain the following formula for the n th term of a GP.

---

n th term of a geometric progression

The *n* th term of a GP with first term *a* and common ratio *r* is:

$$ar^{n-1}$$

We may also have to calculate the sum of a given number of terms in a GP. Again using S_n to denote the sum of the first *n* terms, we have:

$$S_n = a + ar + ar^2 + \cdots + ar^{n-2} + ar^{n-1} \qquad (6)$$

Now, multiplying every term in this expression by *r* gives:

$$r\,S_n = ar + ar^2 + ar^3 + \cdots + ar^{n-1} + ar^n \qquad (7)$$

Subtracting equation (7) from equation (6) so that all the terms apart from the first and the last cancel out, we obtain:

$$S_n - r\,S_n = \left(a + ar + ar^2 + \cdots + ar^{n-2} + ar^{n-1}\right) - \left(ar + ar^2 + ar^3 + \cdots + ar^{n-1} + ar^n\right)$$

$$= a - ar^n$$

So:

$$(1-r)\,S_n = a(1-r^n)$$

Dividing both sides of this equation by $1-r$, we obtain the following formula.

Sum of the first *n* terms of a geometric progression

The sum of the first *n* terms of a GP with first term *a* and common ratio *r* is given by:

$$S_n = \sum_{i=1}^{n} ar^{i-1} = \frac{a(1-r^n)}{1-r}$$

Example 4.26

Evaluate $\displaystyle\sum_{k=1}^{10} \frac{5}{1.06^k}$.

Solution

We have:

$$\sum_{k=1}^{10} \frac{5}{1.06^k} = \frac{5}{1.06} + \frac{5}{1.06^2} + \frac{5}{1.06^3} + \cdots + \frac{5}{1.06^{10}}$$

This is the sum of the first 10 terms of the GP with $a = \dfrac{5}{1.06}$ and $r = \dfrac{1}{1.06}$.

So:

$$\sum_{k=1}^{10} \frac{5}{1.06^k} = \frac{\frac{5}{1.06}\left[1-\left(\frac{1}{1.06}\right)^{10}\right]}{1-\frac{1}{1.06}} = 36.80044$$

Now let's consider what happens to S_n as n increases.

If $-1 < r < 1$, then $r^n \to 0$ as $n \to \infty$, so:

$$S_n \to \frac{a(1-0)}{1-r} = \frac{a}{1-r} \quad \text{as } n \to \infty$$

In this case, we say that the series *converges to a finite limit* as $n \to \infty$. The limit is $\dfrac{a}{1-r}$. We call this limit the *sum to infinity* and denote it by the symbol S_∞.

The sum to infinity of the GP in Example 4.26 is:

$$\frac{\frac{5}{1.06}}{1-\frac{1}{1.06}} = 83\frac{1}{3}$$

As another example, let's consider the GP:

$$1, \frac{1}{2}, \frac{1}{4}, \frac{1}{8}, \dots$$

Here we have $a = 1$ and $r = \frac{1}{2}$. The first ten values of S_n are:

$$S_1 = 1$$

$$S_2 = 1+\frac{1}{2} = 1.5$$

$$S_3 = 1+\frac{1}{2}+\frac{1}{4} = 1.75$$

$$S_4 = 1+\frac{1}{2}+\frac{1}{4}+\frac{1}{8} = 1.875$$

$$S_5 = 1+\frac{1}{2}+\frac{1}{4}+\frac{1}{8}+\frac{1}{16} = 1.9375$$

$$S_6 = 1+\frac{1}{2}+\frac{1}{4}+\frac{1}{8}+\frac{1}{16}+\frac{1}{32} = 1.96875$$

$$S_7 = 1+\frac{1}{2}+\frac{1}{4}+\frac{1}{8}+\frac{1}{16}+\frac{1}{32}+\frac{1}{64} = 1.984375$$

$$S_8 = 1+\frac{1}{2}+\frac{1}{4}+\frac{1}{8}+\frac{1}{16}+\frac{1}{32}+\frac{1}{64}+\frac{1}{128} = 1.9921875$$

$$S_9 = 1+\frac{1}{2}+\frac{1}{4}+\frac{1}{8}+\frac{1}{16}+\frac{1}{32}+\frac{1}{64}+\frac{1}{128}+\frac{1}{256} = 1.99609375$$

$$S_{10} = 1+\frac{1}{2}+\frac{1}{4}+\frac{1}{8}+\frac{1}{16}+\frac{1}{32}+\frac{1}{64}+\frac{1}{128}+\frac{1}{256}+\frac{1}{512} = 1.998046875$$

This pattern suggests that as n increases, S_n gets closer to 2. This is indeed the case since:

$$S_n = \frac{a(1-r^n)}{1-r} = \frac{1-(\frac{1}{2})^n}{1-\frac{1}{2}} \to \frac{1-0}{1-\frac{1}{2}} \text{ as } n \to \infty$$

and:

$$\frac{1-0}{1-\frac{1}{2}} = 2$$

However, if $r \geq 1$ or $r \leq -1$, then S_n does not converge to a finite limit. Equivalently we could say that, if $r \geq 1$ or $r \leq -1$, the series *diverges* or that the *sum to infinity does not exist* (*ie* it is not finite). To illustrate this, let's consider the GP:

3, 6, 12, 24, ...

Here we have $a = 3$ and $r = 2$. The first four values of S_n are:

$$S_1 = 3$$
$$S_2 = 3 + 6 = 9$$
$$S_3 = 3 + 6 + 12 = 21$$
$$S_4 = 3 + 6 + 12 + 24 = 45$$

We can see that the amount being added increases each time as n increases and that S_n does not tend to a finite limit.

Sum to infinity of a geometric progression

If $-1 < r < 1$, then the sum to infinity exists and is given by:

$$S_\infty = \frac{a}{1-r}$$

Example 4.27

Calculate the value of the sum to infinity of the following GP:

4, 3.2, 2.56, 2.048, ...

Solution

We have $a = 4$ and $r = \dfrac{3.2}{4} = 0.8$. Since $-1 < r < 1$ the sum to infinity exists. The sum to infinity is:

$$S_\infty = \frac{4}{1-0.8} = 20$$

◆◆

4.7   *Sums involving positive integers*

In Example 4.25, we used the general formula for the sum of the first n terms of an AP to simplify the expression $1 + 2 + 3 + \cdots + n$. A reminder of this is given in the box below. The expression $1^2 + 2^2 + 3^2 + \cdots + n^2$ can also be simplified. We will state the formula here (but we will not prove it).

Sums involving positive integers

$$\sum_{k=1}^{n} k = \frac{1}{2} n(n+1)$$

$$\sum_{k=1}^{n} k^2 = \frac{1}{6} n(n+1)(2n+1)$$

These formulae are used in the example below.

Example 4.28

Simplify the expression $\displaystyle\sum_{i=1}^{n} (1 + 4i + i^2)$.

Solution

$$\sum_{i=1}^{n}(1 + 4i + i^2) = \sum_{i=1}^{n} 1 + \sum_{i=1}^{n} 4i + \sum_{i=1}^{n} i^2$$

$$= n + 4\sum_{i=1}^{n} i + \sum_{i=1}^{n} i^2$$

$$= n + \tfrac{4}{2} n(n+1) + \tfrac{1}{6} n(n+1)(2n+1)$$

$$= \tfrac{1}{6} n \big(6 + 12(n+1) + (n+1)(2n+1)\big)$$

$$= \tfrac{1}{6} n \big(6 + 12n + 12 + 2n^2 + 2n + n + 1\big)$$

$$= \tfrac{1}{6} n \big(2n^2 + 15n + 19\big) \qquad\qquad \blacklozenge\blacklozenge$$

4.8   Double summations

Earlier in this chapter we introduced sigma notation. We will now consider expressions involving more than one level of summation, *ie* sums of sums. For example, suppose we want to calculate the following sum, which involves a sum over the variable x within another sum over the variable y :

$$\sum_{y=0}^{3} \sum_{x=0}^{y} 2xy$$

The values of y over which we are summing on the outer level are 0, 1, 2 and 3. Let's consider each of these in turn and the values of the inner sum that the various y values give.

When $y = 0$: $\displaystyle\sum_{x=0}^{y} 2xy = 0$

When $y = 1$: $\displaystyle\sum_{x=0}^{y} 2xy = \sum_{x=0}^{1} 2x = 0 + 2 = 2$

When $y = 2$: $\displaystyle\sum_{x=0}^{y} 2xy = \sum_{x=0}^{2} 4x = 0 + 4 + 8 = 12$

When $y = 3$: $\displaystyle\sum_{x=0}^{y} 2xy = \sum_{x=0}^{3} 6x = 0 + 6 + 12 + 18 = 36$

Summing these, we see that:

$$\sum_{y=0}^{3} \sum_{x=0}^{y} 2xy = 0 + 2 + 12 + 36 = 50$$

Another way to evaluate this expression is to swap the order of summation so that the outer summation is over the values of x and the inner summation is over the values of y. However, we have to take care to use the correct limits on each summation.

Looking back at the original expression, we see that $0 \le y \le 3$ and $0 \le x \le y$. Combining these inequalities gives:

$$0 \le x \le y \le 3$$

If we want to use x in the outer summation, we need to use the outermost values in the inequality as the limits. These are 0 and 3. Then, for any given value of x, the values of y will range from x to 3. So:

$$\sum_{y=0}^{3} \sum_{x=0}^{y} 2xy = \sum_{x=0}^{3} \sum_{y=x}^{3} 2xy$$

We can easily check that reversing the order of summation gives the same answer.

When $x = 0$: $\displaystyle\sum_{y=x}^{3} 2xy = 0$

When $x = 1$: $\displaystyle\sum_{y=x}^{3} 2xy = \sum_{y=1}^{3} 2y = 2 + 4 + 6 = 12$

When $x = 2$: $\displaystyle\sum_{y=x}^{3} 2xy = \sum_{y=2}^{3} 4y = 8 + 12 = 20$

When $x = 3$: $\displaystyle\sum_{y=x}^{3} 2xy = \sum_{y=3}^{3} 6y = 18$

Summing these, we see that:

$$\sum_{x=0}^{3}\sum_{y=x}^{3} 2xy = 0 + 12 + 20 + 18 = 50 = \sum_{y=0}^{3}\sum_{x=0}^{y} 2xy$$

4.9   Binomial expansions

In this section we will see how to expand expressions of the form $(a + b)^n$. The formula used depends on whether or not n is a positive integer.

◆ Positive integer powers

The binomial theorem states that for all positive integers n and all real numbers a and b:

$$(a + b)^n = \binom{n}{0}a^n + \binom{n}{1}a^{n-1}b + \binom{n}{2}a^{n-2}b^2 + \cdots + \binom{n}{n-1}ab^{n-1} + \binom{n}{n}b^n$$

The expression on the right-hand side is called the *binomial expansion* of $(a + b)^n$. The expansion involves terms of the form $\binom{n}{r}$, which are defined as follows:

$$\binom{n}{r} = \frac{n!}{r!(n-r)!}$$

Recall that, if k is a positive integer, then:

$$k! = k(k-1)(k-2)\times\ldots\times2\times1$$

and that:

$$0! = 1$$

The function $\binom{n}{r}$ appears as ^nC_r on most calculators. It is read as "n choose r", or sometimes just "n C r". It represents the number of different ways there are of choosing r objects from n when the order of selection is not important. It appears in the binomial expansion because it represents the number of times the term $a^{n-r}b^r$ appears when $(a + b)^n$ is multiplied out. We will study $\binom{n}{r}$ in more detail in Chapter 14.

This binomial expansion of $(a+b)^n$ can also be written using sigma notation as follows:

$$(a+b)^n = \sum_{r=0}^{n} \binom{n}{r} a^{n-r} b^r$$

In addition, writing:

$$\binom{n}{r} = \frac{n!}{r!(n-r)!} = \frac{n(n-1)\cdots(n-r+1)\times(n-r)!}{r!(n-r)!} = \frac{n(n-1)\cdots(n-r+1)}{r!}$$

we see that:

$$(a+b)^n = a^n + na^{n-1}b + \frac{n(n-1)}{2!}a^{n-2}b^2 + \cdots + nab^{n-1} + b^n$$

$$= \sum_{r=0}^{n} \frac{n(n-1)\cdots(n-r+1)}{r!}a^{n-r}b^r$$

Observe that the sum of the powers of a and b is always n, and that the $\binom{n}{r}$ terms can be obtained from the n th row of Pascal's triangle:

```
                        1
                  1           1
            1           2           1
      1           3           3           1
1           4           6           4           1
```

In this triangle, each internal number is obtained by adding the two numbers above it. All the numbers on the edges of the triangle are 1.

Example 4.29

Obtain the binomial expansion of $(2-3x)^4$.

Solution

The binomial expansion is:

$$(2-3x)^4 = \binom{4}{0}2^4 + \binom{4}{1}2^3(-3x) + \binom{4}{2}2^2(-3x)^2 + \binom{4}{3}2(-3x)^3 + \binom{4}{4}(-3x)^4$$

$$= (1\times 16) + (4\times 8 \times(-3x)) + (6\times 4 \times 9x^2) + (4\times 2\times(-27x^3)) + (1\times 81x^4)$$

$$= 16 - 96x + 216x^2 - 216x^3 + 81x^4 \qquad\qquad \blacklozenge\blacklozenge$$

The next example shows how we can determine individual terms in a binomial expansion without writing out the whole expression.

Example 4.30

Determine the coefficient of the term in a^4 in the expansion of $(2a+5b)^6$.

Solution

The binomial expansion is:

$$(2a + 5b)^6 = \sum_{r=0}^{6} \binom{6}{r} (2a)^{6-r} (5b)^r$$

The coefficient of the term in a^4 can be obtained by setting $r = 2$ in this expression. The coefficient is:

$$\binom{6}{2} \times 2^4 \times (5b)^2 = 15 \times 16 \times 25\, b^2 = 6,000\, b^2 \qquad \blacklozenge\blacklozenge$$

◆ *Negative or fractional powers*

If n is not a positive integer, we cannot obtain a value of $\binom{n}{r}$ from Pascal's triangle. So we have to use a slightly different form of the binomial expansion. If n is a negative integer or a fraction, then:

$$(1 + x)^n = 1 + nx + \frac{n(n-1)}{2!} x^2 + \frac{n(n-1)(n-2)}{3!} x^3 + \cdots$$

for $-1 < x < 1$. This result is derived using Maclaurin series, which we will meet in Chapter 6. Unlike the earlier version of the binomial expansion, which has a finite number of terms, the series in this version is an infinite series, *ie* it goes on for ever.

Example 4.31

Expand $(1 - 2x)^{1/2}$ as far as the term in x^3. State the range of values of x for which this expansion is valid.

Solution

The expansion is:

$$(1 - 2x)^{1/2} = 1 + \tfrac{1}{2}(-2x) + \frac{\tfrac{1}{2}\left(-\tfrac{1}{2}\right)}{2!}(-2x)^2 + \frac{\tfrac{1}{2}\left(-\tfrac{1}{2}\right)\left(-\tfrac{3}{2}\right)}{3!}(-2x)^3 + \cdots$$

$$= 1 - x - \tfrac{1}{2}x^2 - \tfrac{1}{2}x^3 + \cdots$$

This expansion is valid for $-1 < -2x < 1$, *ie* for $-\tfrac{1}{2} < x < \tfrac{1}{2}$. $\qquad \blacklozenge\blacklozenge$

When we are applying a binomial expansion with a negative or fractional power, the first term in brackets must be 1. However, we can still use this method if the first term is not 1 by taking out a factor. This is demonstrated in the example below.

Example 4.32

Expand $\dfrac{1 + x}{2 + 3x}$ as a series as far as the term in x^3. State the range of values of x for which this expansion is valid.

Solution

We start by writing $(2+3x)^{-1}$ as $2^{-1}(1+\frac{3}{2}x)^{-1}$. We then expand the term $(1+\frac{3}{2}x)^{-1}$ as follows:

$$(1+\tfrac{3}{2}x)^{-1} = 1 - \tfrac{3}{2}x + \frac{(-1)(-2)}{2!}\left(\tfrac{3}{2}x\right)^2 + \frac{(-1)(-2)(-3)}{3!}\left(\tfrac{3}{2}x\right)^3 + \cdots$$

$$= 1 - \tfrac{3}{2}x + \left(\tfrac{3}{2}x\right)^2 - \left(\tfrac{3}{2}x\right)^3 + \cdots$$

Hence:

$$\frac{1+x}{2+3x} = (1+x)(2+3x)^{-1} = 2^{-1}(1+x)(1+\tfrac{3}{2}x)^{-1}$$

$$= 2^{-1}(1+x)\left(1 - \tfrac{3}{2}x + \left(\tfrac{3}{2}x\right)^2 - \left(\tfrac{3}{2}x\right)^3 + \cdots\right)$$

$$= 2^{-1}(1+x)\left(1 - \tfrac{3}{2}x + \tfrac{9}{4}x^2 - \tfrac{27}{8}x^3 + \cdots\right)$$

$$= \tfrac{1}{2}\left(1 - \tfrac{3}{2}x + \tfrac{9}{4}x^2 - \tfrac{27}{8}x^3 + x - \tfrac{3}{2}x^2 + \tfrac{9}{4}x^3 + \cdots\right)$$

$$= \tfrac{1}{2} - \tfrac{1}{4}x + \tfrac{3}{8}x^2 - \tfrac{9}{16}x^3 + \cdots$$

This expansion is valid for $-1 < \frac{3}{2}x < 1$, ie for $-\frac{2}{3} < x < \frac{2}{3}$.   ♦♦

The formulae for binomial expansions are summarised in the box below.

Binomial expansions

If $n \in \mathbb{Z}^+$, then:

$$(a+b)^n = \binom{n}{0}a^n + \binom{n}{1}a^{n-1}b + \binom{n}{2}a^{n-2}b^2 + \cdots + \binom{n}{n-1}ab^{n-1} + \binom{n}{n}b^n$$

$\forall\, a, b \in \mathbb{R}$.

If $n \notin \mathbb{Z}^+$, then:

$$(1+x)^n = 1 + nx + \frac{n(n-1)}{2!}x^2 + \frac{n(n-1)(n-2)}{3!}x^3 + \cdots$$

for $-1 < x < 1$.

Chapter 4 Practice Questions

◆ Algebraic expressions

Question 4.1

Simplify the expression $2x^b\left(x^2\right)^b + 2x^b x^3$.

Question 4.2

Simplify the expression $2\log_a\left(\dfrac{x}{y}\right) + \log_a y$.

Question 4.3

Express $\dfrac{x+3}{3x+1} - \dfrac{5-2x}{x-1}$ as a single fraction.

◆ Quadratic polynomials

Question 4.4

Simplify $\dfrac{x+3}{2x^2-3x-2} \div \dfrac{x^2+x-6}{2x^2+3x+1}$.

Question 4.5

Factorise the quadratic $2x^2 - 5x - 3$. Hence, or otherwise, determine the roots of the equation $2x^2 - 5x - 3 = 0$.

Question 4.6

Solve the quadratic equation $x^2 - 12x + 12 = 0$.

◆ Simultaneous equations

Question 4.7

Solve the following equations simultaneously:

$$\frac{\alpha}{\alpha+\beta} = 0.75$$

$$\frac{\alpha\beta}{(\alpha+\beta)^2(\alpha+\beta+1)} = 0.0225$$

Question 4.8

If $e^{\mu + \frac{1}{2}\sigma^2} = 3$, and $e^{2\mu + \sigma^2}(e^{\sigma^2} - 1) = 11.2$, calculate the values of μ and σ.

Question 4.9

Solve the following equations simultaneously:

$$\frac{\lambda}{\alpha - 1} = 9 \qquad \frac{\alpha \lambda^2}{(\alpha - 1)^2 (\alpha - 2)} = 162$$

◆ Inequalities

Question 4.10

Determine the values of x that satisfy the inequality $|2x - 3| < 7$.

Question 4.11

Determine the values of x that satisfy the inequality $x^2 - x - 12 < 0$.

◆ Arithmetic and geometric progressions

Question 4.12

Susan has made a New Year's resolution to save money. She decided to deposit £1 in a savings account in the first week of the year, followed by £3 in the second week, £5 in the third week, and so on. Calculate the total amount that Susan deposits in the first 26 weeks of the year.

Question 4.13

Evaluate $\displaystyle\sum_{k=1}^{\infty} \frac{210}{4^k}$.

Question 4.14

Calculate the sum of the first 20 terms of the sequence $1, 1.5, 1.5^2, 1.5^3, \dots$.

◆ Sums involving positive integers

Question 4.15

Evaluate the following sum:

$$51^2 + 52^2 + 53^2 + \dots + 100^2$$

You may use the result $\displaystyle\sum_{k=1}^{n} k^2 = \frac{1}{6}n(n+1)(2n+1)$.

◆ Double summations

Question 4.16

Which of the following expressions is equal to $\displaystyle\sum_{y=1}^{20} y \sum_{x=y}^{20} x^2$?

A $\displaystyle\sum_{x=1}^{20} x^2 \sum_{y=1}^{20} y$

B $\displaystyle\sum_{x=1}^{20} x^2 \sum_{y=x}^{20} y$

C $\displaystyle\sum_{x=y}^{20} x^2 \sum_{y=1}^{20} y$

D $\displaystyle\sum_{x=1}^{20} x^2 \sum_{y=1}^{x} y$

Question 4.17

Evaluate $\displaystyle\sum_{x=1}^{6} \sum_{y=x}^{6} 2x(y-1)$ by swapping the order of summation or otherwise.

You may use the results $\displaystyle\sum_{k=1}^{n} k = \tfrac{1}{2}n(n+1)$ and $\displaystyle\sum_{k=1}^{n} k^3 = \tfrac{1}{4}n^2(n+1)^2$.

◆ Binomial expansions

Question 4.18

Determine the coefficient of $x^5 y^3$ in the expansion of the expression $(x+4y)^8$.

Question 4.19

Obtain the binomial expansion of $(3x+2)^{-2}$ as far as the term in x^3 and state the range of values of x for which this expansion is valid.

5

Numerical Methods II

Learning Objectives

The following learning objectives are covered in this chapter:

- expressing quantities as percentages or per mil
- calculating absolute change, proportionate change and percentage change
- calculating absolute error, proportionate error and percentage error
- using linear interpolation
- solving difference equations.

5.1   Percentages

Actuaries frequently have to calculate a *percentage* of a number, particularly in the context of interest rates. For example, if the annual interest rate is 6% and an investment of £5,000 is made at the start of a year then the interest earned during the year is 6% of £5,000.

Percent literally means *out of a hundred*, so to find a percentage, p, of a number L we calculate:

$$\frac{p}{100} \times L$$

Example 5.1

Calculate 7.5% of $2,500.

Solution

$$\frac{7.5}{100} \times \$2,500 = 0.075 \times \$2,500 = \$187.50 \qquad\qquad \blacklozenge\blacklozenge$$

We might also have to calculate the new value of a number after a percentage increase or decrease. For example, we might need to calculate the total number of members of a pension scheme after an increase of 2% in the number of members. Alternatively, we could be expected to calculate the original number of members given the number after the increase.

Example 5.2

The price of an item in a shop is £15.75. Find the new price if it is:

(i)   increased by 1.2%

(ii)   decreased by 5%.

Solution

(i)   Increasing the price by 1.2% means that it will now be $100\% + 1.2\% = 101.2\%$ of the
        original price:

$$\frac{101.2}{100} \times £15.75 = 1.012 \times £15.75 = £15.94$$

(ii)   Decreasing the price by 5% means that it will now be $100\% - 5\% = 95\%$ of the original
        price:

$$\frac{95}{100} \times £15.75 = 0.95 \times £15.75 = £14.96$$

In each case we have rounded the final answer to two decimal places because we are working in pounds and pence. $\qquad\qquad \blacklozenge\blacklozenge$

Example 5.3

The new price of an item in a shop is £60. Find the *original* price if it was:

(i)   increased by 20%

(ii)   decreased by 20%.

Solution

(i)   If the price was increased by 20% then the new price is $100\% + 20\% = 120\%$ of the original price. Using x to stand for the original price, we have:

$$\frac{120}{100} \times x = 1.20 \times x = £60 \quad \Rightarrow \quad x = \frac{60}{1.20} = £50$$

(ii)   If the price was decreased by 20% then the new price is $100\% - 20\% = 80\%$ of the original price. Using x to stand for the original price, we have:

$$\frac{80}{100} \times x = 0.80 \times x = £60 \quad \Rightarrow \quad x = \frac{60}{0.8} = £75 \qquad \blacklozenge\blacklozenge$$

It is important to be able to express a quantity A as a percentage of another quantity B. Actuaries need to do this in order to calculate measures such as profit margins for an insurance company. Quantity A is calculated as a percentage of quantity B as follows:

$$\frac{A}{B} \times 100\%$$

Example 5.4

At the start of year 1, a group consists of 51,890 people. By the start of year 2, there are 51,548 people still alive. Determine the percentage of the group that died in year 1.

Solution

In the group, $51,890 - 51,548 = 342$ people have died. Expressing this as a percentage of the original group:

$$\frac{342}{51,890} \times 100\% = 0.66\% \qquad \blacklozenge\blacklozenge$$

It is also possible to express a quantity *per mil*, which means *out of a thousand*. Per mil is written as ‰. Actuaries use this notation in connection with insurance premiums, which are often small percentages so writing them per thousand rather than per hundred makes them easier to interpret.

Example 5.5

Express the number of people who have died in Example 5.4 as a rate per mil.

Solution

0.66% is equivalent to 6.6‰ since $\dfrac{0.66}{100} = \dfrac{6.6}{1,000}$. $\qquad \blacklozenge\blacklozenge$

5.2   Changes

Example 5.4 is really asking about the percentage *change* in the population, and in this section we are going to look at different ways of expressing change.

◆▷ Absolute change

The *absolute change* is the difference between two values. The absolute change can be positive or negative.

Absolute change

absolute change = new value − original value

Example 5.6

Calculate the absolute change in the population described in Example 5.4.

Solution

The absolute change is −342, since the population decreased by 342 people.   ◆ ◆

◆▷ Proportionate change

The absolute change gives no indication of the size of the change compared to the original number. For example, there is an absolute change of 1 when a population increases from 3 to 4 people, or from 340,025 to 340,026 people. The *proportionate change* looks at the change relative to the original number. We calculate the proportionate change by dividing the absolute change by the original number.

Proportionate change

$$\text{proportionate change} = \frac{\text{absolute change}}{\text{original value}}$$

Proportionate change is sometimes called *relative change*.

Example 5.7

Calculate the proportionate change in the price of a car that decreases from £9,950 to £9,550.

Solution

The absolute change is −£400, so the proportionate change is $-\dfrac{£400}{£9,950} = -0.04$ to 1SF.   ◆ ◆

This answer has no units of measurement, since we have divided pounds by pounds. We say that quantities without units, such as the proportionate change, are *dimensionless*. We looked at dimensions in Chapter 1.

◆▷ *Percentage change*

The *percentage change* is the proportionate change expressed as a percentage.

Percentage change

$$\text{percentage change} = \frac{\text{absolute change}}{\text{original value}} \times 100\%$$

 ### *Example 5.8*

Calculate the percentage change for Example 5.7.

Solution

The proportionate change is −0.04 so the percentage change is −0.04×100% = 4% to 1SF. ◆◆

5.3   *Errors*

Errors are similar to changes in that they look at differences, but errors refer specifically to differences between an *actual* value and an *estimated* value. For example, if we are given population figures of 42,000 and 42,540 this could represent an absolute change of 540 or −540.

Let's consider that the value 42,540 is the *actual* population figure and that 42,000 is an *estimate* of the population arrived at by a statistician.

The *absolute error* is the difference between the estimated value and the actual value, which is −540 here.

Another way of describing the *estimated* value is the *expected, approximate* or *experimental* value and another way of describing the actual value is the *true* or *accurate* value. By using errors we make it clear how big the difference is and whether the estimated figure is higher or lower than the actual value.

As in Section 5.2 on changes, there are three definitions for errors.

Errors

$$\text{absolute error} = \text{approx value} - \text{true value}$$

$$\text{proportionate error} = \frac{\text{absolute error}}{\text{true value}}$$

$$\text{percentage error} = \frac{\text{absolute error}}{\text{true value}} \times 100\%$$

Example 5.9

The definition of v is $v = \dfrac{1}{1+i}$ and the true value of i is 0.0372534. Calculate the absolute, proportionate, and percentage error that will be introduced in the value of v by rounding i to two decimal places.

Solution

The true value of v is $\dfrac{1}{1.0372534}$. When we round i to 2DP we obtain 0.04, which gives v to be $\dfrac{1}{1.04}$.

The absolute error is $\dfrac{1}{1.04} - \dfrac{1}{1.0372534} = -0.0025$ to 4DP.

The proportionate error is $\dfrac{\dfrac{1}{1.04} - \dfrac{1}{1.0372534}}{\dfrac{1}{1.0372534}} = -0.0026$ to 4DP.

The percentage error is $-0.0026 \times 100\% = -0.26\%$.   ◆◆

5.4 Interpolation

Sometimes it is not possible to find an exact solution to an equation such as $f(x) = 0$ by algebraic methods. However, we can determine an approximate value by using a method called *linear interpolation*. To do this we need to determine two values of the function, evaluated at values of x either side of the true value, say x_1 and x_2. As the name suggests, we then assume that the function is linear between x_1 and x_2. To illustrate the scenario and the difference between the true and approximate solution consider the following diagram:

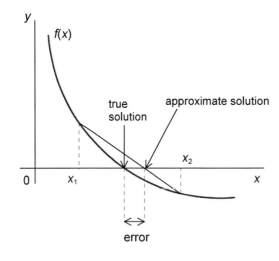

This shows the graph of $y = f(x)$, with the values x_1 and x_2, and the error that this interpolation has introduced. Do be aware however that we have drawn a large-scale diagram with a function with high curvature and we have chosen x_1 and x_2 to be some distance away from the true value just for illustration, so in reality the difference between the true and approximate solution is likely to be smaller.

Example 5.10

If $f(1) = -1$ and $f(2) = 3$, calculate x so that $f(x) = 0$ using linear interpolation.

Solution

Since 0 is 25% of the way from -1 to 3, the solution for x is 25% of the way from 1 to 2 which is 1.25.   ♦♦

We will now look at how we can use an algebraic approach to interpolation. Consider the following diagram:

By considering the ratio of 'lengths' above and below the line, we can write:

$$\frac{x - x_1}{x_2 - x_1} = \frac{f(x) - f(x_1)}{f(x_2) - f(x_1)}$$

This can be rearranged to give:

$$x = x_1 + \frac{f(x) - f(x_1)}{f(x_2) - f(x_1)}(x_2 - x_1)$$

This gives us a formula for x. It doesn't actually matter which value we call x_1 and which we call x_2. This formula will give the same answer either way. It is important to understand how this formula is derived rather than trying to learn it. We will now repeat the previous example using an algebraic approach.

Example 5.11

If $f(1) = -1$ and $f(2) = 3$, calculate x so that $f(x) = 0$ using linear interpolation.

Solution

$$
\begin{array}{ccc}
-1 & 0 & 3 \\
\end{array}
$$

$$
\begin{array}{ccc}
1 & x & 2 \\
\end{array}
$$

By considering the ratio of 'lengths' above and below the line, we can write:

$$\frac{x - 1}{2 - 1} = \frac{0 - (-1)}{3 - (-1)}$$

This can be rearranged to give:

$$x = 1 + \frac{0 - (-1)}{3 - (-1)}(1) = 1.25$$

◆◆

Example 5.12

Determine an approximate solution to the equation $f(x) = 0$ given $f(1.34) = 0.523$ and $f(1.65) = -0.42$.

Solution

We know that the value of x that satisfies $f(x) = 0$ lies somewhere between 1.34 and 1.65, so:

$$\frac{x - 1.65}{1.34 - 1.65} = \frac{0 - (-0.42)}{0.523 - (-0.42)}$$

which gives $x = 1.51$ (to 3SF).

◆◆

Notice that the answer of 1.51 is closer to 1.65 than 1.34 since $f(1.65)$ is closer to zero than $f(1.34)$.

We can use interpolation to find either the value of x or the value of the function.

Example 5.13

This is an extract from a table of values for a function $F(x)$:

x	$F(x)$
0.54	0.70540
0.55	0.70884
0.56	0.71226

Using linear interpolation, determine:

(i)   the value of $F(x)$ when $x = 0.548$

(ii)   the value of x when $F(x) = 0.71$.

Solution

(i)   Using the formula for interpolation:

$$F(0.548) = 0.70540 + \frac{(0.548 - 0.54)}{0.55 - 0.54}(0.70884 - 0.70540) = 0.708$$

(ii)   Using the formula:

$$x = 0.55 + \frac{(0.71 - 0.70884)}{0.71226 - 0.70884}(0.56 - 0.55) = 0.553$$

◆◆

Key points about linear interpolation

The answer obtained will only be close to the true value of x if x_1 and x_2 are relatively close to that true value.

The answer obtained will only be close to the true value of x if $f(x)$ is approximately linear between x_1 and x_2.

The solution is only approximate (unless the function is truly linear).

The main advantage of linear interpolation is that we can obtain an approximate solution to an equation that is otherwise not possible to solve.

We can actually use the same method when x_1 and x_2 both lie on the same side of x, in which case it is called extrapolation, rather than interpolation. However, it is best to use interpolation, as this usually gives more accurate results.

Despite the disadvantages of linear interpolation, this is often the method to use in practice. We just need to be aware that the answer may be slightly inaccurate.

5.5   Difference equations

Another type of equation that we need to solve by a special method is a *difference equation*.

Difference equations arise when we are considering a sequence of numbers and want to define a relationship between its values. For example, consider the 'triangular' numbers:

$$1, \quad 1+2=3, \quad 1+2+3=6, \quad 1+2+3+4=10,\ldots$$

The difference equation that can be used to describe this sequence is $y_t = y_{t-1} + t$. For example, the fourth number in the sequence is $y_4 = y_3 + 4$, *ie* the third value plus 4.

Example 5.14

Given the difference equation $y_t = 3y_{t-1} + t - 1$ and the value $y_1 = 2$, calculate y_2 and y_3.

Solution

Using the difference equation with $t = 2$, we obtain $y_2 = 3y_1 + 2 - 1 = 3 \times 2 + 2 - 1 = 7$ and using the difference equation with $t = 3$, we obtain $y_3 = 3y_2 + 3 - 1 = 3 \times 7 + 3 - 1 = 23$.   ♦♦

We can solve simple difference equations (*ie* determine an expression for y_t that doesn't involve other y values) by repeated substitution.

Example 5.15

Solve the difference equation $y_t = y_{t-1} + 1$ given the value $y_1 = 1$.

Solution

Using the difference equation we can write out expressions for y_{t-1}, y_{t-2} etc:

$$y_{t-1} = y_{t-2} + 1, \; y_{t-2} = y_{t-3} + 1$$

We can substitute these into the expression for y_t:

$$y_t = y_{t-1} + 1$$
$$= (y_{t-2} + 1) + 1 = y_{t-2} + 2$$
$$= (y_{t-3} + 1) + 2 = y_{t-3} + 3$$

We can see a pattern building up, so that in general we would get $y_t = y_{t-a} + a$. We know the value of y_1, so let's use $a = t - 1$ (since we then have $t - a = t - (t - 1) = 1$):

$$y_t = y_{t-(t-1)} + t - 1 = y_1 + t - 1$$

Substituting the value of y_1 into this expression, we obtain:

$$y_t = y_1 + t - 1 = 1 + t - 1 = t \quad \Rightarrow \quad y_t = t \qquad \blacklozenge \blacklozenge$$

So far we have considered *first order* difference equations (where y_t is defined in terms of y_{t-1}), which can be simple to deal with. However we may need to work with *second order* difference equations, where the relationship between three consecutive values is defined. An example of a second order difference equation is $y_t = 3y_{t-1} + 2y_{t-2}$. These are more complicated to solve.

We are now going to set out the steps in the method for solving the second order difference equation $ay_t + by_{t-1} + cy_{t-2} = 0$ to determine a solution of the form $y_t = f(t)$.

We first need to define the *auxiliary equation*. The auxiliary equation is obtained by replacing y_t by λ^2, y_{t-1} by λ and y_{t-2} by 1. So the auxiliary equation for the difference equation $ay_t + by_{t-1} + cy_{t-2} = 0$ is $a\lambda^2 + b\lambda + c = 0$.

Step 1

Solve the auxiliary equation $a\lambda^2 + b\lambda + c = 0$, to obtain the roots λ_1 and λ_2.

Step 2

The *general solution* of the difference equation depends on the roots λ_1 and λ_2 of the auxiliary equation, as follows:

$b^2 - 4ac$	Nature of the roots	General solution of the difference equation
> 0	The auxiliary equation has two distinct real roots: $\lambda_1 \neq \lambda_2$	$y_t = A\lambda_1^t + B\lambda_2^t$
$= 0$	There is only one (repeated) root: $\lambda_1 = \lambda_2 = \lambda$	$y_t = (A + Bt)\lambda^t$

If there are two different roots it doesn't matter which one we call λ_1 and which one we call λ_2.

Step 3

If we are given additional information, called the *boundary conditions*, then we can determine the *particular solution*. This means working out the values of A and B in the above general solutions.

 Example 5.16

Solve the difference equations:

(i) $y_t - 5y_{t-1} + 6y_{t-2} = 0$ given that $y_0 = 0$ and $y_1 = 1$

(ii) $y_{t+2} - 6y_{t+1} + 9y_t = 0$

Solution

(i)   The auxiliary equation is $\lambda^2 - 5\lambda + 6 = 0$, which can be factorised to $(\lambda - 2)(\lambda - 3) = 0$. So the equation has roots 2 and 3.

The general solution is of the form $y_t = A \times 2^t + B \times 3^t$.

However we know that $y_0 = 0$ and $y_1 = 1$, so:

$$y_0 = 0 = A \times 2^0 + B \times 3^0 \quad \Rightarrow \quad 0 = A + B$$
$$y_1 = 1 = A \times 2^1 + B \times 3^1 \quad \Rightarrow \quad 1 = 2A + 3B$$

Subtracting twice the first equation from the second, we obtain $B = 1$ and $A = -1$, so our particular solution is:

$$y_t = (-1) \times 2^t + 1 \times 3^t = 3^t - 2^t$$

We can check that this result is consistent with the boundary conditions $y_0 = 0$ and $y_1 = 1$:

$$y_0 = 3^0 - 2^0 = 1 - 1 = 0$$

$$y_1 = 3^1 - 2^1 = 3 - 2 = 1$$

(ii)   The auxiliary equation is $\lambda^2 - 6\lambda + 9 = 0$, which can be factorised to give $(\lambda - 3)^2 = 0$. The equation has one (repeated) root of 3.

The general solution is of the form $y_t = (A + Bt)3^t$.   ◆◆

Chapter 5 Practice Questions

◆ *Percentages*

Question 5.1

The population on 1 January each year is 5% higher than on the previous 1 January.

(i)   Calculate how many complete years it would take for the population to at least double.

(ii)   If the population was 66,150,000 on 1 January 2012, calculate the population on 1 January 2010.

Question 5.2

The population of a country at the start of the year is 62,400,000. The population at the end of the year is 63,760,000. Express the change in population as a rate per mil.

Question 5.3

An item has increased in cost by 30% to $58.50. Calculate the original cost.

◆ *Changes*

Question 5.4

A man's annual wage has risen from £14,567 to £15,034. Calculate the absolute, proportionate and percentage changes in his wage.

Question 5.5

Calculate the proportionate change in the price of a house that increases from £180,000 to £210,000.

◆ *Errors*

Question 5.6

In an actuarial calculation, a student uses $i = 0.027$, having rounded the precise value of i to 2 significant figures. Calculate the largest magnitude of percentage error that could have been made in the calculated value of $v = \dfrac{1}{1+i}$. Hint: work out the value of v when $i = 0.0265$ and when $i = 0.0275$.

Question 5.7

When calculating $y = \sqrt[3]{x}$, a student uses $x = 50$, having rounded the value of x to 2 significant figures. Calculate the maximum magnitude of absolute error possible here.

Question 5.8

A student knows that a equals 5,000 correct to one significant figure and b equals 0.20 correct to two decimal places. The student calculates a/b to be 25,000. Calculate the greatest percentage by which the student might be overestimating the true value.

◆ Interpolation

Question 5.9

Determine two consecutive integer values either side of the value of x, which satisfies $x^3 - 5x^2 + 3x + 7 = 0$. Hence, using linear interpolation, determine an approximate solution of the equation.

Question 5.10

Given the following values:

$$\Phi(1.20) = 0.88493 \qquad \Phi(1.21) = 0.88686$$

use linear interpolation to calculate the value of $\Phi(1.207)$.

◆ Difference equations

Question 5.11

Solve the difference equations:

(i) $y_t - 8y_{t-1} + 16y_{t-2} = 0$ given that $y_0 = -1$ and $y_1 = 3$

(ii) $y_t = 4y_{t-1} - 4y_{t-2}$

Question 5.12

Determine the solution of the difference equation:

$$y_t + 6y_{t-1} + 8y_{t-2} = 0$$

given that y_0 and y_1 are both equal to 5.

6

Differentiation

Learning Objectives

The following learning objectives are covered in this chapter:

- Understanding that the derivative gives the rate of change of a function as the input variable is changed and that it can be interpreted as the slope of a curve.

- Differentiating the standard functions x^n, e^x, $\ln x$ and c^x.

- Using the product rule, the quotient rule and the chain rule for differentiation.

- Evaluating higher-order derivatives and understanding how these can be used to determine where the maximum or minimum points of a function occur.

- Using partial differentiation to find the extreme values of functions of two variables.

- Applying Maclaurin series and Taylor series to obtain the power series expansion of a function.

6.1   *Differentiation from first principles*

The process of *differentiation* enables us to work out:

- the slope (or gradient) of a curve at a given point on a graph, or equivalently,

- the rate of change of the value of a function, as its input variable changes.

The function obtained as a result of the process of differentiation is known as a *derivative*.

To understand how differentiation can be interpreted in these two ways, we will consider the general function $y = f(x)$ and two points lying on the graph of this function, $P_1 = (x, f(x))$ and $P_2 = (x + h, f(x + h))$, as shown in the diagram below.

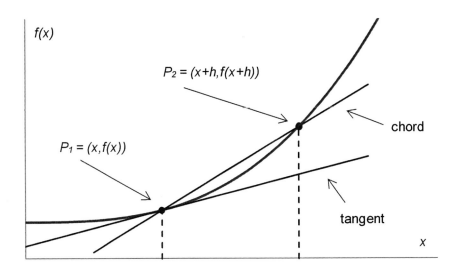

The slope of the curve at the point P_1 will be the same as the slope of the tangent to the curve at that point shown in the diagram. To work out the slope of the tangent, we can start off by considering the straight line joining P_1 to P_2, which is known as a *chord*. The slope of this chord is found by dividing the vertical separation between the two points by the horizontal separation, giving $\dfrac{f(x + h) - f(x)}{h}$.

Now, as h gets smaller and smaller, P_2 slides down the curve towards P_1, and the chord gets closer and closer to the tangent at P_1, until they coincide. Mathematically, this process of letting h get smaller and smaller is known as *taking the limit as h tends to zero*, and is written as $\lim\limits_{h \to 0}$.

So, the gradient of the curve $y = f(x)$ at the point P_1 is given by:

$$\lim_{h \to 0} \frac{f(x + h) - f(x)}{h}$$

This is known as the derivative of the function $y = f(x)$ with respect to x and is written as either $f'(x)$, where the dash denotes differentiation, or $\dfrac{dy}{dx}$.

In order to interpret the derivative as the rate of change of the function $y = f(x)$, first of all we note that the *overall* change in the value of the function between P_1 and P_2 is $f(x+h) - f(x)$. To find the change in $y = f(x)$ from P_1 to P_2 per unit change in x, we divide this overall change by the change in x between the two points, which is h. This gives us the *average rate of change* as $\dfrac{f(x+h) - f(x)}{h}$.

Again, using the idea of letting h get smaller and smaller, so that P_2 gets closer and closer to P_1, we define $\lim\limits_{h \to 0} \dfrac{f(x+h) - f(x)}{h}$ to be the rate of change of $y = f(x)$ with respect to x at the point P_1.

Differentiation from first principles

The derivative of the function $y = f(x)$ with respect to x is given by:

$$f'(x) = \frac{dy}{dx} = \lim_{h \to 0} \frac{f(x+h) - f(x)}{h}$$

Example 6.1

By considering the gradient of the chord joining two points on the curve $y = x^2$, find $\dfrac{dy}{dx}$.

Solution

Consider the points $P_1 = (x, x^2)$ and $P_2 = ((x+h), (x+h)^2)$. The gradient of the chord joining these two points is given by $\dfrac{(x+h)^2 - x^2}{h}$. Simplifying this expression for the gradient gives:

$$\frac{(x+h)^2 - x^2}{h} = \frac{x^2 + 2xh + h^2 - x^2}{h} = \frac{2xh + h^2}{h} = 2x + h$$

So:

$$\frac{dy}{dx} = \lim_{h \to 0} \frac{(x+h)^2 - x^2}{h} = \lim_{h \to 0} (2x + h) = 2x \qquad \blacklozenge\blacklozenge$$

The method used in the above example, where we find a derivative by directly evaluating the limit of the average rate of change, is called *differentiation from first principles*.

Most of the time, we avoid the need for differentiation from first principles by using standard results and rules for finding derivatives, which are covered in the next two sections.

6.2   *Differentiation of standard functions*

In this section, we will consider the derivatives of the standard functions x^n, e^x, $\ln x$ and c^x.

◇ *Differentiating x^n*

In Example 6.1, we saw that the derivative of $y = x^2$ was given by $\dfrac{dy}{dx} = 2x$. We can see in this case that the derivative is obtained by multiplying the function by the original power of x (which was 2) and reducing the power of x by one (from 2 to 1).

This process of 'bringing the old power to the front and reducing the power by one' works for powers of x other than 2, giving us the general rule that if $y = x^n$, then $\dfrac{dy}{dx} = nx^{n-1}$.

This rule can be used for all values of n (including fractions and negative numbers, for example) except $n = 0$. If $n = 0$, then we are considering x^0, which is equal to 1 whatever the value of x. Since 1 is a constant, its derivative (or rate of change) is zero.

Example 6.2

Differentiate the following with respect to x:

(i) $y = 7\sqrt{x}$

(ii) $y = \dfrac{3}{x^2}$

(iii) $y = 5x^3 - 3x^2 + 7x + 2$

Solution

(i)   Recall that $\sqrt{x} = x^{\frac{1}{2}}$, so $y = 7x^{\frac{1}{2}}$. Therefore:

$$\frac{dy}{dx} = 7 \times \frac{1}{2} x^{-\frac{1}{2}} = \frac{7}{2\sqrt{x}}$$

This illustrates that when a function is multiplied by a constant (*eg* the 7), its derivative is also multiplied by the same constant.

(ii)   We can write $\dfrac{3}{x^2}$ as $3x^{-2}$, so:

$$\frac{dy}{dx} = 3 \times (-2) x^{-3} = -\frac{6}{x^3}$$

(iii)   Here we use the idea that the derivative of a sum is the sum of the derivatives to give:

$$\frac{dy}{dx} = 5 \times 3x^2 - 3 \times 2x^1 + 7 \times x^0$$

$$= 15x^2 - 6x + 7$$

Note that the derivative of the +2 term is zero as 2 is a constant.   ♦♦

Differentiating the exponential and natural logarithm functions

The standard results to use when differentiating the exponential function, e^x, and the natural logarithm function, $\ln x$, are:

$$\frac{d}{dx}\left(e^x\right) = e^x$$

and: $$\frac{d}{dx}\left(\ln x\right) = \frac{1}{x}$$

You need to be able to use these results, but you do not need to be able to prove them.

Example 6.3

Differentiate the following with respect to x :

(i) $y = 2e^{x+8} - 1$

(ii) $y = \ln(3x)$

Solution

(i)   We can write e^{x+8} as $e^x \times e^8$ using a power law, so:

$$\frac{dy}{dx} = \frac{d}{dx}\left(2e^{x+8} - 1\right) = \frac{d}{dx}\left(2e^8 \times e^x - 1\right) = 2e^8 \times e^x = 2e^{x+8}$$

(ii)   We can write $\ln(3x)$ as $\ln 3 + \ln x$ using a log law. Since $\ln 3$ is a constant, its derivative is zero, so:

$$\frac{dy}{dx} = \frac{d}{dx}\left(\ln 3x\right) = \frac{d}{dx}\left(\ln 3 + \ln x\right) = \frac{1}{x}$$ ♦♦

Differentiating c^x

We have seen above that the derivative of e^x is itself. We might also want to find the derivative of the function c^x, where c is a positive number not equal to e. In this case, the standard result is:

$$\frac{d}{dx}\left(c^x\right) = c^x \ln c$$

We will derive this result in the next section, using the chain rule.

Example 6.4

Evaluate the derivative of the function $y = 9^x$ when $x = 2$.

Solution

Since $y = 9^x$, we can use the standard result above with $c = 9$ to give:

$$\frac{dy}{dx} = 9^x \ln 9$$

To evaluate this when $x = 2$, we substitute this value of x into the formula for the derivative, to give:

$$9^2 \ln 9 = 81 \ln 9 = 177.975$$

The high value obtained here shows that the graph of this function is very steep at this point. ♦ ♦

The table below summarises the standard results for differentiation that we've met in this section.

Derivatives of standard functions

Function	Derivative
x^n	nx^{n-1}, $n \neq 0$
e^x	e^x
$\ln x$	$\dfrac{1}{x}$
c^x	$c^x \ln c$

6.3   *Rules for differentiation*

We have already seen the following basic rules to use when differentiating:

Basic rules of differentiation

- For any constant c, $\dfrac{d}{dx}(c) = 0$.

- For any two functions, $f(x)$ and $g(x)$, $\dfrac{d}{dx}(f(x) + g(x)) = \dfrac{d}{dx}(f(x)) + \dfrac{d}{dx}(g(x))$.

- For any function $f(x)$ and any constant c, $\dfrac{d}{dx}(cf(x)) = c\dfrac{d}{dx}(f(x))$.

We will now consider three rules that can help when differentiating more complex functions:

- the product rule
- the quotient rule
- the chain rule (which is sometimes referred to as the 'function of a function' rule).

Product rule

We can use the product rule when the function we need to differentiate is a product of functions, such as $f(x) = x \ln x$.

Product rule

If u and v are functions of x, and $f(x) = uv$, then:

$$f'(x) = \frac{df}{dx} = uv' + vu' = u\frac{dv}{dx} + v\frac{du}{dx}$$

Informally, this rule says that to differentiate a product we differentiate each factor in turn (leaving the other factor the same) and then add the results together. It doesn't matter which factor you choose to differentiate first, as we can alternatively state the product rule as:

$$f'(x) = \frac{df}{dx} = u'v + uv' = \frac{du}{dx}v + u\frac{dv}{dx}$$

which gives the same result as in the box above.

 Example 6.5

Differentiate $f(x) = x \ln x$.

Solution

We can set $u = x$ and $v = \ln x$, so that $u' = 1$ and $v' = \dfrac{1}{x}$, which gives:

$$f'(x) = \left(x \times \frac{1}{x}\right) + \left(1 \times \ln x\right) = 1 + \ln x \qquad \blacklozenge\blacklozenge$$

The product rule can also be applied when there are more than two factors involved in the function to be differentiated. For example, if $y = uvw$, then we can treat this first of all as a product of u and vw, and apply the product rule to give $\dfrac{dy}{dx} = u \times \dfrac{d}{dx}(vw) + vw \times \dfrac{du}{dx}$. We can then apply the product rule again to find $\dfrac{d}{dx}(vw) = v \times \dfrac{dw}{dx} + w \times \dfrac{dv}{dx}$. Putting this all together gives:

$$\frac{d}{dx}(uvw) = u \times \frac{d}{dx}(vw) + vw \times \frac{du}{dx}$$

$$= u\left(v \times \frac{dw}{dx} + w \times \frac{dv}{dx}\right) + vw \times \frac{du}{dx}$$

$$= uv\frac{dw}{dx} + uw\frac{dv}{dx} + vw\frac{du}{dx}$$

So, as in the two-factor case, we need to differentiate each factor in turn (leaving the other factors alone) and then add the results together.

◆ *Quotient rule*

We can use the quotient rule when the function we need to differentiate is expressed as a fraction or *quotient* of functions, such as $f(x) = \dfrac{x}{3x+1}$.

Quotient rule

If *u* and *v* are functions of *x*, and $f(x) = \dfrac{u}{v}$, then:

$$f'(x) = \frac{vu' - uv'}{v^2} = \frac{v\frac{du}{dx} - u\frac{dv}{dx}}{v^2}$$

Example 6.6

Differentiate $f(x) = \dfrac{x}{3x+1}$.

Solution

Using the quotient rule, we can set $u = x$ and $v = 3x+1$, so that $u' = 1$ and $v' = 3$, which gives:

$$f'(x) = \frac{(3x+1) \times 1 - x \times 3}{(3x+1)^2} = \frac{1}{(3x+1)^2}$$

◆◆

◆ *Chain rule*

The chain rule is also known as the 'function of a function' rule. It is used to differentiate expressions involving nested functions (*ie* functions of functions).

For example, instead of $y = x^n$ where *y* is a direct function of the value of *x*, we may have $y = (f(x))^n$, in which *y* is a function of $f(x)$, which is itself a function of *x*. Similarly, instead of $y = e^x$, we may have $y = e^{f(x)}$, and instead of $y = \ln x$, we may have $y = \ln f(x)$.

Differentiating these nested functions can be quite difficult or messy using standard techniques alone. For example, to differentiate $(3x^2 + 2x - 1)^5$ without the chain rule we'd have to multiply out the brackets and this would be extremely time consuming!

To use the chain rule, we give the nested function a name. Here, we call it '*u*'.

Chain rule

If *y* is a function of *u*, and *u* is a function of *x*, then:

$$\frac{dy}{dx} = \frac{dy}{du} \times \frac{du}{dx}$$

Example 6.7

If $y = \left(3x^2 + 2x - 1\right)^5$, find an expression for $\dfrac{dy}{dx}$.

Solution

First of all, we set $u = 3x^2 + 2x - 1$, so we have $y = u^5$. Next, we differentiate the two parts:

$$\frac{du}{dx} = 6x + 2$$

$$\frac{dy}{du} = 5u^4$$

To obtain the second of these derivatives, we have differentiated y with respect to u, ie we have treated u as the variable that is changing.

Using these derivatives gives:

$$\frac{dy}{dx} = \frac{dy}{du} \times \frac{du}{dx} = 5u^4 \times (6x + 2)$$

Replacing u gives:

$$\frac{dy}{dx} = 5\left(3x^2 + 2x - 1\right)^4 \times (6x + 2)$$ ◆◆

In practice, these stages are not usually written out in full as the answer can be written down immediately.

The thought process when differentiating $y = \left(f(x)\right)^n$ using the chain rule is to differentiate the bracketed term 'as normal' (ie bringing the old power to the front and reducing the power by one), to give $n\left(f(x)\right)^{n-1}$, and then multiply by the derivative of the bracketed term, $f'(x)$.

Let's now have a look at an example involving the exponential function.

Example 6.8

If $y = e^{5x^3 - 1}$, find an expression for $\dfrac{dy}{dx}$.

Solution

First of all, we set $u = 5x^3 - 1$, so we have $y = e^u$. Next, we differentiate the two parts:

$$\frac{du}{dx} = 15x^2$$

$$\frac{dy}{du} = e^u$$

Hence:

$$\frac{dy}{dx} = \frac{dy}{du} \times \frac{du}{dx} = e^u \times 15x^2$$

Replacing u gives:

$$\frac{dy}{dx} = e^{5x^3-1} \times 15x^2 = 15x^2 e^{5x^3-1}$$

◆◆

The thought process when differentiating $y = e^{f(x)}$ using the chain rule is to differentiate the exponential 'as normal' (*ie* leave it as it is) to give $e^{f(x)}$, and then multiply by the derivative of the power, $f'(x)$.

This approach gives us a method of deriving the standard result for the derivative of c^x, which we met in Section 6.2.

Example 6.9

If $y = c^x$, show that $\frac{dy}{dx} = c^x \ln c$.

Solution

To start off, we can rewrite y in terms of the exponential function as follows:

$$y = c^x = e^{\ln(c^x)} = e^{x \ln c}$$

The first equality here uses the fact that the exponential and natural logarithm functions are the inverse of each other, and the second equality uses a log law. Now that y takes the form $e^{f(x)}$, where $f(x) = x \ln c$, we use the above approach, with $f'(x) = \ln c$, to give:

$$\frac{dy}{dx} = e^{x \ln c} \ln c = c^x \ln c$$

◆◆

Let's now have a look at an example involving the log function.

Example 6.10

Differentiate $y = \ln(3x + 2)$.

Solution

First of all, we set $u = 3x + 2$, so we have $y = \ln u$. Next, we differentiate the two parts:

$$\frac{du}{dx} = 3$$

$$\frac{dy}{du} = \frac{1}{u}$$

Hence:

$$\frac{dy}{dx} = \frac{dy}{du} \times \frac{du}{dx} = \frac{1}{u} \times 3$$

Replacing u gives:

$$\frac{dy}{dx} = \frac{1}{3x+2} \times 3 = \frac{3}{3x+2}$$

◆◆

So, when differentiating $y = \ln f(x)$, we differentiate the log 'as normal' (to give $1/f(x)$), and then multiply by the derivative of the function $f(x)$, *ie* we multiply by $f'(x)$.

The table below summarises these 'shortcut' rules based on the chain rule.

Derivatives using the chain rule

Function	Derivative
$(f(x))^n$	$n(f(x))^{n-1} \times f'(x)$
$e^{f(x)}$	$e^{f(x)} \times f'(x)$
$\ln f(x)$	$\dfrac{1}{f(x)} \times f'(x)$

Before moving on, we'll look at a couple of more complex examples, the first of which involves using the chain rule twice.

Example 6.11

Differentiate $\left[\ln(1 + 2e^x)\right]^2$ with respect to x.

Solution

Using the chain rule to differentiate $(f(x))^n$, we have:

$$\frac{d}{dx}\left[\ln(1 + 2e^x)\right]^2 = 2\left[\ln(1 + 2e^x)\right] \times \frac{d}{dx}\ln(1 + 2e^x)$$

To find $\dfrac{d}{dx}\ln(1 + 2e^x)$ we need to use the chain rule for $\ln f(x)$:

$$\frac{d}{dx}\ln(1 + 2e^x) = \frac{1}{1 + 2e^x} \times \frac{d}{dx}(1 + 2e^x) = \frac{1}{1 + 2e^x} \times 2e^x = \frac{2e^x}{1 + 2e^x}$$

Returning to our original expression, the final answer is:

$$\frac{d}{dx}\left[\ln(1 + 2e^x)\right]^2 = 2\left[\ln(1 + 2e^x)\right] \times \frac{2e^x}{(1 + 2e^x)} = \frac{4e^x}{(1 + 2e^x)}\ln(1 + 2e^x) \qquad \blacklozenge\blacklozenge$$

To differentiate some complex functions, we might need to use a combination of the product, quotient and chain rules. The following example combines the quotient rule and the chain rule.

Example 6.12

If $y = \dfrac{2x + 1}{(3x - 4)^4}$, find an expression for $\dfrac{dy}{dx}$.

Solution

To use the quotient rule, we set $u = 2x + 1$ and $v = (3x - 4)^4$. The derivative of u is $u' = 2$, and the derivative of v is found using the chain rule:

$$v' = 4(3x - 4)^3 \times 3 = 12(3x - 4)^3$$

Now, using the quotient rule:

$$\frac{dy}{dx} = \frac{\left\{(3x - 4)^4 \times 2\right\} - \left\{(2x + 1) \times 12(3x - 4)^3\right\}}{(3x - 4)^8}$$

$$= \frac{2(3x - 4)^3 \left((3x - 4) - 6(2x + 1)\right)}{(3x - 4)^8}$$

$$= -\frac{2(9x + 10)}{(3x - 4)^5}$$

♦♦

6.4   Higher-order derivatives

So far, we have only differentiated each function we have considered once, to obtain $f'(x)$ or $\frac{dy}{dx}$. These are known as the *first derivative* of the function. However, expressions can be differentiated repeatedly to obtain *higher-order derivatives*. For example, if we differentiate the first derivative, we obtain the second derivative, and if we differentiate the second derivative, we obtain the third derivative, and so on.

The notation for these higher-order derivatives is:

$$\frac{d^2y}{dx^2}, \frac{d^3y}{dx^3}, \frac{d^4y}{dx^4}, \text{ etc}$$

or, in function notation, $f''(x), f'''(x)$, etc.

Example 6.13

If the value of a quantity x at time t is given by $x = \ln(2t + 3)$, find expressions for $\frac{d^2x}{dt^2}$ and $\frac{d^3x}{dt^3}$.

Solution

Using the chain rule, the first derivative is:

$$\frac{dx}{dt} = \frac{1}{2t + 3} \times 2 = 2(2t + 3)^{-1}$$

Again, using the chain rule, the second derivative is:

$$\frac{d^2x}{dt^2} = \frac{d}{dt}\left(\frac{dx}{dt}\right) = \frac{d}{dt}\left(2(2t + 3)^{-1}\right) = 2 \times (-1) \times (2t + 3)^{-2} \times 2 = \frac{-4}{(2t + 3)^2}$$

We use the chain rule again to obtain the third derivative:

$$\frac{d^3x}{dt^3} = \frac{d}{dt}\left(\frac{d^2x}{dt^2}\right) = \frac{d}{dt}\left(-4(2t+3)^{-2}\right) = (-4)\times(-2)\times(2t+3)^{-3}\times 2 = \frac{16}{(2t+3)^3} \qquad \blacklozenge\blacklozenge$$

The second derivative tells us about the rate of change of the rate of change of a function, or equivalently, about the rate of change of the gradient of a curve (which is a measure of curvature). Higher-order derivatives can be interpreted in a similar way.

The idea of a second or third derivative may not seem to have many practical applications. However, we will see in the next section that the second derivative at least is often very useful, as it helps us to determine where the maximum and minimum points of a function occur.

6.5   Stationary points

A function has a *stationary point* where the tangent to the graph of the function is horizontal. A stationary point can be a maximum, a minimum or a point of inflexion. Maximum and minimum points may also be called *turning points*.

The graph below shows the function $y = x^3(1-x)^2$. It has 3 stationary points: a minimum at $x = 1$, a maximum at $x = 0.6$, and a point of inflexion (neither a maximum nor a minimum) at $x = 0$.

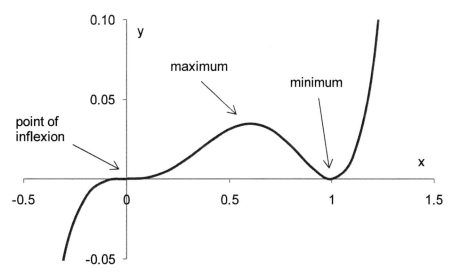

As a *stationary point* is defined to be a point where the tangent to the graph of the function is horizontal, we can find stationary points by looking for solutions to the equation $f'(x) = 0$.

We define the different stationary points mathematically as follows:

- A function $f(x)$ has a *local maximum* at the point $x = b$ if the values of $f(x)$ close to $x = b$ are less than $f(b)$, or a little more formally, if $f(b \pm \varepsilon) < f(b)$, where ε is a small positive number.

- A function $f(x)$ has a *local minimum* at the point $x = b$ if the values of $f(x)$ close to $x = b$ are greater than $f(b)$, or, if $f(b \pm \varepsilon) > f(b)$.

- A function $f(x)$ has a *stationary point of inflexion* at the point $x = b$ if $f'(x) = 0$ and the values of $f(x)$ close to $x = b$ are less than $f(b)$ on one side of $x = b$ and greater than $f(b)$ on the other, that is, if $f(b - \varepsilon) < f(b) < f(b + \varepsilon)$ or $f(b - \varepsilon) > f(b) > f(b + \varepsilon)$.

Determining the nature of stationary points

Once a stationary point has been located, we can check whether it is a maximum, a minimum or a stationary point of inflexion. We do this by finding the second derivative, and substituting in the value of x at the stationary point. Substituting a particular value of x into the expression for a (second) derivative is called *evaluating the (second) derivative* at that point. If the stationary point we are considering occurs when $x = x_0$, then evaluating the second derivative at that point is written as:

$$\left.\frac{d^2 y}{dx^2}\right|_{x=x_0} \quad \text{or} \quad f''(x_0)$$

If the second derivative is negative, the stationary point is a maximum, and if it is positive, the stationary point is a minimum. If the second derivative equals zero, further investigation is required, as the point could be a maximum, a minimum or a stationary point of inflexion. We will see the rationale behind these rules below.

Example 6.14

Find the maximum and minimum points of the function $f(x) = x^3 - x^2 - 8x + 12$.

Solution

First of all, we differentiate the function:

$$f'(x) = 3x^2 - 2x - 8 = (3x + 4)(x - 2)$$

The stationary points occur when $f'(x) = 0$, giving $x = -\frac{4}{3}$ and $x = 2$. To find the y-coordinates of the stationary points, we can substitute these values of x into $f(x)$:

$$f\left(-\tfrac{4}{3}\right) = \left(-\tfrac{4}{3}\right)^3 - \left(-\tfrac{4}{3}\right)^2 - 8\left(-\tfrac{4}{3}\right) + 12 = \tfrac{500}{27}$$

$$f(2) = 2^3 - 2^2 - 8 \times 2 + 12 = 0$$

So the stationary points are $\left(-\tfrac{4}{3}, \tfrac{500}{27}\right)$ and $(2, 0)$. To determine the nature of these stationary points, we consider the second derivative:

$$f''(x) = 6x - 2$$

When $x = -\tfrac{4}{3}$, $f''(x) = -10 < 0$, so $\left(-\tfrac{4}{3}, \tfrac{500}{27}\right)$ is a maximum.

When $x = 2$, $f''(x) = 10 > 0$, so $(2, 0)$ is a minimum.   ◆◆

In order to understand why the second derivative is positive for a minimum and negative for a maximum, it is necessary to consider the sign of the gradient of the graph (which we know is given by $\dfrac{dy}{dx}$ or $f'(x)$).

For a minimum point, the gradient of the graph changes from negative, to zero, to positive. In other words, the gradient is increasing. Since the second derivative is the rate of change of the gradient, the second derivative must be positive for a minimum. By similar reasoning, the second derivative must be negative for a maximum.

We mentioned above that if the second derivative equals zero, then further investigation of the nature of the stationary point is required. To do this further investigation, you need to check the sign of $f'(x)$ to see how the graph is behaving:

- If $f'(x)$ changes from negative to positive as x increases through the stationary point, then the stationary point is a minimum, as shown: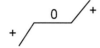

- If $f'(x)$ changes from positive to negative as x increases through the stationary point, then the stationary point is a maximum:

- If $f'(x)$ has the same sign immediately before and after the stationary point, then the stationary point is a stationary point of inflexion:

Example 6.15

Find the location and nature of the stationary point of the function $f(x) = x^4$.

Solution

The first two derivatives of $f(x) = x^4$ are $f'(x) = 4x^3$ and $f''(x) = 12x^2$. Setting $f'(x) = 0$ to find the stationary point gives $x = 0$. So, since $f(0) = 0$, the stationary point is at $(0,0)$.

To find the nature of this stationary point, we consider the second derivative when $x = 0$, which is zero. So, we need to consider the sign of $f'(x)$ on either side of $(0,0)$. We'll consider $x = -0.1$ and $x = 0.1$:

$$f'(-0.1) = 4(-0.1)^3 = -0.004 \quad \text{and} \quad f'(0.1) = 4(0.1)^3 = 0.004$$

Since $f'(x)$ changes from negative to positive as x increases through the stationary point, then the stationary point $(0,0)$ is a minimum.   ♦♦

In fact, the graph of $f(x) = x^n$, where n is any positive even number, will have a minimum at $x = 0$, since we know that $f(0) = 0$ and the function takes positive values everywhere else.

To identify a point of inflexion, it is necessary for $f''(x) = 0$. We must then look at how $f'(x)$ behaves in the vicinity of the stationary point to establish if it is a point of inflexion, as outlined above.

When trying to find the maximum and minimum points of a *positive function* $f(x)$ (that is, a function whose values are always positive, so $f(x) > 0$ for all relevant values of x), we can instead consider the maximum and minimum points of $\ln f(x)$. This is because $\ln x$ (which is only defined for $x > 0$) is steadily increasing with no stationary points, so taking the natural logarithm of a function does not introduce any new stationary points. This means that the x values at which the maximum and minimum points of $\ln f(x)$ occur will be the same as the x values at which the maximum and minimum points of $f(x)$ occur.

This approach of taking logs is useful when the function to be differentiated is a complex product of terms involving powers, as taking logs can make the algebra easier. This is used frequently in statistical work, in particular in a procedure called maximum likelihood estimation, which enables us to estimate parameter values based on observed data.

Example 6.16

Find the maximum value of:

$$f(\lambda) = e^{-25\lambda}\left(1-e^{-\lambda}\right)^{45}, \quad \lambda > 0$$

Solution

For $\lambda > 0$, $e^{-\lambda}$ takes values between 0 and 1, so $1-e^{-\lambda}$ will always take positive values. Since $e^{-25\lambda}$ also always takes positive values, $f(\lambda)$ is a positive function. So, taking logs:

$$\ln f(\lambda) = \ln\left\{e^{-25\lambda}\left(1-e^{-\lambda}\right)^{45}\right\} = -25\lambda + 45\ln\left(1-e^{-\lambda}\right)$$

Differentiating with respect to λ, using the chain rule on the second term, gives:

$$\frac{d}{d\lambda}\ln f(\lambda) = -25 + 45\times\frac{1}{1-e^{-\lambda}}\times\left(-e^{-\lambda}\right)\times(-1) = -25 + \frac{45e^{-\lambda}}{1-e^{-\lambda}}$$

Simplifying the second term, by multiplying the numerator and denominator by e^{λ}, gives:

$$\frac{d}{d\lambda}\ln f(\lambda) = -25 + \frac{45}{e^{\lambda}-1}$$

Setting this equal to zero to find a stationary point, gives:

$$25 = \frac{45}{e^{\lambda}-1}$$
$$25e^{\lambda} - 25 = 45$$
$$25e^{\lambda} = 70$$
$$\lambda = \ln 2.8 = 1.0296$$

To check if this is a maximum, we find the second derivative:

$$\frac{d^2}{d\lambda^2}\ln f(\lambda) = \frac{d}{d\lambda}\left(-25+\frac{45}{e^\lambda-1}\right) = \frac{d}{d\lambda}\left(-25+45\left(e^\lambda-1\right)^{-1}\right) = \frac{-45e^\lambda}{\left(e^\lambda-1\right)^2}$$

Both e^λ and $\left(e^\lambda-1\right)^2$ are always positive, so the second derivative must always be negative, meaning the point we have found must be a maximum.

Finding the value of the function at this point:

$$f(\ln 2.8) = e^{-25\ln 2.8}\left(1-e^{-\ln 2.8}\right)^{45} = 1.5353\times 10^{-20}$$

So the coordinates of the maximum point are $\left(1.0296, 1.5353\times 10^{-20}\right)$. While this maximum value looks very small, the values of the function at other points are even smaller, *eg* when $\lambda = 2$, $f(2) = 2.7760\times 10^{-25}$.   ◆◆

It is not always necessary to look at the second derivative, as the nature of the stationary points might be obvious from the shape of the graph of the function. Looking at Example 6.16, we see that $f(\lambda)$ is always positive, and the value of the function tends to zero as λ tends to zero and as λ tends to infinity. So any stationary point we find must be a 'hump in the middle', *ie* a maximum.

The box below summarises the key points to learn about stationary points:

Stationary points

A stationary point of the function $f(x)$ satisfies the equation $f'(x) = 0$.

If $\left(x_0, f(x_0)\right)$ is a stationary point of $f(x)$, then it is:

- a maximum point if $f''(x_0) < 0$

- a minimum point if $f''(x_0) > 0$.

If $f'(x_0) = 0$ and $f''(x_0) = 0$, then $\left(x_0, f(x_0)\right)$ is:

- a maximum point if $f'(x)$ changes from positive to negative as x increases through x_0

- a minimum point if $f'(x)$ changes from negative to positive as x increases through x_0

- a stationary point of inflexion if $f'(x)$ has the same sign immediately before and after x_0.

The x values at which the stationary points of a positive function $f(x)$ occur are the same as the x values at which the stationary points of $\ln f(x)$ occur.

It is important to be aware that there are occasions when the rules given above do not work. This is particularly true of 'unusual' functions. For example, consider the graph of $y = |x|$, shown below.

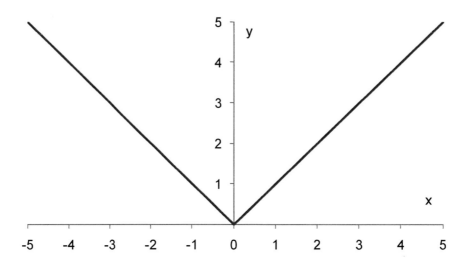

This has a minimum at $x = 0$. However, $\dfrac{dy}{dx}$ is not equal to zero when $x = 0$, as the graph is disjointed at that point, with a slope of -1 on the left and $+1$ on the right, and hence its derivative at that point does not exist. We say that this function is *not differentiable* when $x = 0$.

◆ *Curve sketching*

It is often useful to be able to sketch the graphs of functions, in order to see what is happening.

In some cases, we may be able to sketch a function by applying transformations to the graph of a standard function. We looked at this approach in Chapter 3, where we considered standard functions and their graphs, including variations of those functions, such as $y = e^{4x} + 1$.

The ideas covered in this chapter are also helpful when trying to decide how a particular function behaves. In order to sketch the graph of a function, the following techniques may be useful:

- Find where the function crosses the x- and y-axes.

- Find any stationary points and their nature.

- Consider the sign and gradient of the function, and the ranges of values for which the function is positive or negative.

- Consider the behaviour of the function at extreme values, *ie* when x or y tend to zero or infinity, or at 'impossible' values, such as where the denominator of a fraction would become zero.

Example 6.17

Sketch the graph of $y = e^{-\frac{1}{2}x^2}$.

Solution

We can start off by working out where this graph crosses the axes.

If $x = 0$, then $y = 1$, so the graph crosses the y-axis at $(0,1)$. Since the exponential function is never negative, we know that this function will not *cross* the x-axis. Moreover, as $x \to \pm\infty$, $y \to 0$, so the function approaches zero but does not touch the x-axis for any finite value of x.

To look for stationary points, we consider the first derivative of the function, which, using the chain rule, is:

$$\frac{dy}{dx} = -xe^{-\frac{1}{2}x^2}$$

For a stationary point, we need $\frac{dy}{dx} = 0$, so the only stationary point occurs when $x = 0$ (and $y = 1$). As we've already observed that this function is always positive and tends to zero as $x \to \pm\infty$, this stationary point must be a maximum, but we can check this by considering the second derivative, which, using the product rule and the chain rule, is:

$$\frac{d^2y}{dx^2} = (-x)\times(-x)e^{-\frac{1}{2}x^2} - e^{-\frac{1}{2}x^2}\times 1 = e^{-\frac{1}{2}x^2}(x^2 - 1)$$

When $x = 0$, $\frac{d^2y}{dx^2} = -1 < 0$, so the stationary point at $(0,1)$ is certainly a maximum.

We now have enough information to sketch the graph.

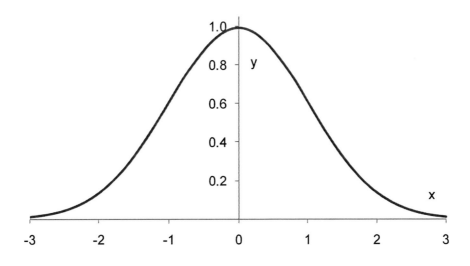

♦♦

6.6   *Partial differentiation*

So far in this chapter, we have looked at functions of one variable only, so it has been clear which variable we were differentiating with respect to, as there was only one. We will now see how to apply the process of differentiation to functions of more than one variable.

Consider the function $f(x,y)$, which is a function of two independent variables x and y. The value of this function will change as x changes *and* as y changes. *Partial differentiation* tells us about the rate of change of the function as each of the input values changes.

The partial derivatives of $f(x,y)$ with respect to x and y are defined to be:

$$\frac{\partial f}{\partial x} = \lim_{h\to 0} \frac{f(x+h,y)-f(x,y)}{h} \qquad \frac{\partial f}{\partial y} = \lim_{h\to 0} \frac{f(x,y+h)-f(x,y)}{h}$$

The notation for partial differentiation uses a 'curly d' ∂, to distinguish it from ordinary differentiation.

These definitions mirror the one given in Section 6.1 for a function of one variable. In the first definition above, the value of x is changed by a small amount h, while the value of y is held constant, and in the second, the value of y is changed by a small amount h, while the value of x is held constant.

This gives us the following approach for working out partial derivatives:

Partial differentiation

The partial derivative of a function f with respect to x, $\dfrac{\partial f}{\partial x}$, is found by differentiating f with respect to x, treating all other variables as constants. This gives the rate of change of the function f when x is varied but all other variables are kept constant.

The partial derivative of a function f with respect to y, $\dfrac{\partial f}{\partial y}$, is found by differentiating f with respect to y, treating all other variables as constants. This gives the rate of change of the function f when y is varied but all other variables are kept constant.

The following alternative notation for partial derivatives may sometimes be used:

$$f'_x(x,y) = \frac{\partial f}{\partial x} \quad \text{and} \quad f'_y(x,y) = \frac{\partial f}{\partial y}$$

where the subscript on the function f indicates the variable used for differentiation.

The rules for differentiation that we have met in this chapter also apply to partial differentiation, in the same way as they apply to ordinary differentiation. In the example below, we use the chain rule.

Example 6.18

Find expressions for $\dfrac{\partial f}{\partial x}$ and $\dfrac{\partial f}{\partial y}$ for the function $f(x,y) = 2x^2y + (x+2y)^3$.

Solution

Differentiating with respect to x, treating y as a constant, gives:

$$\frac{\partial f}{\partial x} = 4xy + 3(x+2y)^2$$

Differentiating with respect to y, treating x as a constant, gives:

$$\frac{\partial f}{\partial y} = 2x^2 + 6(x+2y)^2 \qquad\qquad\qquad \blacklozenge\blacklozenge$$

Higher-order partial derivatives can be found by repeated partial differentiation, in a similar way to higher-order derivatives of functions of just one variable.

The notation used here is $\dfrac{\partial^2 f}{\partial x^2}, \dfrac{\partial^3 f}{\partial x^3}$, etc for partial derivatives with respect to x, and $\dfrac{\partial^2 f}{\partial y^2}, \dfrac{\partial^3 f}{\partial y^3}$, etc for partial derivatives with respect to y.

It is also possible to obtain higher-order partial derivatives by differentiating the function with respect to different variables. For example, $\dfrac{\partial^2 f}{\partial x \partial y}$ means the partial derivative of $\dfrac{\partial f}{\partial y}$ with respect to x, ie:

$$\frac{\partial^2 f}{\partial x \partial y} = \frac{\partial}{\partial x}\left(\frac{\partial f}{\partial y}\right)$$

Example 6.19

If $f(x,y) = (2x + y)e^{xy}$, show that:

(i) $\dfrac{\partial^2 f}{\partial x^2} = y\left(\dfrac{\partial f}{\partial x} + 2e^{xy}\right)$

(ii) $\dfrac{\partial^2 f}{\partial x \partial y} = \dfrac{\partial^2 f}{\partial y \partial x}$

Solution

(i)   Using the product rule to differentiate partially with respect to x (holding y constant):

$$\frac{\partial f}{\partial x} = (2x+y)ye^{xy} + 2e^{xy}$$

$$\frac{\partial^2 f}{\partial x^2} = (2x+y)y^2 e^{xy} + 2ye^{xy} + 2ye^{xy} = (2x+y)y^2 e^{xy} + 4ye^{xy}$$

Also:

$$y\left(\frac{\partial f}{\partial x} + 2e^{xy}\right) = y\left((2x+y)ye^{xy} + 2e^{xy} + 2e^{xy}\right) = (2x+y)y^2 e^{xy} + 4ye^{xy}$$

so the relationship is true.

(ii)   Starting from the result for $\dfrac{\partial f}{\partial x}$ above:

$$\frac{\partial^2 f}{\partial y \partial x} = \frac{\partial}{\partial y}\left(\frac{\partial f}{\partial x}\right) = \frac{\partial}{\partial y}\left((2x+y)ye^{xy} + 2e^{xy}\right) = \frac{\partial}{\partial y}\left(\left(2xy+y^2\right)e^{xy} + 2e^{xy}\right)$$

Using the product rule gives:

$$\frac{\partial^2 f}{\partial y \partial x} = \left(2xy+y^2\right)xe^{xy} + (2x+2y)e^{xy} + 2xe^{xy} = \left(2x^2 y + xy^2 + 4x + 2y\right)e^{xy}$$

Now, differentiating f with respect to y first and then x:

$$\frac{\partial f}{\partial y} = (2x+y)xe^{xy} + e^{xy} = \left(2x^2 + xy\right)e^{xy} + e^{xy}$$

$$\frac{\partial^2 f}{\partial x \partial y} = \frac{\partial}{\partial x}\left(\frac{\partial f}{\partial y}\right) = \left(2x^2 + xy\right)ye^{xy} + \left(4x + y\right)e^{xy} + ye^{xy}$$

This simplifies to:

$$\frac{\partial^2 f}{\partial x \partial y} = \left(2x^2 y + xy^2 + 4x + 2y\right)e^{xy} = \frac{\partial^2 f}{\partial y \partial x}$$

So the relationship is true. ◆◆

The relationship shown in part (ii) of this example holds for all functions, so when partially differentiating with respect to different variables, the order of partial differentiation does not matter.

◆ Total derivatives

If f is a function of x and y, and x and y are both functions of some other variable t, the partial derivatives can be used to find the change in the function f when t is varied by calculating the *total derivative* using the relationship:

$$\frac{df}{dt} = \frac{\partial f}{\partial x}\frac{dx}{dt} + \frac{\partial f}{\partial y}\frac{dy}{dt}$$

This is effectively an extension of the chain rule we met earlier, applied to functions of more than one variable.

Example 6.20

If $f(x,y) = x^2 y$, where $x = e^{t^2}$ and $y = t^3$, find an expression for the total derivative $\dfrac{df}{dt}$.

Solution

We start off by working out the partial derivatives of f with respect to x and y:

$$\frac{\partial f}{\partial x} = 2xy \quad \text{and} \quad \frac{\partial f}{\partial y} = x^2$$

Next, differentiate x and y with respect to t:

$$\frac{dx}{dt} = 2te^{t^2} \quad \text{and} \quad \frac{dy}{dt} = 3t^2$$

Finally, the total derivative is given by:

$$\frac{df}{dt} = \frac{\partial f}{\partial x}\frac{dx}{dt} + \frac{\partial f}{\partial y}\frac{dy}{dt} = 2xy \times 2te^{t^2} + x^2 \times 3t^2$$

Writing this entirely in terms of t:

$$\frac{df}{dt} = 2e^{t^2}t^3 \times 2te^{t^2} + \left(e^{t^2}\right)^2 \times 3t^2 = \left(4t^2 + 3\right)t^2 e^{2t^2}$$ ◆◆

6.7   Extreme values of functions of two variables

Extreme values in three-dimensional space are equivalent to stationary points in two-dimensional space.

Functions of two variables can have three types of extreme point: maximum points, minimum points and saddle points. Maximum and minimum points have their usual interpretations, whereas a saddle point can be thought of as resembling a horse's saddle, *ie* such a point is a minimum in one direction (going from the front of the horse to the back) and a maximum in the other (going from one side of the horse to the other).

To find these extreme points, we need to find the values $x = x_0$, $y = y_0$ such that:

$$\frac{\partial f}{\partial x} = 0 \quad \text{and} \quad \frac{\partial f}{\partial y} = 0$$

To discover the nature of an extreme point, we find the roots of the following equation for λ:

$$\left(\left. \frac{\partial^2 f}{\partial y^2} \right|_{\substack{x=x_0 \\ y=y_0}} - \lambda \right) \left(\left. \frac{\partial^2 f}{\partial x^2} \right|_{\substack{x=x_0 \\ y=y_0}} - \lambda \right) - \left(\left. \frac{\partial^2 f}{\partial y \, \partial x} \right|_{\substack{x=x_0 \\ y=y_0}} \right)^2 = 0$$

and apply the following conditions:

- if both the roots are positive, there is a local minimum

- if both the roots are negative, there is a local maximum

- if the roots are of differing signs, there is a saddle point.

We will not look at the reasoning behind this procedure here, but note that it is similar to solving the equation $f'(x) = 0$ to find stationary points in two-dimensional space, and then looking at $f''(x)$ to determine their nature.

Example 6.21

Find the extreme points of the function $f(x,y) = 2x^2 + y^2$ and determine their nature.

Solution

Partially differentiating with respect to *x* and *y* gives:

$$\frac{\partial f}{\partial x} = 4x \quad \text{and} \quad \frac{\partial f}{\partial y} = 2y$$

Setting these equal to zero gives $x = 0$ and $y = 0$, *ie* $(0,0)$ is an extreme point.

Next, finding the second derivatives gives:

$$\frac{\partial^2 f}{\partial x^2} = 4 , \quad \frac{\partial^2 f}{\partial y^2} = 2 \quad \text{and} \quad \frac{\partial^2 f}{\partial y \, \partial x} = 0$$

Substituting these values into the required equation:

$$(2 - \lambda)(4 - \lambda) = 0 \quad \Rightarrow \quad \lambda = 2 \text{ or } 4$$

Since both these values are positive, the extreme point is a local minimum.

This is what we would expect since, if $y = 0$, the function $2x^2$ has a minimum value at $x = 0$ and, if $x = 0$, the function y^2 also has a minimum value at $y = 0$.   ◆◆

6.8   *Maclaurin series and Taylor series*

A series whose terms involve increasing or decreasing powers of a variable is called a *power series*. We have already met some examples of these when we looked at binomial expansions in Chapter 4, such as $(2-3x)^4$ and $(1-2x)^{0.5}$. In this section, we will look at how other functions can be expressed as power series, using Maclaurin series and Taylor series.

◆ *Maclaurin series*

We will consider the function $f(x)$, and assume that it can be expanded as an infinite series of increasing powers of x:

$$f(x) = a_0 + a_1 x + a_2 x^2 + a_3 x^3 + \cdots + a_r x^r + \cdots$$

where $a_0, a_1, a_2, a_3, \ldots, a_r, \ldots$ are constants to be determined.

Assuming that $f(x)$ can be differentiated repeatedly, we can establish the values of these constants using the following process.

Evaluating the function at the point $x = 0$ gives $f(0) = a_0$.

Evaluating the first derivative:

$$f'(x) = a_1 + 2a_2 x^1 + 3a_3 x^2 + \cdots + ra_r x^{r-1} + \cdots$$

at the point $x = 0$, gives $f'(0) = a_1$.

Evaluating the second derivative:

$$f''(x) = 2 \times 1 a_2 + 3 \times 2 a_3 x^1 + \cdots + r \times (r-1) a_r x^{r-2} + \cdots$$

at the point $x = 0$, gives:

$$f''(0) = 2 \times 1 a_2 \quad \Rightarrow \quad a_2 = \frac{f''(0)}{2 \times 1} = \frac{f''(0)}{2!}$$

Evaluating the third derivative:

$$f'''(x) = 3 \times 2 \times 1 a_3 + \cdots + r \times (r-1) \times (r-2) a_r x^{r-3} + \cdots$$

at the point $x = 0$, gives:

$$f'''(0) = 3 \times 2 \times 1 a_3 \quad \Rightarrow \quad a_3 = \frac{f'''(0)}{3 \times 2 \times 1} = \frac{f'''(0)}{3!}$$

We can continue this process for higher-order derivatives. Denoting the r th derivative by $f^{(r)}$, we have:

$$a_r = \frac{f^{(r)}(0)}{r!}$$

Using these constants, we obtain the *Maclaurin series* for $f(x)$, which is the power series expansion of $f(x)$ about the point $x = 0$. The range of values of x for which the series is valid, *ie* when it converges to the function, will depend on the particular function involved.

Maclaurin series

The Maclaurin series for the function $f(x)$ is given by:

$$f(x) = f(0) + f'(0)x + \frac{f''(0)}{2!}x^2 + \frac{f'''(0)}{3!}x^3 + \cdots + \frac{f^{(r)}(0)}{r!}x^r + \cdots$$

Maclaurin series are useful for finding series expansions for basic functions such as e^x and $\ln(1+x)$, which we will look at in the following examples.

Example 6.22

Obtain the expansion of e^x, as far as the term in x^3.

Solution

If we let $f(x) = e^x$, then repeated differentiation gives $f^{(n)}(x) = e^x$ for all values of n. Since $f(0) = e^0 = 1$ and $f^{(n)}(0) = 1$ for all n, the Maclaurin series (up to the x^3 term) is given by:

$$f(x) = 1 + x + \frac{x^2}{2!} + \frac{x^3}{3!} + \cdots$$

♦♦

Using the pattern established above, we can write e^x as an infinite series as:

$$e^x = \sum_{r=0}^{\infty} \frac{x^r}{r!}$$

where $0! = 1$. This series is valid for all values of x.

Example 6.23

Obtain the expansion of $\ln(1+x)$, as far as the term in x^3.

Solution

If we let $f(x) = \ln(1+x)$, then:

$$f(0) = \ln(1) = 0$$

$$f'(x) = \frac{1}{1+x} \quad \Rightarrow \quad f'(0) = 1$$

$$f''(x) = -\frac{1}{(1+x)^2} \quad \Rightarrow \quad f''(0) = -1$$

$$f'''(x) = \frac{2}{(1+x)^3} \quad \Rightarrow \quad f'''(0) = 2$$

So, the Maclaurin series (up to the x^3 term) is given by:

$$\ln(1+x) = x + \tfrac{1}{2!}(-1)x^2 + \tfrac{1}{3!}(2)x^3 + \cdots$$

$$= x - \tfrac{1}{2}x^2 + \tfrac{1}{3}x^3 + \cdots$$

♦♦

Using the pattern established above, we can write $\ln(1+x)$ as an infinite series as:

$$\ln(1+x) = \sum_{r=1}^{\infty} (-1)^{r+1} \frac{x^r}{r}$$

This infinite series will only converge to a finite limit for $-1 < x \le 1$.

◆ *Taylor series for functions of one variable*

A Maclaurin series cannot be found for all functions. For example, there is no Maclaurin series for $\ln x$, as the natural logarithm function is not defined at the point $x = 0$.

A *Taylor series* is similar to a Maclaurin series, except that the power series expansion is about the point $x = a$ (where $a \ne 0$) rather than about $x = 0$.

We can derive the form of a Taylor series for the function $f(x)$ by expressing it as an infinite series of increasing powers of $x - a$:

$$f(x) = a_0 + a_1(x-a) + a_2(x-a)^2 + a_3(x-a)^3 + \cdots + a_r(x-a)^r + \cdots$$

and establishing the values of the constants $a_0, a_1, a_2, a_3, \ldots, a_r, \ldots$ by evaluating each successive derivative at the point $x = a$, in a similar way to that shown above for the Maclaurin series.

Taylor series for functions of one variable

The Taylor series about the point $x = a$ for the function $f(x)$ is given by:

$$f(x) = f(a) + f'(a)(x-a) + \frac{f''(a)}{2!}(x-a)^2 + \frac{f'''(a)}{3!}(x-a)^3 + \cdots + \frac{f^{(r)}(a)}{r!}(x-a)^r + \cdots$$

Example 6.24

Find the Taylor series about the point $x = e$ for the function $\ln x$, as far as the term in $(x-e)^3$.

Solution

Using the general form of the Taylor series given above, with $f(x) = \ln x$ and $a = e$, we have:

$$f(x) = \ln x \quad \Rightarrow \quad f(e) = \ln e = 1$$

$$f'(x) = \frac{1}{x} \quad \Rightarrow \quad f'(e) = \frac{1}{e}$$

$$f''(x) = \frac{-1}{x^2} \quad \Rightarrow \quad f''(e) = \frac{-1}{e^2}$$

$$f'''(x) = \frac{2}{x^3} \quad \Rightarrow \quad f'''(e) = \frac{2}{e^3}$$

So, the Taylor series for $\ln x$ about the point $x = e$ is:

$$\ln x = 1 + \frac{1}{e}(x-e) + \frac{1}{2!}\left(-\frac{1}{e^2}\right)(x-e)^2 + \frac{1}{3!}\left(\frac{2}{e^3}\right)(x-e)^3 + \cdots$$

$$= 1 + \frac{1}{e}(x-e) - \frac{1}{2e^2}(x-e)^2 + \frac{1}{3e^3}(x-e)^3 + \cdots \qquad \blacklozenge\blacklozenge$$

Taylor series can be used to look at the effect on $f(x)$ of a small change in the value of x.

Example 6.25

Expand the function $f(i) = (1+i)^{-2} + (1+i)^{-5}$ as a Taylor series about $i = 0.1$, as far as the term in $(i - 0.1)^3$, and use this Taylor series to comment on how the value of this function will change if i increases from 0.1 to 0.11.

Solution

Using the general form of the Taylor series with $x = i$, $f(i) = (1+i)^{-2} + (1+i)^{-5}$, and $a = 0.1$, we have:

$$f(0.1) = (1.1)^{-2} + (1.1)^{-5} = 1.447$$

Evaluating the derivatives:

$$f'(i) = -2(1+i)^{-3} - 5(1+i)^{-6} \quad \Rightarrow \quad f'(0.1) = -4.325$$

$$f''(i) = (-2)(-3)(1+i)^{-4} + (-5)(-6)(1+i)^{-7} \quad \Rightarrow \quad f''(0.1) = 19.493$$

$$f'''(i) = (-2)(-3)(-4)(1+i)^{-5} + (-5)(-6)(-7)(1+i)^{-8} \quad \Rightarrow \quad f'''(0.1) = -112.869$$

Substituting these values into the general form gives:

$$f(i) = 1.447 - 4.325(i - 0.1) + 19.493\frac{(i-0.1)^2}{2!} - 112.869\frac{(i-0.1)^3}{3!} + \cdots$$

$$= 1.447 - 4.325(i - 0.1) + 9.746(i - 0.1)^2 - 18.811(i - 0.1)^3 + \cdots$$

If we evaluate this expression when i is equal to 0.11, then $i - 0.1 = 0.01$. As 0.01^2, 0.01^3 and higher-powered terms will be very small, we will ignore them and just consider the first two terms in the series:

$$f(0.11) \approx 1.447 - 4.325(0.01)$$

Since $f(0.1) = 1.447$, this can be written as

$$f(0.11) \approx f(0.1) - 4.325(0.01)$$

So, we can see that changing i from 0.1 to 0.11 would change the value of the function by approximately $-4.325 \times 0.01 = -0.04325$.

Indeed, since the coefficient of the second term in the Taylor series is negative, we can tell straightaway that a small increase in the value of i will reduce the value of $f(i)$. $\qquad \blacklozenge\blacklozenge$

We can re-express the general form of the Taylor series given above in terms of a small change in the input variable, by setting $x - a = h$ (so that $x = a + h$), to give:

$$f(a+h) = f(a) + hf'(a) + \frac{h^2}{2!}f''(a) + \frac{h^3}{3!}f'''(a) + \cdots + \frac{h^r}{r!}f^{(r)}(a) + \cdots$$

This then tells us about the value of the function when the input value is changed by a small amount from a to $a+h$.

Chapter 6 Practice Questions

◆ Differentiation from first principles

Question 6.1

If $f(x) = 5x$, give an expression for $\dfrac{f(x+h) - f(x)}{h}$, and hence find $f'(x)$.

Question 6.2

Differentiate $y = 2x^2 + 3x + 4$, using a first principles approach.

◆ Differentiation of standard functions

Question 6.3

Differentiate the following functions with respect to x:

(i) $2\sqrt[3]{x^4}$

(ii) $2\ln\left(3x^2\right)$

(iii) $3e^x + 1$

(iv) $\dfrac{4}{x^{3/5}}$

Question 6.4

Differentiate $f(t) = 5\left(4^t\right)$ with respect to t.

Question 6.5

Calculate the gradient of $y = 2x^3 - x^2 + 3$ when $x = 2$.

◆ The product rule, the quotient rule and the chain rule

Question 6.6

A pension scheme receives money from its investments continuously. The amount of money received at time t is given by $p(t) = 100te^{2t}$. Calculate the rate at which the payment is increasing at time $t = 1.5$.

Question 6.7

Evaluate $\dfrac{dP(i)}{di}$ at the point $i = 0.05$, where:

$$P(i) = \frac{100}{(1+i)^{10}} + 5\left(\frac{1-(1+i)^{-10}}{i}\right)$$

Question 6.8

If $p = \left(3r^2 - 4\right)^6$, find an expression for $\dfrac{dp}{dr}$.

Question 6.9

Calculate $M'(0)$ where:

(i) $M(t) = e^{\mu t + \frac{1}{2}\sigma^2 t^2}$

(ii) $M(t) = -\alpha \ln\left(1 - \dfrac{t}{\lambda}\right)$

Question 6.10

Differentiate the following functions with respect to x:

(i) $y = \left(5x^2 - 7\right)^9$

(ii) $y = e^{-3x^2}$

(iii) $y = 2\ln\left(4x^3 - 5x + 1\right)$

(iv) $y = \exp\left\{\lambda\left(e^{2x^2} - 1\right)\right\}$

(v) $y = (x+1)^2 e^x$

(vi) $y = \dfrac{\ln x}{\left(e^{2x} + 1\right)^2}$

(vii) $y = (2x + 7)^4 \ln(4x + 3)^2$

(viii) $y = (4 - 3x)\left(x^2 - 2x + 1\right)^5$

◆ *Higher-order derivatives*

Question 6.11

Find an expression for $f''(x)$ in each of the following cases:

(i) $f(x) = \left(3x^2 + 2x + 3\right)^2$

(ii) $f(x) = \dfrac{x}{\sqrt{x+1}}$

(iii) $f(x) = \ln x^{x+1}$

(iv) $f(x) = 32x^2 e^{-4x}$

Question 6.12

Evaluate the second derivative of $y = \dfrac{3x^2}{e^x}$ when $x = 1$.

Question 6.13

Find an expression for the third derivative of the function $2^x + \dfrac{1}{x}$.

◆ *Stationary points and curve sketching*

Question 6.14

Which of the following is a graph of $y = x(x+3)(x-5)$?

A

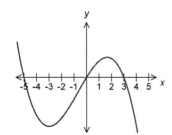

B

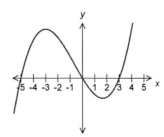

C

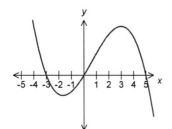

D

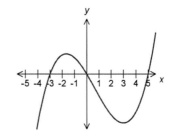

Question 6.15

Calculate the maximum value of the function $f(x) = 5 - 2x - 3x^2$.

Question 6.16

Find the stationary points of the function $f(x) = x^3 - x^2 - x + 7$ and determine their nature.

Question 6.17

For the curve $y = 4x^3 - 3x^2 - 90x + 6$, find the stationary points and determine their nature.

Question 6.18

Consider the function $f(x) = 45x^4 e^{-3x}$, where $x > 0$. By taking logs, or otherwise, find the value of x for which $f(x)$ has a maximum point.

Question 6.19

Sketch the graph of $y = \dfrac{x^2 - 4x}{x^2 - 4x + 3}$.

Question 6.20

Consider the function $y = 4\lambda x^3 \left(\lambda + x^4\right)^{-2}$ where $x > 0$ and λ is a positive constant. By taking logs, or otherwise, find an expression in terms of λ for the maximum value of y attained.

Question 6.21

According to a mortality table, the instantaneous rate of mortality at age x, which is denoted by $\mu(x)$, is calculated from the formula:

$$\mu(x) = a_0 + a_1\left(\frac{x-70}{50}\right) + \exp\left[b_0 + b_1\left(\frac{x-70}{50}\right)\right], \quad x \geq 17$$

where $a_0 = -0.00338415$, $a_1 = -0.00386512$, $b_0 = -3.352236$ and $b_1 = 4.656042$.

Find the age in the range $20 \leq x \leq 40$ at which the function μ is stationary, rounding your answer to the nearest month, and indicate the nature of this point.

◇ Partial differentiation

Question 6.22

If $f(x,y) = axy + b(xy)^2 + c(xy)^3$ where a, b and c are constants, find an expression for $\dfrac{\partial f}{\partial x}$.

Question 6.23

Find $\dfrac{\partial f}{\partial x}, \dfrac{\partial f}{\partial y}, \dfrac{\partial^2 f}{\partial x^2}, \dfrac{\partial^2 f}{\partial y^2}$, and $\dfrac{\partial^2 f}{\partial x \partial y}$ for the function $f(x,y) = (3x+y)^4 - 2x^2 y^2 + (4-7x)^3$.

Question 6.24

If $f(x,y,z) = (xyz)^2$, find an expression for $\dfrac{\partial^3 f}{\partial z \partial y \partial x} \times \dfrac{\partial f}{\partial x}$.

◆ Extreme values of functions of two variables

Question 6.25

Find the extreme points of the function $f(x,y) = x^3 - 2x^2 + 2y^2$ and determine their nature.

◆ Maclaurin series and Taylor series

Question 6.26

By using the first four terms of the Maclaurin series for e^x, calculate an approximate value for e^2.

Question 6.27

By considering the Taylor series for the function $f(x) = x^{-1}$ about the point $x=1$, calculate the values of the constants a and b in the expansion:

$$f(x) = 1 - (x-1) + a(x-1)^2 + b(x-1)^3 + \cdots$$

Integration

Learning Objectives

The following learning objectives are covered in this chapter:

- Understanding that integration is the opposite of differentiation, and that an integral can be interpreted as the sum of infinitesimally small elements or as the area enclosed between a curve and the x-axis.

- Integrating the standard functions x^n, e^x and a^x.

- Evaluating integrals by inspection, by substitution, using integration by parts, or using partial fractions.

- Determining when a definite integral converges.

7.1   *Introduction to integration*

We can consider *integration* to be the 'reverse' of differentiation. The process of integration can also be interpreted as:

- calculating the area enclosed between a curve and the *x*-axis (often called the *area under a curve*)

- evaluating a sum consisting of infinitesimally small elements.

In this section, we will consider two different kinds of integration: *indefinite integration* and *definite integration*.

◆ *Indefinite integration*

By considering integration to be the reverse of differentiation, this means that we're trying to 'undo' the differentiation of a function. So, we're trying to answer the question:

'If $f(x)$ is a derivative, what function is it the derivative of?'

If we call the answer to this question $F(x)$, then mathematically, we want to determine $F(x)$ such that:

$$F'(x) = \frac{d}{dx}F(x) = f(x)$$

We call the function $F(x)$ the *integral* of the function $f(x)$ with respect to x. We write this as:

$$F(x) = \int f(x)\,dx$$

The integral of a function can also be referred to as the *anti-derivative* of the function.

Example 7.1

If $f(x) = x^2$, find a general expression for $F(x)$, the integral of $f(x)$ with respect to x.

Solution

To find the integral of $f(x) = x^2$, we need to work out what function we would start off with if, after differentiating, we have x^2.

We know from Chapter 6 that to obtain the derivative of x raised to a given power, we bring the power to the front and reduce the power by one. So, when we differentiate x^3 we get $3x^2$.

This means that if we differentiate $\frac{1}{3}x^3$, we get $\frac{1}{3} \times 3x^2 = x^2$.

Using the notation above, if $F(x) = \frac{1}{3}x^3$, then $f(x) = x^2$, ie:

$$f(x) = F'(x) = \frac{d}{dx}F(x) = \frac{d}{dx}\left(\frac{1}{3}x^3\right) = x^2$$

However, $F(x) = \frac{1}{3}x^3$ isn't the only function that gives x^2 when it is differentiated.

We know that differentiating a constant gives 0, so, for example, $\frac{1}{3}x^3 + 6$ and $\frac{1}{3}x^3 - 4$ both

have derivative x^2. This means that any function of the form $\frac{1}{3}x^3 + c$, where c is a constant,

has derivative x^2. So, the most general expression we can give for the integral of $f(x) = x^2$ is

$\frac{1}{3}x^3 + c$, and we write this as:

$$\int x^2 dx = \frac{1}{3}x^3 + c \qquad \qquad \blacklozenge\blacklozenge$$

Most of the time, we can avoid the need to go through the thought process used above to determine the integral of a function. Instead, we can use standard results and rules for integration, which we will look at in Section 7.2 and Section 7.3 of this chapter.

Example 7.1 is an illustration of *indefinite integration*, which means that we establish the most general function that, when differentiated, gives $f(x)$. When doing indefinite integration, we should include a constant, c, called the *constant of integration*.

Indefinite integration

If $F'(x) = f(x)$, then the indefinite integral of the function $f(x)$ with respect to x is given by:

$$\int f(x)dx = F(x) + c$$

◆ *Definite integration*

The process of *definite integration* applies when we are integrating over a specific range of values of x. Definite integrals have numbers at the top and bottom of the integral sign, such as:

$$\int_2^6 f(x)dx \quad \text{or} \quad \int_2^6 f(x)dx$$

The numbers at the top and bottom of the integral sign are called the *upper limit* and *lower limit*, respectively.

To evaluate a definite integral, we first of all determine the function $F(x)$ whose derivative is $f(x)$, ignoring the constant of integration. The value of the definite integral is then equal to $F(x)$ evaluated at the upper limit minus $F(x)$ evaluated at the lower limit.

Definite integration

If $F'(x) = f(x)$, then the definite integral of the function $f(x)$ with respect to x, evaluated between the limits a and b is given by:

$$\int_a^b f(x)dx = \left[F(x)\right]_a^b = F(b) - F(a)$$

The reason we can ignore the constant of integration when performing a definite integral is that, if one was included, it would cancel out in the subtraction $F(b) - F(a)$.

The square bracket notation $\left[F(x) \right]_a^b$ is just shorthand notation for $F(b) - F(a)$. An alternative to this notation is to use a line after the function with limits at the top and bottom, as follows:

$$\int_a^b f(x)\,dx = F(x)\Big|_a^b = F(b) - F(a)$$

Example 7.2

Evaluate the integral $\displaystyle\int_2^5 x^2\,dx$.

Solution

We know from Example 7.1 that if $f(x) = x^2$, $F(x) = \dfrac{1}{3}x^3$. So, we have:

$$\int_2^5 x^2\,dx = \left[\frac{1}{3}x^3 \right]_2^5 = \left(\frac{1}{3} \times 5^3 \right) - \left(\frac{1}{3} \times 2^3 \right) = \frac{125}{3} - \frac{8}{3} = \frac{117}{3} = 39$$

◆ ◆

Using definite integration to find the area under a curve

The practical application of definite integration is that it gives the sum of infinitesimally small elements and one use of this is to find the area under a curve.

To illustrate this, we will consider the area enclosed by the curve $y = f(x)$, between $x = a$ and $x = b$, as shown in the diagram below.

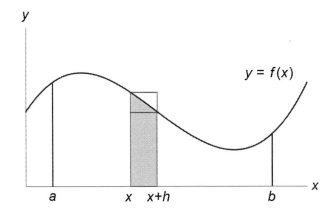

To approximate the area under the curve we can divide up the interval from $x = a$ to $x = b$ into short sections each of length h, and then draw rectangles of width h underneath the curve, such as the shorter of the two rectangles shown on the diagram. The sum of the area of all these rectangles is an estimate of the area under the curve.

To make the estimate of the area more accurate, we can reduce the width of the rectangles. As a result, we have more rectangles, each of which fits more closely just beneath the curve. As the width of the rectangles gets smaller and smaller, the sum of their areas gets closer and closer to the true area underneath the curve.

To link this to the process of integration, let's focus on the small section of area under the curve between x and $x+h$, as marked on the diagram.

If we denote the area under the curve up to the general point x by $A(x)$, then the area under the curve bounded by x and $x+h$ (shaded on the above diagram) is given by $A(x+h)-A(x)$. Now, this area is less than the area of the taller rectangle shown on the diagram (which has height $f(x)$), but it is greater than the area of the shorter rectangle (which has height $f(x+h)$), so we can state:

$$h \times f(x+h) \le A(x+h)-A(x) \le h \times f(x)$$

Dividing by h gives:

$$f(x+h) \le \frac{A(x+h)-A(x)}{h} \le f(x)$$

Now, as h becomes smaller and smaller, the quantity $\frac{A(x+h)-A(x)}{h}$ is sandwiched between two values which get closer and closer together, so we can say that as h tends to zero, $\frac{A(x+h)-A(x)}{h}$ tends to $f(x)$. Mathematically, we write:

$$\lim_{h \to 0} \frac{A(x+h)-A(x)}{h} = f(x)$$

Recalling the idea of differentiation from first principles from Chapter 6, we recognise the left-hand side of this equation as being the definition of the derivative $\frac{dA}{dx}$, so:

$$\frac{dA}{dx} = f(x)$$

Expressing this using our integral notation, we have:

$$A(x) = \int f(x)\, dx$$

This is a general expression for the area under the curve $f(x)$ up to the point x. The area enclosed between $x=a$ and $x=b$ is $A(b)-A(a)$, which is given by the definite integral $\int_a^b f(x)\, dx$.

In the explanation given above, the curve in the diagram was sloping downwards between x and $x+h$. The same result is obtained if the function is instead sloping upwards.

Area under a curve

The area enclosed by the curve $f(x)$ and the x-axis between $x=a$ and $x=b$ is given by:

$$\int_a^b f(x)\, dx = \left[F(x) \right]_a^b = F(b)-F(a)$$

where $F'(x) = f(x)$.

When evaluating a definite integral to obtain the area enclosed by the curve and the x-axis, it is important to note that if the area is below the x-axis, the result of the integration will be a negative number.

We will illustrate this by considering the function $f(x) = x^3$, which takes negative values if x is negative. Here is the graph of $f(x) = x^3$:

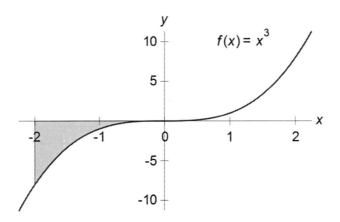

To find the shaded area enclosed by the curve and the x-axis between $x = -2$ and $x = 0$, we need to work out the integral of the function $f(x) = x^3$ between the limits of $x = -2$ and $x = 0$:

$$\int_{-2}^{0} x^3 \, dx$$

To evaluate this integral, we start off by finding a function that has derivative x^3. We know that differentiating x^4 gives $4x^3$, so differentiating $\frac{1}{4}x^4$ gives $\frac{1}{4} \times 4x^3 = x^3$. This means $\frac{1}{4}x^4$ is the integral of x^3. So:

$$\int_{-2}^{0} x^3 \, dx = \left[\frac{1}{4}x^4 \right]_{-2}^{0} = \frac{1}{4} \times 0^4 - \frac{1}{4} \times (-2)^4 = -4$$

Here, the area enclosed by the curve and the x-axis between $x = -2$ and $x = 0$ is 4, but the integral gives the value -4 as the curve is below the x-axis over this range of values.

The fact that the definite integral gives a negative value if the function lies below the x-axis can cause problems when finding the area between the curve and the x-axis for a function that is sometimes above the x-axis and sometimes below it. This is because the negative value obtained from the part of the function that lies below the x-axis cancels out all or part of the positive value obtained from the part of the function that lies above the x-axis.

Example 7.3

Calculate the total area enclosed by the x-axis and the function $f(x) = x^3$ between $x = -2$ and $x = 2$, as shaded on the following graph.

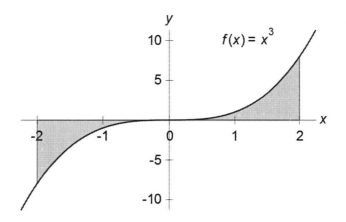

Solution

The function $f(x) = x^3$ takes negative values for $x < 0$, and positive values for $x > 0$.

Therefore, to obtain the correct value for the area enclosed by the curve and the x-axis between $x = -2$ and $x = 2$, we need to split the calculation down into two parts: one part covering the section of the interval where the curve is below the x-axis (from –2 to 0) and one part covering the section of the interval where the curve is above the x-axis (from 0 to 2).

So:

$$\int_{-2}^{0} x^3\, dx = \left[\frac{1}{4}x^4\right]_{-2}^{0} = \frac{1}{4}\times 0^4 - \frac{1}{4}\times(-2)^4 = -4 \quad \text{(as previously)}$$

and:

$$\int_{0}^{2} x^3\, dx = \left[\frac{1}{4}x^4\right]_{0}^{2} = \frac{1}{4}\times 2^4 - \frac{1}{4}\times 0^4 = 4$$

The area enclosed by the x-axis and the function $f(x) = x^3$ between $x = -2$ and $x = 2$ is therefore:

$$\int_{0}^{2} x^3\, dx - \int_{-2}^{0} x^3\, dx = 4 - (-4) = 8$$

In this last step, the second integral is subtracted as it is negative, and we need the magnitude of the answer to work out the overall area.   ◆◆

In the above example, we might have thought about evaluating the integral:

$$\int_{-2}^{2} x^3\, dx = \left[\frac{1}{4}x^4\right]_{-2}^{2} = \frac{1}{4}\times 2^4 - \frac{1}{4}\times(-2)^4 = 0$$

While this is the correct value for the integral, it is not the correct answer for the area enclosed by the x-axis and the function $f(x) = x^3$ between $x = -2$ and $x = 2$, which is not actually 0. In this calculation, the negative value obtained from the part of the function that lies below the x-axis cancels out all of the positive value obtained from the part of the function that lies above the x-axis.

As a final point, when performing definite integration, we also need to be careful if the function being integrated tends to $\pm\infty$ in the range considered. We'll look at this issue in more detail in Section 7.4, on convergence of integrals.

◆ *Other applications of integration*

Integration is not only used to find the area under a graph. We mentioned that it can also be used to evaluate a sum consisting of infinitesimal elements, and this is an important application of integration in actuarial work.

For example, where payments are made very frequently, we often approximate this situation by assuming that they occur *continuously* over the time period. To work out the total amount of payments received over a given time period, we can think about the amount of money received in each very short time interval over the period, and then sum all these amounts. As this involves summing infinitesimal elements, this summation would be expressed as an integral.

Another important application of integration in actuarial work is where we want to calculate probabilities for a variable that can take any value on a continuous scale. To do this we need to sum the infinitesimal probabilities of the variable taking each possible value in the relevant range. Again, this sum is expressed as an integral. We will cover this in more detail in a later chapter.

7.2 *Integrals of standard functions*

In this section, we will look at the integrals of some standard functions.

◆ *Integrating a constant, k*

As integration reverses the process of differentiation, to work out the integral of a constant k (where k can be any number we choose), we need to find a function that has derivative k. If we differentiate kx, the result is k, so the integral of the constant k is kx.

We write this as:

$$\int k\, dx = kx + c$$

remembering to include a constant of integration, c, as this is an indefinite integral.

◆ *Integrating x^n (where $n \neq -1$)*

To work out the integral of the function x^n, we need to find a function that has derivative x^n.

Recall from Chapter 6 that when differentiating a function of x to a given power, we bring the power to the front and reduce the power by one. So, if we differentiate x^{n+1}, we get $(n+1)x^n$.

This means that if we differentiate $\dfrac{1}{n+1}x^{n+1}$ we get $\dfrac{1}{n+1}(n+1)x^n = x^n$. Therefore, the integral of x^n is $\dfrac{1}{n+1}x^{n+1}$, and we write:

$$\int x^n\, dx = \frac{1}{n+1}x^{n+1} + c$$

In words, this tells us that if we wish to integrate x raised to a power, we need to increase the power by one, and divide by the new power.

This result applies for all values of n (including values that are not integers) except for $n = -1$. If we did set $n = -1$ in the general result, it would give:

$$\int x^{-1}\,dx = \frac{1}{-1+1}x^{-1+1} + c = \frac{1}{0}x^0 + c = \frac{1}{0} + c$$

which is a problem as 1 divided by 0 is undefined. This means we need a separate result to integrate x^{-1}, which we will meet shortly.

Example 7.4

Integrate the following functions:

(i) $\sqrt{x}$

(ii) $3x^4 + 2x^3 - x^2 + 5$

Solution

(i)   Writing $\sqrt{x}$ as $x^{\frac{1}{2}}$ and using the result above with $n = \frac{1}{2}$:

$$\int \sqrt{x}\,dx = \int x^{\frac{1}{2}}\,dx = \frac{x^{\frac{3}{2}}}{\frac{3}{2}} + c = \tfrac{2}{3}x^{\frac{3}{2}} + c = \tfrac{2}{3}\sqrt{x^3} + c$$

(ii)   Here we use the idea that the integral of a sum is the sum of the integrals, and apply the result above repeatedly:

$$\int \left(3x^4 + 2x^3 - x^2 + 5\right)dx = 3\left(\tfrac{1}{5}\right)x^5 + 2\left(\tfrac{1}{4}\right)x^4 - \left(\tfrac{1}{3}\right)x^3 + 5x + c$$

$$= \tfrac{3}{5}x^5 + \tfrac{1}{2}x^4 - \tfrac{1}{3}x^3 + 5x + c \qquad\qquad ◆◆$$

Integrating x^{-1}

To integrate x^{-1} or, equivalently, $\dfrac{1}{x}$, we need to find a function that gives x^{-1} when differentiated. We know that the derivative of $\ln x$ is x^{-1}, so the integral of x^{-1} is $\ln x$.

We need to be careful when stating the general result in this case, as the natural logarithm function, $\ln x$, is only defined for $x > 0$, but the function x^{-1} that we're integrating is defined for negative values of x as well, so we should be able to integrate it over any range. To ensure we obtain a suitable answer even when x is negative, we define the integral of x^{-1} to be $\ln|x|$, so that the natural logarithm function is applied to a positive value.

So, our general result is:

$$\int x^{-1}\,dx = \int \frac{1}{x}\,dx = \ln|x| + c$$

Example 7.5

Evaluate the following integrals

(i) $\int_{1}^{2} \frac{1}{x} dx$

(ii) $\int_{-2}^{-1} \frac{1}{x} dx$

and comment on the answers.

Solution

(i)   Using the general result for integrating $\frac{1}{x}$:

$$\int_{1}^{2} \frac{1}{x} dx = \left[\ln|x|\right]_{1}^{2} = \ln 2 - \underset{=0}{\underline{\ln 1}} = \ln 2$$

(ii)   Again, using the general result:

$$\int_{-2}^{-1} \frac{1}{x} dx = \left[\ln|x|\right]_{-2}^{-1} = \ln|-1| - \ln|-2| = \underset{=0}{\underline{\ln 1}} - \ln 2 = -\ln 2$$

Below is a sketch of the hyperbola $f(x) = \frac{1}{x}$, with the areas corresponding to these integrals shaded:

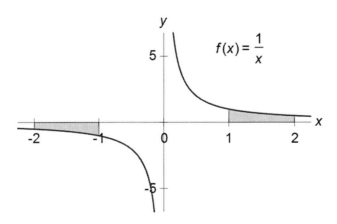

Since this hyperbola has rotational symmetry about the origin, we expect the two shaded areas to be equal. This ties in with our results, as the two integrals we've evaluated give the same answer, except for the fact that the integral relating to the area between $x = -2$ and $x = -1$ is negative, because over that range the curve is below the x-axis.   ♦♦

Integrating functions of the form $\dfrac{f'(x)}{f(x)}$

In Chapter 6, we met the result that the derivative of $\ln f(x)$ is $\dfrac{f'(x)}{f(x)}$, which was obtained using the chain rule. We therefore have the equivalent result for integration that:

$$\int \frac{f'(x)}{f(x)} dx = \ln|f(x)| + c$$

As mentioned above, we take the modulus of the function being logged, as the natural logarithm function, $\ln x$, is only defined for values of $x > 0$.

The trick to using this standard result is spotting that the function we need to integrate can be expressed as a fraction where the numerator is the derivative of the denominator.

Example 7.6

Integrate the following functions:

(i) $\dfrac{2}{x+1}$

(ii) $\dfrac{e^x}{e^x+1}$

(iii) $\dfrac{x^2}{\frac{1}{3}\left(x^3-1\right)}$

Solution

(i)   First of all, we can pull the constant 2 through the integral to simplify it:

$$\int \frac{2}{x+1} dx = 2\int \frac{1}{x+1} dx$$

The numerator of the function to be integrated is equal to the derivative of the denominator, so using the general result with $f(x) = x+1$:

$$\int \frac{2}{x+1} dx = 2\ln|x+1| + c$$

Note that the integral $\int \dfrac{1}{x+1} dx$ *can also be written as* $\int \dfrac{dx}{x+1}$.

(ii)   The derivative of e^x+1 is e^x, so we can use the general result directly, with $f(x) = e^x+1$:

$$\int \frac{e^x}{e^x+1} dx = \ln\left(e^x+1\right) + c$$

Here we do not need to include the modulus signs, as the function $f(x) = e^x+1$ is always positive.

(iii)   If we rewrite the integral as:

$$\int \frac{x^2}{\frac{1}{3}\left(x^3 - 1\right)}\, dx = \int \frac{3x^2}{x^3 - 1}\, dx$$

then it's clear that the numerator of the function being integrated is the derivative of the denominator. So we can use the general result with $f(x) = x^3 - 1$ to obtain:

$$\int \frac{3x^2}{x^3 - 1}\, dx = \ln\left|x^3 - 1\right| + c \qquad \blacklozenge\blacklozenge$$

◆ *Integrating the exponential function*

By using the chain rule for differentiation, we know that, for any constant k, the derivative of $\frac{1}{k}e^{kx}$ is $\frac{1}{k} \times ke^{kx} = e^{kx}$. This means that the integral of e^{kx} is $\frac{1}{k}e^{kx}$, giving the general result:

$$\int e^{kx}\, dx = \frac{1}{k}e^{kx} + c$$

Example 7.7

Evaluate $\int_0^{\ln 2} 2e^{5x}\, dx$.

Solution

Using this general result:

$$\int_0^{\ln 2} 2e^{5x}\, dx = \left[2 \times \tfrac{1}{5}e^{5x}\right]_0^{\ln 2} = \tfrac{2}{5}e^{5\ln 2} - \tfrac{2}{5}e^0$$

Since $e^{5\ln 2} = e^{\ln 2^5} = 2^5 = 32$, this simplifies to:

$$\tfrac{2}{5} \times 32 - \tfrac{2}{5} = \tfrac{62}{5} = 12.4 \qquad \blacklozenge\blacklozenge$$

◆ *Integrating a^x*

In Chapter 6, we used the chain rule to obtain a general result for the derivative of a^x, where a is any positive constant:

$$\frac{d}{dx}a^x = a^x \ln a$$

This tells us that the derivative of $\frac{a^x}{\ln a}$ is a^x, giving us the general integral result:

$$\int a^x\, dx = \frac{a^x}{\ln a} + c$$

Instead of using the above general result, integrals of this form can be performed by rewriting the function to be integrated in terms of the exponential function. As we saw in Chapter 6, when looking at differentiating functions of this form, we can write $a^x = e^{\ln(a^x)} = e^{x \ln a}$, so that the integral becomes:

$$\int a^x \, dx = \int e^{x \ln a} \, dx = \frac{e^{x \ln a}}{\ln a} + c = \frac{a^x}{\ln a} + c$$

Here, we have used the general result for integrating the exponential function to carry out the integration.

 ### *Example 7.8*

Integrate 7^{2x} .

Solution

Using a power law, this can be written as:

$$7^{2x} = \left(7^2\right)^x = 49^x$$

So, using the general result:

$$\int 7^{2x} dx = \int 49^x dx = \frac{49^x}{\ln 49} + c$$ ◆◆

The table below summarises the standard integration results that we've met in this section.

Integrals of standard functions	
Function	***Integral***
k	$kx + c$
x^n	$\dfrac{x^{n+1}}{n+1} + c, n \neq -1$
$\dfrac{1}{x}$	$\ln|x| + c$
$\dfrac{f'(x)}{f(x)}$	$\ln|f(x)| + c$
e^{kx}	$\dfrac{e^{kx}}{k} + c$
a^x	$\dfrac{a^x}{\ln a} + c$

7.3   Techniques for integration

In this section, we consider four techniques that can be used when integrating more complex functions:

- inspection
- using partial fractions
- substitution
- integration by parts.

◆ Integration by inspection

Certain expressions can be integrated by inspection, that is, the answer is immediately recognisable and can simply be written down. This relies on the technique of writing down what we think is the correct answer for the integral, and then checking that it is correct by differentiating it, hopefully to obtain the original function that we started with. If the answer is of the correct form, but has the wrong coefficient, we can adjust it, by multiplying by a factor, until it does give the original function when differentiated.

Often, the key to successful integration by inspection is to spot an exact derivative (or a multiple of an exact derivative) as part of the integral.

We will look at some examples below.

Example 7.9

Integrate the following expressions with respect to x:

(i) $(x+2)^4$

(ii) $x\left(x^2+6\right)^5$

(iii) $3xe^{x^2}$

Solution

(i)   We know that integrating involves increasing the power of a function, so we might consider the integral of $(x+2)^4$ to be $(x+2)^5$. If we differentiate $(x+2)^5$ using the chain rule, we obtain $5(x+2)^4 \times 1 = 5(x+2)^4$, which is close to our original function, except for the factor of 5. If we differentiate $\frac{1}{5}(x+2)^5$, we will obtain our original function, so:

$$\int (x+2)^4 \, dx = \frac{1}{5}(x+2)^5 + c$$

(ii)   If we differentiate $\left(x^2 + 6\right)^6$ using the chain rule, we obtain $6\left(x^2 + 6\right)^5 \times 2x$. This is the same as the function we are trying to integrate, except for the factor of 12. If we differentiate $\dfrac{1}{12}\left(x^2 + 6\right)^6$, we will obtain our original function, so:

$$\int x\left(x^2 + 6\right)^5 dx = \frac{1}{12}\left(x^2 + 6\right)^6 + c$$

(iii)   As the derivative of e^{x^2} is $2xe^{x^2}$ (using the chain rule), we know that the integral of $2xe^{x^2}$ is e^{x^2}. So, to integrate $3xe^{x^2}$ by inspection, we can rewrite the integral as follows:

$$\int 3xe^{x^2} dx = \frac{3}{2}\int 2xe^{x^2} dx$$

and use the fact the we know how to integrate $2xe^{x^2}$ to give:

$$\int 3xe^{x^2} dx = \frac{3}{2}e^{x^2} + c$$ ◆◆

The technique used here, where we have made an adjustment to the integral to turn it into an exact derivative will work where the adjustment involves numbers only. It cannot be done by adjusting using factors that are functions of x.

◆ Integration using partial fractions

This technique involves splitting up a single fraction into separate parts, known as *partial fractions*. Using this technique, expressions that cannot be integrated directly can be written as expressions that can.

Example 7.10

Find $\int \dfrac{x + 7}{(x + 1)(x - 2)} dx$.

Solution

To integrate this using partial fractions the first step is to express the function $\dfrac{x + 7}{(x + 1)(x - 2)}$ as a sum of simpler fractions. We look for values of A and B such that:

$$\frac{x + 7}{(x + 1)(x - 2)} = \frac{A}{x + 1} + \frac{B}{x - 2}$$

Multiplying both sides of this equation by $(x + 1)(x - 2)$ gives:

$$x + 7 = A(x - 2) + B(x + 1)$$

Setting $x = -1$ (so that the coefficient of B in the above equation is zero) gives:

$$-1 + 7 = A(-1 - 2) + B(-1 + 1) \;\Rightarrow\; 6 = -3A \;\Rightarrow\; A = -2$$

and setting $x = 2$ (so that the coefficient of A is zero) gives:

$$2 + 7 = A(2 - 2) + B(2 + 1) \;\Rightarrow\; 9 = 3B \;\Rightarrow\; B = 3$$

So:

$$\frac{x+7}{(x+1)(x-2)} = \frac{-2}{x+1} + \frac{3}{x-2}$$

An alternative approach to establishing the values of A and B is to compare the constants and the coefficients of the terms in x on both sides of the equation:

$$x+7 = A(x-2) + B(x+1)$$

to make them match. Equating the constants, we have:

$$7 = -2A + B$$

and equating the coefficients of the terms in x, we have:

$$1 = A + B$$

Solving these two equations simultaneously gives the values $A = -2$ and $B = 3$, as before.

We can now rewrite the integral as:

$$\int \frac{x+7}{(x+1)(x-2)}dx = \int \left(\frac{-2}{x+1} + \frac{3}{x-2}\right)dx$$

This can now be integrated directly, using the standard result for integrating functions of the form $\frac{f'(x)}{f(x)}$.

So, we have:

$$\int \left(\frac{-2}{x+1} + \frac{3}{x-2}\right)dx = -2\ln|x+1| + 3\ln|x-2| + c = \ln\left|\frac{(x-2)^3}{(x+1)^2}\right| + c \qquad \blacklozenge\blacklozenge$$

When using the technique of partial fractions, it is important to make sure that the denominator is fully factorised, for example, by writing a quadratic as the product of two linear factors. This is illustrated below.

Example 7.11

Find $\int \frac{9x-2}{9x^2-4}dx$.

Solution

In order to integrate this using partial fractions, we first need to factorise the denominator:

$$9x^2 - 4 = (3x+2)(3x-2)$$

Next, we need to split up the single fraction into two fractions that are added together. We search for A and B such that:

$$\frac{9x-2}{(3x+2)(3x-2)} = \frac{A}{3x+2} + \frac{B}{3x-2}$$

Multiplying this equation through by $(3x+2)(3x-2)$ gives:

$$9x - 2 = A(3x-2) + B(3x+2)$$

Setting $x = -\dfrac{2}{3}$ (so that the coefficient of B in the above equation is zero), we have:

$$9 \times \left(-\dfrac{2}{3}\right) - 2 = A\left(3 \times \left(-\dfrac{2}{3}\right) - 2\right) \quad \Rightarrow \quad -8 = -4A \quad \Rightarrow \quad A = 2$$

Setting $x = \dfrac{2}{3}$ (so that the coefficient of A is zero), we have:

$$9 \times \dfrac{2}{3} - 2 = B\left(3 \times \dfrac{2}{3} + 2\right) \quad \Rightarrow \quad 4 = 4B \quad \Rightarrow \quad B = 1$$

As in Example 7.10, we can alternatively establish the values of A and B by comparing the constants and the coefficients of the terms in x in the equation:

$$9x - 2 = A(3x - 2) + B(3x + 2)$$

and solving the equations simultaneously. This gives the values $A = 2$ and $B = 1$, as before.

Using the values of A and B that we have determined, we can rewrite the integral as:

$$\int \dfrac{9x - 2}{9x^2 - 4}\, dx = \int \left(\dfrac{2}{3x + 2} + \dfrac{1}{3x - 2}\right) dx$$

To evaluate this integral using the standard result for integrating functions of the form $\dfrac{f'(x)}{f(x)}$, we can think of it as:

$$\int \left(\dfrac{2}{3x + 2} + \dfrac{1}{3x - 2}\right) dx = \dfrac{2}{3}\int \dfrac{3}{3x + 2}\, dx + \dfrac{1}{3}\int \dfrac{3}{3x - 2}\, dx$$

So:

$$\int \left(\dfrac{2}{3x + 2} + \dfrac{1}{3x - 2}\right) dx = \dfrac{2}{3}\ln|3x + 2| + \dfrac{1}{3}\ln|3x - 2| + c$$

$$= \dfrac{1}{3}\ln\left|(3x + 2)^2(3x - 2)\right| + c \qquad \blacklozenge\blacklozenge$$

◆ *Integration by substitution (or change of variable)*

This technique involves the replacement of one variable by another, enabling expressions to be simplified and hence integrated.

The steps to follow are:

- Decide what substitution to use, by defining a new variable, u, say. Generally, we set u equal to the 'complicated' part of the expression to be integrated or the part of the expression in brackets (if there is one).

- Find $\dfrac{du}{dx}$, and use this to change dx into du.

- Express the function to be integrated in terms of u.

- If this method is being applied to a definite integral, the limits should be changed so that they correspond to the new variable u.

- Evaluate the simpler integral.

Let's look at a couple of examples using this technique.

Example 7.12

Evaluate $\int_0^1 x(2x+3)^4 dx$.

Solution

We could evaluate this integral by multiplying out the function and then integrating it term by term, but that would be quite time-consuming. Instead, we will use integration by substitution.

The most complicated part of the expression to be integrated is $(2x+3)^4$, so we will let $u = 2x+3$, meaning that this part of the integral becomes u^4. Since $u = 2x+3$, we know that $x = \dfrac{u-3}{2}$, so the function to be integrated, $x(2x+3)^4$, is $\left(\dfrac{u-3}{2}\right)u^4$ in terms of the new variable u.

If $u = 2x+3$, then $\dfrac{du}{dx} = 2$. By 'splitting the derivative', we can write $du = 2dx$, or equivalently, $dx = \dfrac{1}{2}du$.

As this is a definite integral, we need to work out the new values for the limits. When $x = 0$ (the value at the lower limit), $u = 3$, so the new lower limit is 3, and when $x = 1$ (the value at the upper limit), $u = 5$, so the new upper limit is 5.

We are now in a position to rewrite the integral in terms of u:

$$\int_0^1 x(2x+3)^4 dx = \int_3^5 \left(\frac{u-3}{2}\right)u^4 \times \frac{1}{2}\,du$$

$$= \frac{1}{4}\int_3^5 \left(u^5 - 3u^4\right)du$$

This is now simple to integrate:

$$\frac{1}{4}\int_3^5 \left(u^5 - 3u^4\right)du = \frac{1}{4}\left[\frac{u^6}{6} - \frac{3u^5}{5}\right]_3^5$$

$$= \frac{1}{4}\left(\frac{5^6}{6} - \frac{3 \times 5^5}{5}\right) - \frac{1}{4}\left(\frac{3^6}{6} - \frac{3 \times 3^5}{5}\right)$$

$$= 188\tfrac{11}{30} \qquad \qquad \blacklozenge \blacklozenge$$

This technique of integration can be used in place of integration by inspection. If it is difficult to write down an answer by inspection, using a substitution can make life easier as it formalises the process to work through.

Integration by substitution can also be used as an alternative to applying results for integrating standard functions.

To illustrate these points, we'll revisit some of our earlier examples.

Example 7.13

Integrate the following functions with respect to x:

(i) $\dfrac{e^x}{e^x + 1}$

(ii) $3xe^{x^2}$

Solution

(i)   We looked at this integral in part (ii) of Example 7.6, where we applied the standard result for integrating functions of the form $\dfrac{f'(x)}{f(x)}$.

The denominator is the most complicated part of this function, so let's set $u = e^x + 1$. With this substitution, $\dfrac{du}{dx} = e^x$, and 'splitting the derivative' gives $du = e^x \, dx$. This is a convenient relationship, because the integral in question:

$$\int \frac{e^x}{e^x + 1} \, dx$$

features $e^x \, dx$ in the numerator. So, making the substitution, the integral becomes:

$$\int \frac{1}{u} \, du = \ln|u| + c$$

Writing this in terms of x, and removing the modulus as $e^x + 1$ is always positive, we have:

$$\int \frac{e^x}{e^x + 1} \, dx = \ln\left(e^x + 1\right) + c$$

(ii)   We looked at this integral in part (iii) of Example 7.9, where we used integration by inspection.

The awkward part of the function to be integrated is the x^2 in the power of the exponential function. Since we know how to integrate e^x easily, we will use the substitution $u = x^2$, so that e^{x^2} becomes e^u.

If $u = x^2$, then $\dfrac{du}{dx} = 2x$, and 'splitting the derivative' gives $du = 2x \, dx$. Since our integral includes $x \, dx$, the relationship $\dfrac{1}{2} du = x \, dx$ will be useful in rewriting the integral.

So, in terms of the new variable u the integral becomes:

$$\int 3xe^{x^2} \, dx = \int 3e^u \times \frac{1}{2} \, du = \frac{3}{2} \int e^u \, du$$

This is more straightforward to integrate than the original expression. Integrating gives:

$$\frac{3}{2} \int e^u \, du = \frac{3}{2} e^u + c$$

Writing this in terms of the original variable x:

$$\int 3xe^{x^2} dx = \frac{3}{2}e^{x^2} + c$$

◆◆

◆ *Integration by parts*

Integration by parts gives us a method for integrating products of functions.

We can obtain the formula for integration by parts by starting with the product rule for differentiation, which was introduced in Chapter 6. This tells us that if u and v are functions of x, then:

$$\frac{d}{dx}(uv) = u\frac{dv}{dx} + v\frac{du}{dx}$$

We can rearrange this to give:

$$u\frac{dv}{dx} = \frac{d}{dx}(uv) - v\frac{du}{dx}$$

The first term on the right-hand side is the derivative of the function uv with respect to x. If we integrate this with respect to x, we obtain uv, as integration is the reverse of differentiation. So, integrating the equation above with respect to x gives:

$$\int u\frac{dv}{dx} dx = uv - \int v\frac{du}{dx} dx$$

This is the formula for integration by parts. It can be presented in the form of indefinite integration as above, or in the form of definite integration, with lower limit a and upper limit b, as shown in the box below. The basic procedure is the same whether the integrals are definite or indefinite, but for indefinite integration, the final answer will need to include a constant of integration.

Integration by parts

If u and v are functions of x, then:

$$\int u\frac{dv}{dx} dx = uv - \int v\frac{du}{dx} dx$$

and

$$\int_a^b u\frac{dv}{dx}dx = \left[uv\right]_a^b - \int_a^b v\frac{du}{dx}dx$$

Looking at the formula for integration by parts in more detail, we see that on the left-hand side, the product to be integrated is split down into two parts, u and $\frac{dv}{dx}$. The right-hand side features u, v and $\frac{du}{dx}$. Of these, we already know what u is, as it is one of the functions on the left-hand side, but we will have to work out v and $\frac{du}{dx}$.

This helps us when choosing which function to associate with u in the formula, and which to associate with $\dfrac{dv}{dx}$: we should try to make these associations so that we can easily *differentiate* the function u and easily *integrate* the function $\dfrac{dv}{dx}$.

Another issue that affects our choice of u and $\dfrac{dv}{dx}$ is the fact that the right-hand side of the formula for integration by parts features:

$$\int v\frac{du}{dx}dx$$

The process of integration by parts is therefore only useful if the integral we are faced with on the right-hand side is easier to work out than the one we started with on the left-hand side, and ensuring this is the case also affects our choice of u and $\dfrac{dv}{dx}$.

It is not always straightforward to decide which function to associate with u (the function to differentiate) and which to associate with $\dfrac{dv}{dx}$ (the function to integrate), but it does get easier with practice. We'll take a look at some examples to highlight the issues.

Example 7.14

Integrate xe^x with respect to x.

Solution

Both x and e^x can be easily differentiated and integrated, so we should choose u and $\dfrac{dv}{dx}$ so that the resulting integral is easier than the original one. One thing to note here is that if we set u to be a linear function of x, then its derivative will be a constant, which is likely to make the integral on the right-hand side easier to deal with.

Letting $u = x$ and $\dfrac{dv}{dx} = e^x$, so that $\dfrac{du}{dx} = 1$ and $v = e^x$, we have:

$$\int \underbrace{x}_{u}\underbrace{e^x}_{\frac{dv}{dx}}dx = \underbrace{x}_{u}\underbrace{e^x}_{v} - \int \underbrace{1}_{\frac{du}{dx}}\underbrace{e^x}_{v}dx$$

Carrying out the integration on the right-hand side gives:

$$\int xe^x dx = xe^x - e^x + c = (x-1)e^x + c \qquad\qquad ♦♦$$

Let's see what would have happened in Example 7.14 if we had chosen u and $\dfrac{dv}{dx}$ to be the other way around, so $u = e^x$ and $\dfrac{dv}{dx} = x$. In this case, $\dfrac{du}{dx} = e^x$ and $v = \dfrac{1}{2}x^2$, so the formula for integration by parts gives:

$$\int \underbrace{x}_{\frac{dv}{dx}}\underbrace{e^x}_{u}dx = \underbrace{e^x}_{u}\times\underbrace{\frac{1}{2}x^2}_{v} - \int \underbrace{e^x}_{\frac{du}{dx}}\times\underbrace{\frac{1}{2}x^2}_{v}dx$$

Now the integral on the right-hand side looks more complicated than the one we started with, as it involves x^2 instead of x. So this choice of u and $\frac{dv}{dx}$ is not worth pursuing.

In the following example, suitable choices for u and $\frac{dv}{dx}$ are harder to establish.

Example 7.15

Integrate $x^3 e^{x^2}$ with respect to x.

Solution

Here the function to be integrated is the product of x^3 and e^{x^2}. Since e^{x^2} cannot be directly integrated, we might think that setting $\frac{dv}{dx} = x^3$ would be a good idea. However, integrating this gives $v = \frac{1}{4}x^4$, meaning that the integral on the right-hand side will be more complicated than the original integral. This choice of u and $\frac{dv}{dx}$ is therefore not suitable.

Instead, we will split up the x^3 term into x^2 multiplied by x. Then we can write the function to be integrated as $x^2 \times xe^{x^2}$. The expression xe^{x^2} can be integrated, either by inspection (as we saw in part (iii) of Example 7.9) or by substitution (as we saw in part (ii) of Example 7.13).

So, letting $u = x^2$ and $\frac{dv}{dx} = xe^{x^2}$, so that $\frac{du}{dx} = 2x$ and $v = \frac{1}{2}e^{x^2}$, we have:

$$\int \underbrace{x^3 e^{x^2}}\, dx = \int \underbrace{x^2}_{u} \times \underbrace{xe^{x^2}}_{\frac{dv}{dx}}\, dx = \underbrace{x^2}_{u} \times \underbrace{\frac{1}{2}e^{x^2}}_{v} - \int \underbrace{2x}_{\frac{du}{dx}} \times \underbrace{\frac{1}{2}e^{x^2}}_{v}\, dx$$

This simplifies as follows:

$$\int x^3 e^{x^2}\, dx = \frac{1}{2}x^2 e^{x^2} - \int xe^{x^2}\, dx$$

The remaining integral on the right-hand side is exactly the same as the one we did to obtain v from $\frac{dv}{dx}$, so:

$$\int x^3 e^{x^2}\, dx = \frac{1}{2}x^2 e^{x^2} - \frac{1}{2}e^{x^2} + c = \frac{1}{2}(x^2 - 1)e^{x^2} + c \qquad\qquad \blacklozenge\blacklozenge$$

One omission from our set of integrals of standard functions in Section 7.2 was the natural logarithm function, $\ln x$. In fact, to integrate $\ln x$, we use integration by parts as shown in the following example.

Example 7.16

Evaluate $\displaystyle\int_1^2 \ln x\, dx$.

Solution

The function to be integrated here, $\ln x$, is not obviously a product, suggesting that we cannot use integration by parts. However, we will rewrite it as $1 \times \ln x$, so the integral becomes:

$$\int_1^2 (1 \times \ln x)\, dx$$

Since we are trying to find the integral of $\ln x$, it would not make sense to let $\dfrac{dv}{dx} = \ln x$, as we would need to integrate this to find v.

Instead, letting $u = \ln x$ and $\dfrac{dv}{dx} = 1$, so that $\dfrac{du}{dx} = \dfrac{1}{x}$, and $v = x$, we have:

$$\int_1^2 (1 \times \ln x)\, dx = \left[x \ln x \right]_1^2 - \int_1^2 \left(\frac{1}{x} \times x \right) dx$$

$$= \left[x \ln x \right]_1^2 - \int_1^2 1\, dx$$

The integral on the right-hand side is now very straightforward, and this can be evaluated to give:

$$\int_1^2 \ln x\, dx = \left[x \ln x \right]_1^2 - \left[x \right]_1^2 = (2 \times \ln 2 - 1 \times \ln 1) - (2 - 1) = 2\ln 2 - 1 = \ln 4 - 1 \qquad \blacklozenge\blacklozenge$$

It is important to note that there is not always a unique way of integrating. We saw this in Example 7.13 in which we revisited earlier examples. In addition, Example 7.12 could have been carried out using integration by parts with $u = x$ and $\dfrac{dv}{dx} = (2x + 3)^4$. Where more than one approach could be taken to perform an integral, the key thing is to try to use the most efficient method.

7.4   *Convergence of integrals*

So far we have only considered integrals where the upper and lower limits have been finite. However, it is possible that we will need to evaluate integrals where either the upper or lower limit (or both) is infinite. In order to do this, we define:

$$\int_a^\infty f(x)\, dx = \lim_{k \to \infty} \int_a^k f(x)\, dx$$

and:

$$\int_{-\infty}^b f(x)\, dx = \lim_{k \to -\infty} \int_k^b f(x)\, dx$$

so that an integral with an infinite limit is expressed in terms of an integral with a finite limit, k, which we allow to tend to infinity. If these integrals tend to a finite limit as k tends to $\pm\infty$, the integrals are said to *converge*; otherwise the integrals do not converge.

Example 7.17

Establish whether the integral $\int_1^\infty \frac{1}{x^2}\,dx$ converges. If it does converge, state its value.

Solution

Using the definition given above for an integral with an infinite upper limit, we have:

$$\int_1^\infty \frac{1}{x^2}\,dx = \lim_{k\to\infty}\int_1^k \frac{1}{x^2}\,dx = \lim_{k\to\infty}\left[-\frac{1}{x}\right]_1^k = \lim_{k\to\infty}\left(-\frac{1}{k}-(-1)\right)$$

As k tends to infinity, $\frac{1}{k}$ tends to zero. This means that the limit as k tends to infinity exists, and the integral converges to the value 1.   ♦♦

In practice, when evaluating integrals such as the one in Example 7.17, we consider the limit, but do not explicitly write it down. So, we would usually present the solution as:

$$\int_1^\infty \frac{1}{x^2}\,dx = \left[-\frac{1}{x}\right]_1^\infty = 0-(-1) = 1$$

Convergence of integrals is also an issue when the function being integrated tends to $\pm\infty$ at a certain point, eg $\frac{1}{x}$ when $x=0$.

Example 7.18

Explain why the following integrals do not converge:

(i) $\int_0^\infty \frac{1}{x^2}\,dx$

(ii) $\int_0^N \frac{1}{x}\,dx$

(iii) $\int_1^\infty \frac{1}{x}\,dx$

Solution

(i) $\int_0^\infty \frac{1}{x^2}\,dx = \lim_{k\to\infty}\int_0^k \frac{1}{x^2}\,dx = \lim_{k\to\infty}\left[-\frac{1}{x}\right]_0^k$ which is not defined at the lower limit of 0.

(ii) $\int_0^N \frac{1}{x}\,dx = \lim_{k\to0}\int_k^N \frac{1}{x}\,dx = \lim_{k\to0}\left[\ln|x|\right]_k^N$ does not converge, as $\ln k$ tends to negative infinity as k tends to zero.

(iii) $\displaystyle\int_1^\infty \frac{1}{x}\,dx = \lim_{k\to\infty}\int_1^k \frac{1}{x}\,dx = \lim_{k\to\infty}\Big[\ln|x|\Big]_1^k = \lim_{k\to\infty}\ln k$ does not converge, as $\ln k$ tends to

infinity as k tends to infinity.   ◆◆

One consequence of these integrals not converging is that the area represented by each of them is infinite.

Chapter 7 Practice Questions

◆ Introduction to integration

Question 7.1

Which of the following is NOT true?

A $\quad \displaystyle\int_a^b f(x)\,dx = -\int_b^a f(x)\,dx$

B $\quad \displaystyle\int_a^b f(x)\,dx = \int_0^b f(x)\,dx - \int_0^a f(x)\,dx$

C $\quad \displaystyle\int_a^b \frac{d}{dx}f(x)\,dx = f(b) - f(a)$

D $\quad \displaystyle\int_a^b \frac{d}{dx}f(x)\,dx$ is used to find the area enclosed by the function $f(x)$ and the x-axis between the lines $x = a$ and $x = b$.

Question 7.2

Calculate the area under the curve $y = 3x^2$ between $x = 1$ and $x = 3$.

◆ Integrals of standard functions

Question 7.3

Integrate the following functions with respect to x:

(i) $\quad 6x^2 + 6x + 6$

(ii) $\quad \dfrac{2}{x^2} + 4\sqrt[3]{x^2}$

(iii) $\quad \frac{1}{2}e^{2x}$

(iv) $\quad 6^{\frac{1}{2}x}$

(v) $\quad \dfrac{2x+5}{x^2+5x+7}$

Question 7.4

Evaluate the following integrals:

(i) $\displaystyle\int_{1}^{2} x^{0.75}\,dx$

(ii) $\displaystyle\int_{2}^{4} 5^{x}\,dx$

(iii) $\displaystyle\int_{0}^{3} \lambda e^{-\lambda x}\,dx$

(iv) $\displaystyle\int_{0}^{10} \frac{5}{x+1}\,dx$

Question 7.5

Find the area of the region enclosed by the x-axis and the curve $y = 6 + x - 2x^2$.

◆ Techniques for integration

Question 7.6

Use integration by inspection to find the following:

(i) $\displaystyle\int \frac{4x+6}{\left(x^2+3x+4\right)^5}\,dx$

(ii) $\displaystyle\int 7x e^{3x^2-4}\,dx$

(iii) $\displaystyle\int x\sqrt{e^{2x^2}}\,dx$

Question 7.7

By first expressing the function $f(x) = \dfrac{x-7}{x^2-1}$ in terms of partial fractions, integrate $f(x)$ with respect to x.

Question 7.8

By using a suitable substitution, evaluate:

(i) $\displaystyle\int_{2}^{5}\frac{2x}{\sqrt{(x-1)}}\,dx$

(ii) $\displaystyle\int_{0}^{1}\frac{4}{2e^{3x}+1}\,dx$

Question 7.9

Use integration by parts to find:

(i) $\displaystyle\int x(x+1)^{6}dx$

(ii) $\displaystyle\int x\ln x\,dx$

Question 7.10

Evaluate $\displaystyle\int_{1}^{2}\frac{x}{(5+x)^{2}}\,dx$

(a)   by substitution

(b)   using integration by parts

(c)   using partial fractions.

Question 7.11

Evaluate:

(i) $\displaystyle\int_{0}^{1}\frac{x^{5}}{\left(10+x^{6}\right)^{3}}\,dx$

(ii) $\displaystyle\int_{1}^{2}\frac{3x^{2}+3}{2x^{3}+6x+1}\,dx$

(iii) $\displaystyle\int_{3}^{5}\frac{2x+5}{(2x-4)(x+1)}\,dx$

(iv) $\displaystyle\int_{0}^{1}xe^{2x}\,dx$

◆ *Convergence*

Question 7.12

Which one of the following integrals does NOT converge?

A $\displaystyle\int_{1}^{\infty} e^{-2x}\,dx$

B $\displaystyle\int_{0}^{1} \ln x\,dx$

C $\displaystyle\int_{1}^{\infty} x^{-2}\,dx$

D $\displaystyle\int_{1}^{\infty} \frac{6}{x^3}\,dx$

Question 7.13

Evaluate $\displaystyle\int_{0}^{\infty} x^3 e^{-5x^4}\,dx$.

Question 7.14

Evaluate $\displaystyle\int_{0}^{\infty} x e^{-2x}\,dx$.

8

Vectors and matrices

Learning Objectives

The following learning objectives are covered in this chapter:

- Carrying out simple calculations involving vectors, including the use of row/column vectors and unit vectors.

- Determining the magnitude and direction of a vector, and the angle between two vectors.

- Carrying out calculations involving matrices, including calculating the determinant and inverse of a 2×2 matrix.

8.1 *Vectors*

A *vector* is defined as a quantity that has a magnitude (or length) and a direction.

In this chapter, we will work with two and three-dimensional vectors, but note that the results can easily be extended to the *n*-dimensional case.

◆ **Notation**

We will use the convention that vectors (and later, matrices) are written in bold. In handwritten work, vectors and matrices can be underlined to distinguish them from single numbers (which we call *scalars*). So, an equation involving the scalar λ, the vector **v** and the matrices **M** and **I** might look like this:

$$\mathbf{Mv} = \lambda\mathbf{Iv} \quad \text{or} \quad \underline{M}\underline{v} = \lambda\underline{I}\underline{v}$$

We'll start off with a couple of examples to illustrate how vectors work.

Example 8.1

Write down the vector, **a**, joining the point $(0,0)$ to the point $(3,-2)$ in two-dimensional space.

Solution

To move from $(0,0)$ to $(3,-2)$, we need to go 3 units in the x direction and -2 units in the y direction. This vector, **a**, is written as:

$$\begin{pmatrix} 3 \\ -2 \end{pmatrix}$$

◆◆

We can use the same idea in three dimensions.

Example 8.2

Calculate the coordinates of the point arrived at by following the vector:

$$\mathbf{b} = \begin{pmatrix} -1 \\ 4 \\ -2 \end{pmatrix}$$

from the starting point $(1,3,5)$.

Solution

We need to move -1 units in the x direction, taking us from $x = 1$ to $x = 0$, 4 units in the y direction, taking us from $y = 3$ to $y = 7$, and -2 units in the z direction, taking us from $z = 5$ to $z = 3$.

So, we arrive at the point $(0,7,3)$.

◆◆

Vectors can be expressed in the form of a column vector, *eg* $\mathbf{b} = \begin{pmatrix} -1 \\ 4 \\ -2 \end{pmatrix}$, or, equivalently, in the

form of a row vector, *eg* $\mathbf{b} = (-1 \quad 4 \quad -2)$. We will work with column vectors in this chapter, although similar rules to those described here for column vectors also apply to row vectors.

◆ *Basic vector arithmetic*

Any vector can be multiplied by a scalar (*ie* a single number), simply by multiplying each of the individual elements by the scalar. Vectors of equal dimensions can be added or subtracted, again by simply adding or subtracting the individual elements.

Addition, subtraction and scalar multiplication of a vector in 3 dimensions

$$\begin{pmatrix} a \\ b \\ c \end{pmatrix} + \begin{pmatrix} d \\ e \\ f \end{pmatrix} = \begin{pmatrix} a+d \\ b+e \\ c+f \end{pmatrix} \qquad \begin{pmatrix} a \\ b \\ c \end{pmatrix} - \begin{pmatrix} d \\ e \\ f \end{pmatrix} = \begin{pmatrix} a-d \\ b-e \\ c-f \end{pmatrix} \qquad k\begin{pmatrix} a \\ b \\ c \end{pmatrix} = \begin{pmatrix} ka \\ kb \\ kc \end{pmatrix}$$

Similar results to these hold in 2, and higher, dimensions.

Showing addition and multiplication pictorially:

 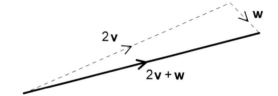

Example 8.3

If $\mathbf{a} = \begin{pmatrix} 2 \\ 4 \\ -4 \end{pmatrix}$ and $\mathbf{b} = \begin{pmatrix} 3 \\ -5 \\ 1 \end{pmatrix}$, calculate:

(i) $2\mathbf{a}$

(ii) $\mathbf{a} + \mathbf{b}$

(iii) $3\mathbf{a} - 4\mathbf{b}$

Solution

(i) $2\mathbf{a} = 2\begin{pmatrix} 2 \\ 4 \\ -4 \end{pmatrix} = \begin{pmatrix} 2\times 2 \\ 2\times 4 \\ 2\times(-4) \end{pmatrix} = \begin{pmatrix} 4 \\ 8 \\ -8 \end{pmatrix}$

(ii) $\mathbf{a} + \mathbf{b} = \begin{pmatrix} 2 \\ 4 \\ -4 \end{pmatrix} + \begin{pmatrix} 3 \\ -5 \\ 1 \end{pmatrix} = \begin{pmatrix} 2+3 \\ 4+(-5) \\ (-4)+1 \end{pmatrix} = \begin{pmatrix} 5 \\ -1 \\ -3 \end{pmatrix}$

(iii) $\quad 3\mathbf{a} - 4\mathbf{b} = 3\begin{pmatrix} 2 \\ 4 \\ -4 \end{pmatrix} - 4\begin{pmatrix} 3 \\ -5 \\ 1 \end{pmatrix} = \begin{pmatrix} 6 \\ 12 \\ -12 \end{pmatrix} - \begin{pmatrix} 12 \\ -20 \\ 4 \end{pmatrix} = \begin{pmatrix} -6 \\ 32 \\ -16 \end{pmatrix}$ ♦♦

◆ *Magnitude*

The *magnitude* of a vector is just its length, which can be calculated using Pythagoras' theorem in two dimensions, or an extended version of Pythagoras' theorem in higher dimensions. The magnitude of vector **a** is written as *a* or $|\mathbf{a}|$.

Magnitude of a vector

In two dimensions, if $\mathbf{a} = \begin{pmatrix} p \\ q \end{pmatrix}$, then $a = |\mathbf{a}| = \sqrt{p^2 + q^2}$.

In three dimensions, if $\mathbf{a} = \begin{pmatrix} p \\ q \\ r \end{pmatrix}$, then $a = |\mathbf{a}| = \sqrt{p^2 + q^2 + r^2}$.

Example 8.4

Calculate the magnitude of the vector $\mathbf{a} = \begin{pmatrix} 1 \\ -2 \\ 4 \end{pmatrix}$.

Solution

$a = \sqrt{1^2 + (-2)^2 + 4^2} = \sqrt{21}$ ♦♦

◆ *Unit vectors*

A vector with a magnitude of 1 is called a *unit vector*.

All vectors in two-dimensional space can be written in terms of the *base vectors* **i** and **j**, which are the unit vectors in the *x* and *y* directions on a graph. So, **i** lies along the *x*-axis (taking us from the origin to the point (1,0)), and **j** lies along the *y*-axis (taking us from the origin to the point (0,1)). This means we can write:

$$\mathbf{i} = \begin{pmatrix} 1 \\ 0 \end{pmatrix} \text{ and } \mathbf{j} = \begin{pmatrix} 0 \\ 1 \end{pmatrix}$$

Similarly, all vectors in three-dimensional space can be written in terms of the base vectors **i**, **j** and **k**, which are the unit vectors in the *x*, *y* and *z* directions on a three-dimensional graph. So:

$$\mathbf{i} = \begin{pmatrix} 1 \\ 0 \\ 0 \end{pmatrix}, \ \mathbf{j} = \begin{pmatrix} 0 \\ 1 \\ 0 \end{pmatrix} \text{ and } \mathbf{k} = \begin{pmatrix} 0 \\ 0 \\ 1 \end{pmatrix}$$

Using these base vectors gives us an alternative way of writing vectors. For example, the vector **a** from Example 8.4 can be written in terms of **i**, **j** and **k** as:

$$\mathbf{a} = \begin{pmatrix} 1 \\ -2 \\ 4 \end{pmatrix} = \mathbf{i} - 2\mathbf{j} + 4\mathbf{k}$$

The base vectors **i**, **j** and **k** are unit vectors in the direction of each of the axes in three-dimensional space, but we can find a unit vector in *any* direction, by taking a vector in that direction and dividing by its magnitude.

Example 8.5

Find the unit vector in the direction of $3\mathbf{i} + 4\mathbf{j} - 2\mathbf{k}$.

Solution

The magnitude of the vector is $\sqrt{3^2 + 4^2 + (-2)^2} = \sqrt{29}$, so the unit vector in that direction is

$\dfrac{1}{\sqrt{29}}(3\mathbf{i} + 4\mathbf{j} - 2\mathbf{k})$.   ◆◆

◆ Scalar (or dot) product

The *scalar product* is one way of multiplying two vectors together. The multiplication sign used for a scalar product is written as a dot, so it is also known as the 'dot product'.

The scalar product is calculated by multiplying the corresponding coefficients of the unit vectors **i** and **j** (in two dimensions) or **i**, **j** and **k** (in three dimensions), and then summing.

Scalar product

In two dimensions, if $\mathbf{a} = \begin{pmatrix} d \\ e \end{pmatrix}$ and $\mathbf{b} = \begin{pmatrix} f \\ g \end{pmatrix}$, then $\mathbf{a} \cdot \mathbf{b} = \begin{pmatrix} d \\ e \end{pmatrix} \cdot \begin{pmatrix} f \\ g \end{pmatrix} = df + eg$.

In three dimensions, if $\mathbf{a} = \begin{pmatrix} p \\ q \\ r \end{pmatrix}$ and $\mathbf{b} = \begin{pmatrix} s \\ t \\ u \end{pmatrix}$, then $\mathbf{a} \cdot \mathbf{b} = \begin{pmatrix} p \\ q \\ r \end{pmatrix} \cdot \begin{pmatrix} s \\ t \\ u \end{pmatrix} = ps + qt + ru$.

Example 8.6

Calculate $\mathbf{a} \cdot \mathbf{b}$, where $\mathbf{a} = \begin{pmatrix} 1 \\ -4 \\ 5 \end{pmatrix}$ and $\mathbf{b} = \begin{pmatrix} 2 \\ 3 \\ -6 \end{pmatrix}$.

Solution

$\mathbf{a} \cdot \mathbf{b} = (1)(2) + (-4)(3) + (5)(-6) = 2 - 12 - 30 = -40$ ◆◆

The answer here is a scalar (*ie* a number) not a vector, hence the name 'scalar product'.

Based on the definition of the scalar product given above, the following rules are straightforward to derive:

Scalar product rules

For any vectors **a**, **b** and **c**, and any scalar λ:

- $\mathbf{a}.\mathbf{b} = \mathbf{b}.\mathbf{a}$

- $\mathbf{a}.(\mathbf{b}+\mathbf{c}) = \mathbf{a}.\mathbf{b}+\mathbf{a}.\mathbf{c}$

- $(\lambda\mathbf{a}).\mathbf{b} = \lambda(\mathbf{a}.\mathbf{b})$

For example, if $\mathbf{a} = \begin{pmatrix} a_1 \\ a_2 \end{pmatrix}$, $\mathbf{b} = \begin{pmatrix} b_1 \\ b_2 \end{pmatrix}$ and $\mathbf{c} = \begin{pmatrix} c_1 \\ c_2 \end{pmatrix}$, then the second of these rules can be seen to be true as follows:

$$\mathbf{a}.(\mathbf{b}+\mathbf{c}) = \begin{pmatrix} a_1 \\ a_2 \end{pmatrix} . \begin{pmatrix} b_1 + c_1 \\ b_2 + c_2 \end{pmatrix}$$

$$= a_1(b_1 + c_1) + a_2(b_2 + c_2)$$

$$= a_1 b_1 + a_2 b_2 + a_1 c_1 + a_2 c_2$$

$$= \begin{pmatrix} a_1 \\ a_2 \end{pmatrix} . \begin{pmatrix} b_1 \\ b_2 \end{pmatrix} + \begin{pmatrix} a_1 \\ a_2 \end{pmatrix} . \begin{pmatrix} c_1 \\ c_2 \end{pmatrix}$$

$$= \mathbf{a}.\mathbf{b}+\mathbf{a}.\mathbf{c}$$

◆ *Finding the angle between two vectors*

The scalar product of two vectors also has a geometric interpretation and can be defined in terms of the magnitude of the two vectors and the angle between them.

Scalar product

For vectors **a** and **b**, with magnitudes a and b respectively:

$$\mathbf{a}.\mathbf{b} = ab\cos\theta$$

where θ is the angle between the vectors in the plane containing **a** and **b**.

The angle between the vectors, θ, is shown on the diagram below.

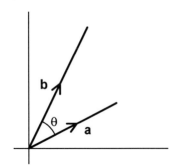

Combining this definition of the scalar product with the earlier definition given provides a means of calculating the angle between two vectors.

Example 8.7

Calculate the angle between the vectors $\mathbf{a} = \begin{pmatrix} 3 \\ 6 \\ -1 \end{pmatrix}$ and $\mathbf{b} = \begin{pmatrix} -3 \\ 3 \\ 4 \end{pmatrix}$.

Solution

$\mathbf{a} \cdot \mathbf{b} = (3)(-3) + (6)(3) + (-1)(4) = 5$, $a = \sqrt{3^2 + 6^2 + (-1)^2} = \sqrt{46}$, and $b = \sqrt{(-3)^2 + 3^2 + 4^2} = \sqrt{34}$

So:

$$\mathbf{a} \cdot \mathbf{b} = ab\cos\theta \quad \Rightarrow \quad \cos\theta = \frac{5}{\sqrt{46}\sqrt{34}} = 0.1264$$

$$\theta = \cos^{-1}(0.1264) = 82.7°$$

◆◆

An important result occurs when $\mathbf{a} \cdot \mathbf{b} = 0$, since this means that the angle between the vectors is $90°$, *ie* they are perpendicular. When this occurs, the vectors are called *orthogonal*.

Example 8.8

Find p such that $\mathbf{a}$ and $\mathbf{b}$ are orthogonal, where $\mathbf{a} = \begin{pmatrix} 1 \\ -7 \end{pmatrix}$, $\mathbf{b} = \begin{pmatrix} 3p \\ 4 \end{pmatrix}$.

Solution

For $\mathbf{a}$ and $\mathbf{b}$ to be orthogonal, their scalar product must equal zero.

$$\mathbf{a} \cdot \mathbf{b} = 3p - 28 = 0, \text{ hence } p = \tfrac{28}{3}.$$

◆◆

8.2   Matrices

A *matrix* is a rectangular array of numbers whose size is referred to by the number of rows and the number of columns. The plural of matrix is *matrices*.

Example 8.9

Describe the size of the matrix $\begin{pmatrix} 1 & -1 & 3 & 5 \\ 3 & 4 & 6 & -4 \end{pmatrix}$.

Solution

As it has 2 rows and 4 columns, this is a 2×4 matrix.

◆◆

A *column vector* is a special case of a matrix where the number of columns is one. A *row vector* is a special case of a matrix where the number of rows is one. A *square matrix* is one where the number of columns equals the number of rows.

Matrices have many uses, such as describing transformations, solving simultaneous equations, carrying out statistical calculations involving several variables, and calculating probabilities based on actuarial models.

◆ *Basic matrix arithmetic*

The *transpose* of a matrix is found by swapping the rows and the columns, so that row i becomes column i, and vice versa. The transpose of a matrix $\mathbf{A}$ is written as $\mathbf{A}^T$ or $\mathbf{A}'$.

Example 8.10

If $\mathbf{A} = \begin{pmatrix} 1 & -3 \\ 2 & 5 \\ 0 & 9 \end{pmatrix}$, write down $\mathbf{A}^T$.

Solution

$$\mathbf{A}^T = \begin{pmatrix} 1 & 2 & 0 \\ -3 & 5 & 9 \end{pmatrix}$$

◆◆

Transposing converts an $m \times n$ matrix to an $n \times m$ matrix and vice versa. Similarly, transposing converts a row vector to a column vector:

$$(1 \quad 2 \quad 3)^T = \begin{pmatrix} 1 \\ 2 \\ 3 \end{pmatrix}$$

Addition and subtraction of matrices of equal size are performed by adding or subtracting the corresponding elements in the matrices.

Addition of matrices

For 2×2 matrices:

$$\begin{pmatrix} a & b \\ c & d \end{pmatrix} + \begin{pmatrix} e & f \\ g & h \end{pmatrix} = \begin{pmatrix} a+e & b+f \\ c+g & d+h \end{pmatrix}$$

Similar results hold for subtraction, and for matrices of higher dimensions.

Example 8.11

If $\mathbf{A} = \begin{pmatrix} 2 & 4 & 5 \\ -4 & 2 & -6 \\ 7 & 1 & 3 \end{pmatrix}$ and $\mathbf{B} = \begin{pmatrix} 4 & 3 & -2 \\ -8 & -5 & 1 \\ 3 & 6 & 0 \end{pmatrix}$, calculate $\mathbf{A} + \mathbf{B}$.

Solution

$$A + B = \begin{pmatrix} 2 & 4 & 5 \\ -4 & 2 & -6 \\ 7 & 1 & 3 \end{pmatrix} + \begin{pmatrix} 4 & 3 & -2 \\ -8 & -5 & 1 \\ 3 & 6 & 0 \end{pmatrix} = \begin{pmatrix} 6 & 7 & 3 \\ -12 & -3 & -5 \\ 10 & 7 & 3 \end{pmatrix}$$ ◆◆

The matrix with zero as all of its elements is called the *zero matrix*. For example, the 2×2 zero matrix is $0 = \begin{pmatrix} 0 & 0 \\ 0 & 0 \end{pmatrix}$.

A matrix such as $\begin{pmatrix} 4 & 0 & 0 \\ 0 & 3 & 0 \\ 0 & 0 & 1 \end{pmatrix}$, where all the elements not on the leading diagonal (*ie* from the top left to the bottom right) are zero, is called a *diagonal matrix*.

If a matrix is equal to its transpose, *ie* $A = A^T$, then it is called *symmetric*. A symmetric matrix must be a square matrix (otherwise the matrix and its transpose would be different sizes and could therefore not be equal) and the elements reflected about the leading diagonal must be equal. An example of a 3×3 symmetric matrix is:

$$\begin{pmatrix} 2 & 0 & 3 \\ 0 & -4 & -5 \\ 3 & -5 & 1 \end{pmatrix}$$

◆ Matrix multiplication

Matrices can be multiplied by a scalar or by another matrix (or a vector). When multiplying by a scalar, we multiply each element in the matrix by that number.

Example 8.12

If $A = \begin{pmatrix} 3 & 3 \\ -5 & 6 \end{pmatrix}$, calculate $2A$.

Solution

$$2A = 2\begin{pmatrix} 3 & 3 \\ -5 & 6 \end{pmatrix} = \begin{pmatrix} 2 \times 3 & 2 \times 3 \\ 2 \times (-5) & 2 \times 6 \end{pmatrix} = \begin{pmatrix} 6 & 6 \\ -10 & 12 \end{pmatrix}$$ ◆◆

To multiply two matrices together, the elements in the rows of the first matrix are multiplied individually by the elements in the columns of the second matrix and then summed. More precisely, the element in row *i* and column *j* of the product is derived from the elements in row *i* of the first matrix and column *j* of the second matrix.

Multiplication of matrices

For 2×2 matrices: $\begin{pmatrix} a & b \\ c & d \end{pmatrix}\begin{pmatrix} e & f \\ g & h \end{pmatrix} = \begin{pmatrix} ae+bg & af+bh \\ ce+dg & cf+dh \end{pmatrix}$

For 3×3 matrices: $\begin{pmatrix} a & b & c \\ d & e & f \\ g & h & i \end{pmatrix}\begin{pmatrix} j & k & l \\ m & n & o \\ p & q & r \end{pmatrix} = \begin{pmatrix} aj+bm+cp & ak+bn+cq & al+bo+cr \\ dj+em+fp & dk+en+fq & dl+eo+fr \\ gj+hm+ip & gk+hn+iq & gl+ho+ir \end{pmatrix}$

Example 8.13

If $\mathbf{A} = \begin{pmatrix} 3 & 1 \\ -5 & -4 \end{pmatrix}$ and $\mathbf{B} = \begin{pmatrix} 4 & -2 \\ 3 & -1 \end{pmatrix}$, calculate $\mathbf{AB}$.

Solution

$\mathbf{AB} = \begin{pmatrix} 3 & 1 \\ -5 & -4 \end{pmatrix}\begin{pmatrix} 4 & -2 \\ 3 & -1 \end{pmatrix}$

$= \begin{pmatrix} (3\times4)+(1\times3) & (3\times-2)+(1\times-1) \\ (-5\times4)+(-4\times3) & (-5\times-2)+(-4\times-1) \end{pmatrix}$

$= \begin{pmatrix} 15 & -7 \\ -32 & 14 \end{pmatrix}$ ♦♦

Example 8.14

If $\mathbf{A} = \begin{pmatrix} 1 & -2 & 4 \\ 3 & 2 & -3 \\ 0 & 1 & -1 \end{pmatrix}$ and $\mathbf{B} = \begin{pmatrix} -4 & 1 & 1 \\ -5 & 0 & 2 \\ 1 & 5 & 3 \end{pmatrix}$, calculate $\mathbf{AB}$ and $\mathbf{BA}$.

Solution

$\mathbf{AB} = \begin{pmatrix} (1\times-4)+(-2\times-5)+(4\times1) & (1\times1)+(-2\times0)+(4\times5) & (1\times1)+(-2\times2)+(4\times3) \\ (3\times-4)+(2\times-5)+(-3\times1) & (3\times1)+(2\times0)+(-3\times5) & (3\times1)+(2\times2)+(-3\times3) \\ (0\times-4)+(1\times-5)+(-1\times1) & (0\times1)+(1\times0)+(-1\times5) & (0\times1)+(1\times2)+(-1\times3) \end{pmatrix}$

$= \begin{pmatrix} 10 & 21 & 9 \\ -25 & -12 & -2 \\ -6 & -5 & -1 \end{pmatrix}$

Similarly:

$\mathbf{BA} = \begin{pmatrix} (-4\times1)+(1\times3)+(1\times0) & (-4\times-2)+(1\times2)+(1\times1) & (-4\times4)+(1\times-3)+(1\times-1) \\ (-5\times1)+(0\times3)+(2\times0) & (-5\times-2)+(0\times2)+(2\times1) & (-5\times4)+(0\times-3)+(2\times-1) \\ (1\times1)+(5\times3)+(3\times0) & (1\times-2)+(5\times2)+(3\times1) & (1\times4)+(5\times-3)+(3\times-1) \end{pmatrix}$

$= \begin{pmatrix} -1 & 11 & -20 \\ -5 & 12 & -22 \\ 16 & 11 & -14 \end{pmatrix}$ ♦♦

In this example, we see that we obtain different answers if we compute **AB** (called *pre-multiplying* **B** by **A**, as matrix **A** is before matrix **B**) and **BA** (called *post-multiplying* **B** by **A**, as matrix **A** is after matrix **B**). This is generally the case with matrix multiplication – unlike ordinary arithmetic, matrix multiplication is not commutative, *ie* the order of multiplication matters.

An important exception to this occurs with powers of a square matrix, where matrix multiplication *is* commutative. This is illustrated in the following example.

Example 8.15

If $P = \begin{pmatrix} 2 & 0 \\ -1 & 3 \end{pmatrix}$, calculate:

(i) P^2

(ii) P^3

Solution

(i) $P^2 = \begin{pmatrix} 2 & 0 \\ -1 & 3 \end{pmatrix}\begin{pmatrix} 2 & 0 \\ -1 & 3 \end{pmatrix} = \begin{pmatrix} (2\times 2)+(0\times -1) & (2\times 0)+(0\times 3) \\ (-1\times 2)+(3\times -1) & (-1\times 0)+(3\times 3) \end{pmatrix} = \begin{pmatrix} 4 & 0 \\ -5 & 9 \end{pmatrix}$

(ii) $P^3 = P^2 P = \begin{pmatrix} 4 & 0 \\ -5 & 9 \end{pmatrix}\begin{pmatrix} 2 & 0 \\ -1 & 3 \end{pmatrix} = \begin{pmatrix} (4\times 2)+(0\times -1) & (4\times 0)+(0\times 3) \\ (-5\times 2)+(9\times -1) & (-5\times 0)+(9\times 3) \end{pmatrix} = \begin{pmatrix} 8 & 0 \\ -19 & 27 \end{pmatrix}$

We could alternatively calculate P^3 as:

$$P^3 = PP^2 = \begin{pmatrix} 2 & 0 \\ -1 & 3 \end{pmatrix}\begin{pmatrix} 4 & 0 \\ -5 & 9 \end{pmatrix} = \begin{pmatrix} (2\times 4)+(0\times -5) & (2\times 0)+(0\times 9) \\ (-1\times 4)+(3\times -5) & (-1\times 0)+(3\times 9) \end{pmatrix} = \begin{pmatrix} 8 & 0 \\ -19 & 27 \end{pmatrix}$$

So, $P^2 P$ gives the same answer as PP^2.   ◆◆

It is also important to note that not all matrices can be multiplied together – the number of columns in the first matrix must be the same as the number of rows in the second. An $m\times n$ matrix multiplied by an $n\times q$ matrix gives an $m\times q$ matrix.

Example 8.16

Calculate $\begin{pmatrix} 0 & 2 & -3 \\ 4 & 2 & 1 \\ 0 & 5 & -1 \end{pmatrix}\begin{pmatrix} 1 \\ 2 \\ -1 \end{pmatrix}$.

Solution

$$\begin{pmatrix} 0 & 2 & -3 \\ 4 & 2 & 1 \\ 0 & 5 & -1 \end{pmatrix}\begin{pmatrix} 1 \\ 2 \\ -1 \end{pmatrix} = \begin{pmatrix} 0\times 1+2\times 2+(-3)\times(-1) \\ 4\times 1+2\times 2+1\times(-1) \\ 0\times 1+5\times 2+(-1)\times(-1) \end{pmatrix} = \begin{pmatrix} 7 \\ 7 \\ 11 \end{pmatrix}$$ ◆◆

Here we have multiplied a 3×3 matrix and a 3×1 column vector to obtain another 3×1 column vector. These could not have been multiplied the other way round.

Now let's consider a special square matrix, **I**.

Example 8.17

If $\mathbf{M} = \begin{pmatrix} a & b \\ c & d \end{pmatrix}$ and $\mathbf{I} = \begin{pmatrix} 1 & 0 \\ 0 & 1 \end{pmatrix}$, calculate **MI** and **IM**.

Solution

$$\mathbf{MI} = \begin{pmatrix} a \times 1 + b \times 0 & a \times 0 + b \times 1 \\ c \times 1 + d \times 0 & c \times 0 + d \times 1 \end{pmatrix} = \begin{pmatrix} a & b \\ c & d \end{pmatrix} \text{ and } \mathbf{IM} = \begin{pmatrix} 1 \times a + 0 \times c & 1 \times b + 0 \times d \\ 0 \times a + 1 \times c & 0 \times b + 1 \times d \end{pmatrix} = \begin{pmatrix} a & b \\ c & d \end{pmatrix} \quad \blacklozenge\blacklozenge$$

From this example, we can see that both pre-multiplying and post-multiplying by **I** leaves the original matrix unchanged, *ie* **MI** = **IM** = **M**. Due to this property, any square matrix with 1's along the leading diagonal and 0's elsewhere is called the *identity matrix* and is written as **I**.

◆ *Determinants*

A *determinant* is a scalar quantity associated with a square matrix.

The determinant of a 2×2 matrix is equal to the product of the numbers on the leading diagonal minus the product of the numbers on the other diagonal. It is written as $\det \mathbf{A}$, $|\mathbf{A}|$ or just Δ when it is clear which matrix is involved.

Determinant of a 2×2 matrix

If $\mathbf{A} = \begin{pmatrix} a & b \\ c & d \end{pmatrix}$, then $\det \mathbf{A} = |\mathbf{A}| = \begin{vmatrix} a & b \\ c & d \end{vmatrix} = ad - bc$.

Example 8.18

Calculate $\det \mathbf{A}$ where $\mathbf{A} = \begin{pmatrix} 2 & -6 \\ 4 & 3 \end{pmatrix}$.

Solution

$$\det \mathbf{A} = (2 \times 3) - (4 \times -6) = 30 \quad \blacklozenge\blacklozenge$$

◆ *Inverses*

The *inverse* of a square matrix **A**, written as $\mathbf{A}^{-1}$, is a matrix such that $\mathbf{AA}^{-1} = \mathbf{A}^{-1}\mathbf{A} = \mathbf{I}$. It is the matrix equivalent of the reciprocal of a number, as it 'undoes' or 'reverses' multiplication by the matrix **A**.

To find the inverse of a 2×2 matrix, we:

- swap the elements on the leading diagonal,

- change the sign of the elements on the other diagonal, and

- divide by the determinant.

Inverse of a 2×2 matrix

If $\mathbf{A} = \begin{pmatrix} a & b \\ c & d \end{pmatrix}$, then $\mathbf{A}^{-1} = \dfrac{1}{\det \mathbf{A}} \begin{pmatrix} d & -b \\ -c & a \end{pmatrix}$.

Example 8.19

(i)   Calculate $\mathbf{A}^{-1}$, where $\mathbf{A} = \begin{pmatrix} 3 & 2 \\ 5 & 4 \end{pmatrix}$.

(ii) Verify that $\mathbf{A}\mathbf{A}^{-1} = \mathbf{A}^{-1}\mathbf{A} = \mathbf{I}$.

Solution

(i)   To calculate $\mathbf{A}^{-1}$, we start by calculating the determinant of $\mathbf{A}$:

$$\det \mathbf{A} = (3 \times 4) - (2 \times 5) = 2$$

So, the inverse of $\mathbf{A}$ is given by:

$$\mathbf{A}^{-1} = \frac{1}{2} \begin{pmatrix} 4 & -2 \\ -5 & 3 \end{pmatrix} = \begin{pmatrix} 2 & -1 \\ -2.5 & 1.5 \end{pmatrix}$$

(ii) Pulling the factor of $\frac{1}{2}$ to the front, we can calculate $\mathbf{A}\mathbf{A}^{-1}$ as:

$$\frac{1}{2} \begin{pmatrix} 3 & 2 \\ 5 & 4 \end{pmatrix} \begin{pmatrix} 4 & -2 \\ -5 & 3 \end{pmatrix} = \frac{1}{2} \begin{pmatrix} (3\times4)+(2\times-5) & (3\times-2)+(2\times3) \\ (5\times4)+(4\times-5) & (5\times-2)+(4\times3) \end{pmatrix} = \frac{1}{2} \begin{pmatrix} 2 & 0 \\ 0 & 2 \end{pmatrix} = \begin{pmatrix} 1 & 0 \\ 0 & 1 \end{pmatrix}$$

Similarly, calculating $\mathbf{A}^{-1}\mathbf{A}$ gives:

$$\frac{1}{2} \begin{pmatrix} 4 & -2 \\ -5 & 3 \end{pmatrix} \begin{pmatrix} 3 & 2 \\ 5 & 4 \end{pmatrix} = \frac{1}{2} \begin{pmatrix} (4\times3)+(-2\times5) & (4\times2)+(-2\times4) \\ (-5\times3)+(3\times5) & (-5\times2)+(3\times4) \end{pmatrix} = \frac{1}{2} \begin{pmatrix} 2 & 0 \\ 0 & 2 \end{pmatrix} = \begin{pmatrix} 1 & 0 \\ 0 & 1 \end{pmatrix}$$

So $\mathbf{A}\mathbf{A}^{-1} = \mathbf{A}^{-1}\mathbf{A} = \mathbf{I}$.   ◆◆

A matrix whose determinant is equal to zero is called *singular*, and its inverse does not exist (as it would involve dividing by zero).

Example 8.20

Calculate the value of x for which the matrix $\mathbf{A} = \begin{pmatrix} 4 & -2 \\ x & 3 \end{pmatrix}$ is singular.

Solution

For the matrix $\mathbf{A}$ to be singular, it must have a determinant of zero. So:

$$\det \mathbf{A} = (4 \times 3) - (-2 \times x) = 0 \quad \Rightarrow \quad 12 + 2x = 0$$

So $x = -6$.   ◆◆

Chapter 8 Practice Questions

◆ *Vectors*

Question 8.1

Determine the vector joining the point $(3,7,-10)$ to the point $(6,-1,-15)$.

Question 8.2

If $\mathbf{a} = \begin{pmatrix} 3 \\ -2 \\ 8 \end{pmatrix}$ and $\mathbf{b} = \begin{pmatrix} 1 \\ 6 \\ -2 \end{pmatrix}$, calculate:

(i) $3\mathbf{b} - 2\mathbf{a}$

(ii)   the values of p and q such that $p\mathbf{a} + q\mathbf{b} = \begin{pmatrix} 5 \\ -50 \\ 46 \end{pmatrix}$.

Question 8.3

If $\mathbf{c} = \begin{pmatrix} 7 \\ 12 \end{pmatrix}$ and $\mathbf{d} = \begin{pmatrix} -3 \\ 4 \end{pmatrix}$, calculate the vector $\mathbf{e}$ such that $3\mathbf{c} - 4\mathbf{d} + \mathbf{e} = \begin{pmatrix} 2 \\ 0 \end{pmatrix}$.

Question 8.4

Calculate the magnitude of the vector $2\mathbf{i} - 5\mathbf{j} + 3\mathbf{k}$.

Question 8.5

Give an expression for the unit vector in the direction of $3\mathbf{i} - 2\mathbf{j} + 4\mathbf{k}$.

Question 8.6

By using the scalar product, calculate the angle between the vectors:

(i) $\mathbf{a} = 2\mathbf{i} + 3\mathbf{j} - 5\mathbf{k}$ and $\mathbf{b} = -3\mathbf{i} + 2\mathbf{j} + 8\mathbf{k}$

(ii) $\begin{pmatrix} 4 \\ -1 \\ 3 \end{pmatrix}$ and $\begin{pmatrix} 1 \\ 3 \\ -2 \end{pmatrix}$.

Question 8.7

Calculate the value of x so that $x\mathbf{i} - 4\mathbf{j} + 4\mathbf{k}$ is orthogonal to $3\mathbf{i} - 2\mathbf{j} + \mathbf{k}$.

Question 8.8

Let $\mathbf{a} = \begin{pmatrix} 1 \\ 0 \\ 1 \end{pmatrix}$ and $\mathbf{b} = \begin{pmatrix} 0 \\ x \\ y \end{pmatrix}$. If the magnitude of $\mathbf{b}$ is 2, and the angle between $\mathbf{a}$ and $\mathbf{b}$ is $45°$, calculate x and y.

Question 8.9

(i)   By considering expressions involving scalar products, find a unit vector of the form $a\mathbf{i} + b\mathbf{j} + c\mathbf{k}$ that is perpendicular to the vectors $-2\mathbf{i} + 3\mathbf{j}$ and $10\mathbf{i} + \mathbf{k}$.

(ii)   Write down the other unit vector perpendicular to $-2\mathbf{i} + 3\mathbf{j}$ and $10\mathbf{i} + \mathbf{k}$.

◆ Matrices

Question 8.10

If $\mathbf{A} = \begin{pmatrix} 3 & -1 \\ 4 & 2 \end{pmatrix}$, $\mathbf{B} = \begin{pmatrix} 2 & 1 & 0 & 4 \\ 3 & -3 & -2 & 1 \end{pmatrix}$ and $\mathbf{I}$ is the 2×2 identity matrix, calculate:

(i) $\mathbf{A} + 2\mathbf{A}^T - 3\mathbf{I}$

(ii) $\mathbf{AB}$

(iii) $\mathbf{B}^T\mathbf{A}$.

Question 8.11

If $\mathbf{A} = \begin{pmatrix} 1 & 2 \\ -3 & -4 \end{pmatrix}$ and $\mathbf{B} = \begin{pmatrix} -2 & 4 \\ -3 & 5 \end{pmatrix}$, calculate $\mathbf{AB}$.

Question 8.12

Calculate $\begin{pmatrix} 2 & 1 & 3 \end{pmatrix} \begin{pmatrix} 1 \\ 3 \\ -2 \end{pmatrix}$.

Question 8.13

If $\mathbf{A} = \begin{pmatrix} 1 & 7 & 0 \\ 2 & 5 & 3 \\ -1 & -2 & 4 \end{pmatrix}$, calculate $\mathbf{A}^2$ and $\mathbf{A}^3$.

Question 8.14

Calculate the determinant of the following matrices:

(i) $\quad \mathbf{P} = \begin{pmatrix} 3 & 5 \\ -2 & -7 \end{pmatrix}$

(ii) $\quad \mathbf{Q} = \begin{pmatrix} \frac{1}{2} & -\frac{1}{3} \\ 9 & 4 \end{pmatrix}$

Question 8.15

If $\mathbf{A} = \begin{pmatrix} 2 & 1 \\ 4 & 0 \end{pmatrix}$ and $\mathbf{B} = \begin{pmatrix} 3 & -1 \\ -2 & 1 \end{pmatrix}$, calculate:

(i) $\quad \mathbf{A}^{-1}$

(ii) $\quad \mathbf{B}^{-1}$

(iii) $\quad \mathbf{AB}$

(iv) $\quad \mathbf{B}^{-1}\mathbf{AB}$

(v) $\quad \mathbf{ABB}^{-1}$

Types of data and statistical diagrams

Learning Objectives

The following learning objective is covered in this chapter:

- Summarise a set of data using a table or frequency distribution, and display it graphically using a lineplot, a boxplot, a bar chart, histogram, stem and leaf plot, or other appropriate elementary device.

9.1   *Types of data*

The word *data* means facts or information collected for reference or analysis. Examples of data used in actuarial science include claim amounts, claim numbers and ages at death.

Data may be classified into various types. Firstly, we can divide data into two groups, namely numerical data and categorical data.

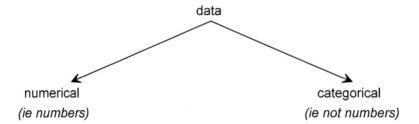

Numerical data values are numbers or quantities (*eg* 3.5 years, 1.2 *kg*, $-4\ ms^{-1}$, $\frac{7}{8}\ m^{3}$, ...).
An alternative term for numerical data is *quantitative data*.

Categorical data values are not numerical in nature (*eg* sex, eye colour, type of policy) but relate to categories (*eg* male/female, blue/green/brown/..., whole life assurance/term assurance/...). An alternative term for categorical data is *qualitative data*.

We can further subdivide numerical data into two types:

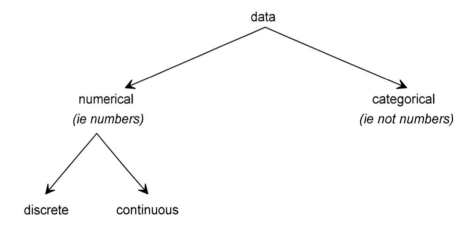

Discrete data can only take particular distinct numerical values. For example, the number of claims must be a whole number (0, 1, 2, 3, ...). It cannot take any value that lies between those listed, *eg* it cannot be 1.5. Typically we obtain discrete data from counting, *eg* number of actuaries, number of claims, number of deaths.

Continuous data can take *any* numerical value in a specified range, *eg* (0,1) or $(-\infty, \infty)$.
For example, the length of time between claims can take *any* positive value. Typically we obtain continuous data from measuring, *eg* height or time.

Since continuous data can take an infinite number of different values, we always round to some extent when we record these values. For example, we might record claim amounts to the nearest £.

Example 9.1

State whether the following data values are numerical or categorical:

(i)   weight

(ii)   place of birth

(iii)   number of claims to be processed

(iv)   nature of car insurance claim

(v)   age

(vi)   amount of claim.

Solution

(i)   Weight is numerical (*eg* 75kg, 200g, 3 tonnes).

(ii)   Place of birth is categorical (*eg* London, Mumbai, Hong Kong).

(iii)   Number of claims to be processed is numerical (*eg* 12 claims, 193 claims).

(iv)   Nature of car insurance claims is categorical (*eg* theft, fire, accident).

(v)   Age is numerical (*eg* 23 years, 65 years and 2 months).

(vi)   Amount of claim is numerical (*eg* £180, €2m, $740.99).   ♦ ♦

Example 9.2

State whether the following types of numerical data are discrete or continuous:

(i)   weight

(ii)   number of claims to be processed

(iii)   age

(iv)   amount of claim.

Solution

(i)   Weight is continuous (as it can be any positive value).

(ii)   Number of claims to be processed is discrete (as the number of claims must be a whole number).

(iii)   Age could be discrete or continuous. When we give our age we usually give our age *last birthday* (*eg* 23 years), which is discrete, rather than our exact age (*eg* 23 years, 3 months, 2 days, 14 hours, …), which is continuous.

(iv)   In theory, claim amounts are discrete. However, because there are so many discrete values, very close to one another in size, the data can be treated as continuous.   ♦ ♦

We can also subdivide categorical data.

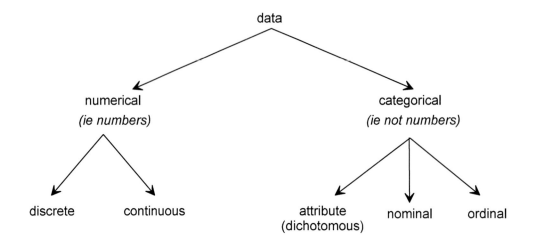

Attribute (or *dichotomous*) data values have only two categories, *eg* claim/no claim, dead/alive or male/female.

Nominal data values cannot be ordered in any natural way, *eg* type of policy (whole life assurance, term assurance or endowment assurance) or nature of claim (fire, theft, accident, earthquake, *etc*).

Ordinal data values can be ordered in a natural way, *eg* exam grades (A, B, C ,...), level of agreement (strongly agree, agree, neutral, disagree, strongly disagree).

In the remainder of this chapter, we will concentrate on numerical data.

9.2 Summarising data in tables

One way to summarise a list of data values is to use a table.

◆ Frequency distributions

Suppose that the numbers of claims reported each day to a small general insurance company over the last 28 working days are as follows:

4 2 0 3 2 1 1 4 2 5 0 3 2 1 3 4 3 5 1 2 4 2 3 1 4 2 3 2

In this list, we have two days when 0 claims were reported, five days when 1 claim was reported, eight days when 2 claims were reported, and so on. A summary of the data is given in the table below:

Claims reported each day	Frequency
0	2
1	5
2	8
3	6
4	5
5	2

This table is called a *frequency distribution*. It shows the number of times that each value has been observed.

A frequency distribution is suitable for categorical or discrete numerical data.

 ### Example 9.3

Explain how we can obtain the following from the above frequency distribution table:

(i)   the total number of observations (data items)

(ii)   the total number of claims reported.

Solution

(i)   The total number of observations is the sum of the frequencies, *ie*:

$$2 + 5 + 8 + 6 + 5 + 2 = 28$$

(ii)   From the table, we have 2 days with 0 claims (total $= 2 \times 0 = 0$ claims), 5 days with 1 claim (total $= 5 \times 1 = 5$ claims), 8 days with 2 claims (total $= 8 \times 2 = 16$ claims), 6 days with 3 claims (total $= 6 \times 3 = 18$ claims), 5 days with 4 claims (total $= 5 \times 4 = 20$ claims) and 2 days with 5 claims (total $= 2 \times 5 = 10$ claims). So, altogether, the total number of claims reported is $0 + 5 + 16 + 18 + 20 + 10 = 69$.   ♦♦

Grouped frequency distributions

Below is a list of the ages last birthday at death of 30 male policyholders who held life assurance policies with a particular insurance company:

57   68   75   66   72   86   80   81   70   78   76   72   88   84   69

77   83   90   48   63   74   81   94   51   73   96   81   66   77   101

The smallest value in this list is 48 and the largest is 101. We could construct a frequency distribution for these data values but, since there are many ages for which the frequency is 0 or 1, it would not be very helpful.

A better way to proceed is to put the data into groups (or classes or bands) and then count the number of observations in each group.

We have 1 result (48) that is between 40 and 49, 2 results (51 and 57) that are between 50 and 59, 5 results (63, 66, 66, 68 and 69) that are between 60 and 69, and so on. We can use the following grouped frequency distribution to summarise the data:

Age last birthday at death	Frequency
40 – 49	1
50 – 59	2
60 – 69	5
70 – 79	10
80 – 89	8
90 – 99	3
100 – 109	1

For continuous data it does not really make sense to construct ungrouped frequency distributions, because each data value is likely to be unique. So, for continuous data, it will always be necessary to group the data in some way.

Cumulative frequency tables

In a cumulative frequency table, we sum the frequencies to give a *running total*.

Cumulative frequency

Cumulative frequency is the sum of all the frequencies up to and including the current point.

For example, using the age last birthday at death data listed above, we have:

Age last birthday at death	Frequency	Cumulative frequency	
40 – 49	1	1	$1 + 2 = 3$
50 – 59	2	3	
60 – 69	5	8	$3 + 5 = 8$
70 – 79	10	18	
80 – 89	8	26	$8 + 10 = 18$
90 – 99	3	29	
100 – 109	1	30	

This table shows that there is one death before (exact) age 50, a total of three deaths before (exact) age 60, a total of 8 deaths before (exact) age 70, and so on. Alternatively, we could present the cumulative frequency table as follows:

Age last birthday at death	Cumulative frequency
up to 49	1
up to 59	3
up to 69	8
up to 79	18
up to 89	26
up to 99	29
up to 109	30

9.3   *Summarising data in diagrams*

Instead of presenting data in the form of a table, we could use a statistical diagram. We will introduce six types of diagrams in the remainder of this chapter.

◆ *Bar charts*

A bar chart can be drawn for discrete numerical data or for categorical data. For each observed value, we draw a bar to show the number of times that the value has occurred (*ie* its frequency).

For example, suppose that a general insurance company has analysed the types of claims it received over the last month, with the following results:

Claim type	Frequency
House theft	57
House fire	48
Car theft	156
Car accident	245

The bar chart for the data is shown below:

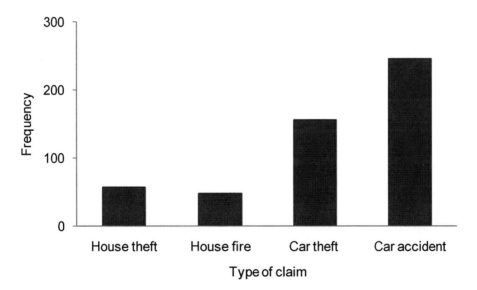

Usually the *x*-axis is used to show the observations and the *y*-axis is used to show the frequency. The axes can, however, be swapped around. A bar chart is a useful tool for showing the shape of a data set.

◆ *Histograms*

A histogram is similar to a bar chart but there are a few important differences.

Constructing a histogram

A histogram is used to display continuous data. We therefore use a continuous scale with no spaces between the bars. In addition, we use *frequency density* rather than frequency on the vertical axis.

Frequency density

Frequency density is defined as follows:

$$frequency\ density = \frac{frequency}{class\ width}$$

Class width is the difference between the largest possible value in the group (or class) and the smallest.

By setting the height of each bar equal to its frequency density, the area of each bar is equal to its frequency.

For example, suppose that a general insurance company has recorded the claim amounts that it received over the last week and that the results are as follows:

Claim amount (x)	Frequency
$0 < x \le 500$	6
$500 < x \le 1,000$	10
$1,000 < x \le 1,500$	9
$1,500 < x \le 2,000$	8
$2,000 < x \le 2,500$	3
$2,500 < x \le 3,000$	2
$3,000 < x \le 3,500$	1
$3,500 < x \le 4,000$	1

In this example, the groups all have the same width (500). The frequency densities are shown in the following table:

Claim amount (x)	Frequency density
$0 < x \le 500$	$6 \div 500 = 0.012$
$500 < x \le 1,000$	$10 \div 500 = 0.020$
$1,000 < x \le 1,500$	$9 \div 500 = 0.018$
$1,500 < x \le 2,000$	$8 \div 500 = 0.016$
$2,000 < x \le 2,500$	$3 \div 500 = 0.006$
$2,500 < x \le 3,000$	$2 \div 500 = 0.004$
$3,000 < x \le 3,500$	$1 \div 500 = 0.002$
$3,500 < x \le 4,000$	$1 \div 500 = 0.002$

The histogram for this data set is given below:

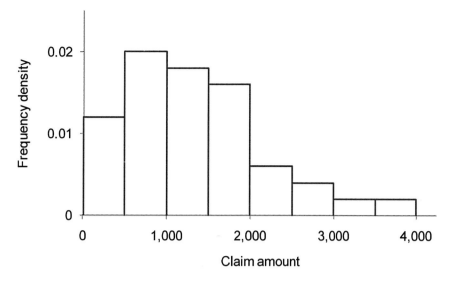

In practice, we might have groups of different class widths. For example, we might combine the last four groups and so have the following frequencies:

Claim amount (x)	Frequency
$0 < x \leq 500$	6
$500 < x \leq 1,000$	10
$1,000 < x \leq 1,500$	9
$1,500 < x \leq 2,000$	8
$2,000 < x \leq 4,000$	7

The width of the first four classes is still 500, but the width of the final class is 2,000. This gives us the following frequency densities:

Claim amount (x)	Frequency density
$0 < x \leq 500$	$6 \div 500 = 0.012$
$500 < x \leq 1,000$	$10 \div 500 = 0.020$
$1,000 < x \leq 1,500$	$9 \div 500 = 0.018$
$1,500 < x \leq 2,000$	$8 \div 500 = 0.016$
$2,000 < x \leq 4,000$	$7 \div 2,000 = 0.0035$

Hence, the histogram looks like this:

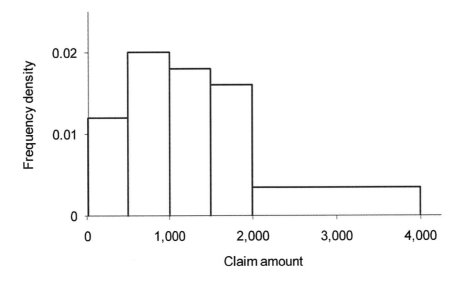

The total area of the bars in both of these histograms is 40 (the total number of data values).

In general, a histogram is drawn with vertical bars and a continuous scale on the *x*-axis. However, the axes can be swapped round and the histogram will then take the form of horizontal bars.

Now here's an example where we have to determine the frequencies of each group from a histogram.

Example 9.4

The histogram below shows the journey times (in minutes) of employees to their offices:

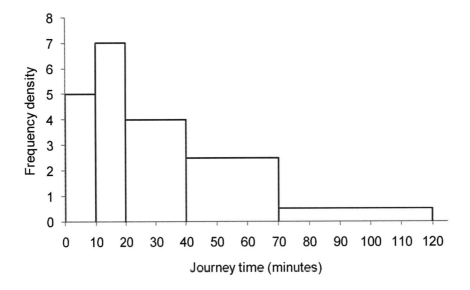

Complete the frequency table for the journey times data:

Time	Frequency
$0 < t \leq 10$	50
$10 < t \leq 20$	
$20 < t \leq 40$	

Solution

Since frequency is given by the area of each bar, we have:

Time	Frequency
$0 < t \leq 10$	50
$10 < t \leq 20$	$7 \times 10 = 70$
$20 < t \leq 40$	$4 \times 20 = 80$
$40 < t \leq 70$	$2.5 \times 30 = 75$
$70 < t \leq 120$	$0.5 \times 50 = 25$

♦♦

◆▷ Calculating class widths

Once we know the width of the group it is easy to calculate the frequency density. However, we must take care to calculate the class widths correctly.

For example, suppose we are measuring time to the nearest minute and one of our groups is:

$10 - 19$ minutes

Since the times are rounded to the nearest minute, the smallest value that could be included in this group is 9.5 minutes (as this will round up to 10 minutes). Similarly, the largest value that could be included in this group is (just below) 19.5 minutes (as this will round down to 19 minutes). Therefore the class width is:

$19.5 - 9.5 = 10$ minutes

So, when we construct our histogram, we should draw the $10 - 19$ minutes bar between 9.5 minutes and 19.5 minutes.

Another type of group is one that involves ages. For example, suppose we are recording age last birthday and one of our groups is:

$11 - 20$ years

The youngest *actual* age that could be included in this group is 11 years (as people would join this group on their 11th birthdays). The oldest actual age that could be included in this group is (just below) 21 years (as people would leave this group on their 21st birthdays). So the width of this class is:

$21 - 11 = 10$ years

So, when we construct our histogram we should draw the $11 - 20$ years bar between 11 and 21 years.

Example 9.5

Write down the class width of each of these groups:

(i)   £150 ≤ x < £170   where x represents a claim amount

(ii)   £150 – £169   for claim amounts recorded to the nearest £

(iii)   £0 – £149   for claim amounts recorded to the nearest £

(iv)   30 – 35 years   for age last birthday.

Solution

(i)   The group ranges from exactly £150 to (just below) £170. Hence the class width is:

$$£170 - £150 = £20$$

(ii)   Since the amounts are rounded to the nearest £, the smallest value that could be included in this group is £149.50 (as this would round up to £150). Similarly (treating the amounts as continuous) the largest value that could be included in this group is (just below) £169.50. Hence the class width is:

$$£169.50 - £149.50 = £20$$

(iii)   This is very similar to part (ii) except that claims smaller than £0 cannot occur. Therefore the smallest value that could be included is £0. Hence the class width is:

$$£149.50 - £0 = £149.50$$

(iv)   People would join this group on their 30th birthdays and would leave this group on their 36th birthdays. So the class width is:

$$36 - 30 = 6 \text{ years}$$ ♦♦

◆ Stem and leaf diagrams

A stem and leaf diagram is an alternative to a histogram.

Constructing a stem and leaf diagram

A stem and leaf diagram is a tabular display of a data set. The observations are split into two parts – a stem and a leaf – and are arranged in ascending order along each leaf. To make it clear what each value represents, it is best to include a key with the graph.

For example, suppose that the ages (last birthday) of 9 individuals in a company, arranged in ascending order, are as follows:

      17   19   19   24   25   27   28   30   31

A stem and leaf diagram of these data is shown below:

```
                    1 | 7  9  9
      stem  ──→     2 | 4  5  7  8   ←──── leaves
                    3 | 0  1
```

The single number on the left-hand side is called the *stem* and the numbers on the right-hand side are the *leaves* associated with the stems For this example, we need to state:

Key: 2|4 represents 24

This key tells us that each stem represents the number of tens and each leaf represents the number of units.

Since the data points are arranged in increasing order, we can use a stem and leaf diagram to find the middle value (the *median*) and the values that are one quarter and three quarters of the way through the data (the *lower* and *upper quartiles*). We'll come back to these ideas in the next two chapters.

Example 9.6

Write down the data values represented by this stem and leaf diagram:

```
1 | 7  9  9
2 | 4  5  7  8
3 | 0  1
```

Key: 2|4 represents 2.4

Solution

The data values represented by the stem and leaf diagram are:

   1.7   1.9   1.9   2.4   2.5   2.7   2.8   3.0   3.1   ◆ ◆

In the previous example each of the numbers had only two digits. In cases where we have more than two digits, we can either place more digits on the stem or round the values so that they each have exactly two digits.

For example, consider the following data values:

56.2	61.0	62.8	63.9	64.5
61.8	59.4	58.6	65.1	62.1
60.3	57.9	62.3	62.1	60.7
59.4	61.4	58.7	63.0	70.5
68.3	61.9	60.5	63.2	64.8

Using 61|4 to represent 61.4, the stem and leaf diagram is as follows:

```
56 | 2
57 | 9
58 | 6  7
59 | 4  4
60 | 3  5  7
61 | 0  4  8  9
62 | 1  1  3  8
63 | 0  2  9
64 | 5  8
65 | 1
66 |
67 |
68 | 3
69 |
70 | 5
```

Alternatively, rounding each of the data values to the nearest whole number and using 5|8 to represent 58, we obtain:

```
5 | 6  8  9  9  9  9
6 | 0  1  1  1  1  2  2  2  2  2  3  3  3  4  5  5  5  8
7 | 1
```

◆ *Dotplots*

A *dotplot* (or *lineplot*) is another alternative to a histogram.

Constructing a dotplot

To construct a dotplot, we mark each data value on a number line using a dot or a cross. If a value is observed more that once, we use an appropriate number of dots (or crosses) on top of each other.

Suppose that the values below represent the starting salaries (in £000s) of 10 new employees of a company, arranged in ascending order:

21   23   24   24   25   25   25   27   27   28

A dotplot of these data values is shown below.

◆ *Cumulative frequency curves*

In Section 9.2 we saw how to construct a cumulative frequency table. We can use a cumulative frequency table to draw a *cumulative frequency curve*.

Constructing a cumulative frequency curve

To obtain the curve, we plot a graph of the cumulative frequencies against the upper limit of each class and join the points.

As we will see in the examples below, we also need to include a point marking the left-hand end of the distribution.

In this chapter, we will join the points on a cumulative frequency curve with straight lines. By doing so, we are assuming linearity between adjacent data points. However, some form of curve could also be fitted, and this may be a better reflection of reality.

Also, as we mentioned earlier in the section on class widths, we must take care to ensure that we correctly identify the upper limit of each class.

Suppose once again that we have the following frequency distribution for claim amount data, which we used for the histograms:

Claim amount (x)	Frequency
$0 < x \le 500$	6
$500 < x \le 1,000$	10
$1,000 < x \le 1,500$	9
$1,500 < x \le 2,000$	8
$2,000 < x \le 4,000$	7

The corresponding cumulative frequency table is:

Claim amount (x)	Cumulative frequency
$x \le 500$	6
$x \le 1,000$	16
$x \le 1,500$	25
$x \le 2,000$	33
$x \le 4,000$	40

For the data given above, the points to be plotted are $(500, 6)$, $(1,000, 16)$, $(1,500, 25)$, $(2,000, 33)$ and $(4,000, 40)$. Joining up these points with straight line segments and extending the graph to the origin, we obtain the following cumulative frequency diagram:

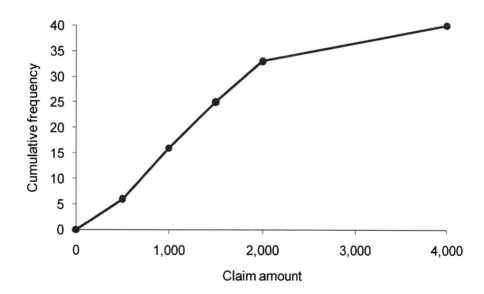

Since claim amounts cannot be negative, it makes sense to start this graph at the origin. However, this will not be true in all situations, *eg* the height of a person cannot be zero, so each situation must be considered carefully.

Cumulative frequency curves can be used to estimate particular features of a data set. For example, we could estimate the number of claims that are less than 750 by locating 750 on the *x*-axis and reading off the corresponding cumulative frequency from the *y*-axis, as shown in the next diagram:

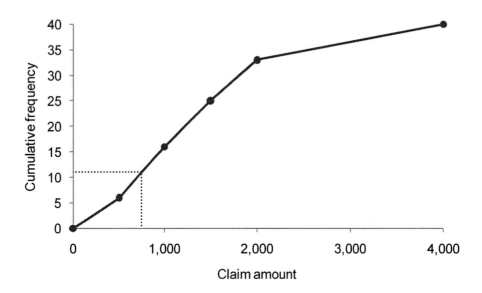

So, from the graph, we estimate that there are 11 claims that are less than 750.

Similarly, we could estimate the middle value (or median) of the data set by locating 20 (*ie* half of 40) on the *y*-axis and reading off the corresponding value from the *x*-axis:

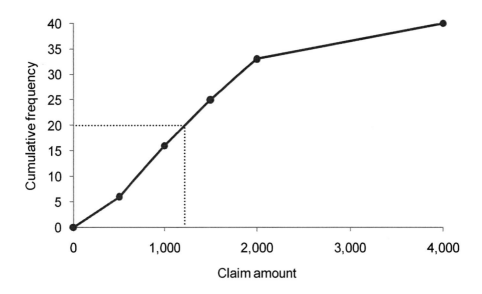

From the graph, we estimate that the middle value is about 1,225.

◆ Boxplots

A *boxplot* (or *box and whisker plot*) is another diagram that can be used to illustrate a data set. Typically, a boxplot looks like this:

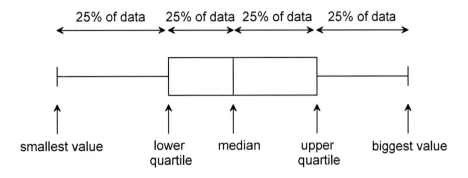

Constructing a boxplot

We draw a rectangle (or box) to represent the central 50% of the data set. We divide the box with a vertical line to show the midpoint (or median) of the data set, and we add lines (or whiskers) to the left and the right of the box. These lines extend outwards to the smallest and largest values in the data set.

9.4   *Using statistical diagrams to compare data sets*

We can use statistical diagrams to help us compare two or more data sets. In particular, we may want to compare the location, the spread and the shape (or *skewness*) of data sets.

◆ Location

The location of a data set tells us about the typical size of the observations. One way to compare locations is through the use of stem and leaf diagrams. As an example, let's consider the diagrams below, which show the claim amounts (in dollars) for two different types of insurance:

```
        Type A                           Type B

   0 | 2  7                        0 | 8
   1 | 1  1  3  6  8  9            1 | 0  2  3
   2 | 3  4  4  4  7               2 | 1  4  6  8
   3 | 0  5                        3 | 2  3  3  6  9  9
   4 | 1                          4 | 0  1  5
   5 | 2                          5 | 4
```

Key: 2|5 represents $250

Type A claims are mostly between $100 and $300 whereas Type B claims are mostly between $200 and $400. So we could say the Type B claims are greater *on average* than Type A claims.

In the next chapter we will use the mean, median and mode to measure the location of a set of data more precisely.

◆ *Spread*

We can easily compare the spreads of two or more data sets using dotplots. The dotplots below show the numbers of telephone calls received each hour over a six-hour period in two different departments of the same company:

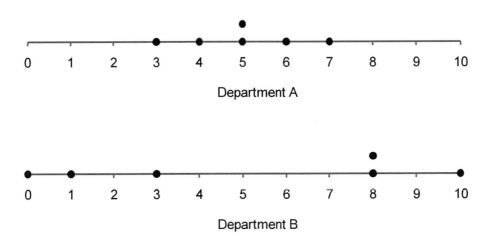

In total, there were 30 calls in each department, but for Department A the observations are closely grouped together around 5 per hour, whereas for Department B they are very spread out, and range from 0 to 10. So we would say that the number of telephone calls per hour is more spread out for Department B than for Department A.

In Chapter 11, we will introduce other measures of spread (*interquartile range* and *standard deviation*).

◆ *Skewness (shape)*

The skewness tells us how symmetrical a data set is – the greater its asymmetry, the greater the magnitude of its skewness.

To illustrate skewness, let's consider the following histograms, which show the age distributions of the population in two different towns:

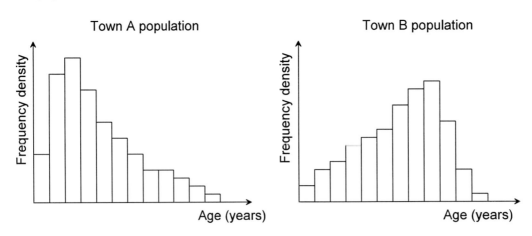

We can see that the age distribution in Town A is skewed (*ie* it is not symmetric) as the peak is towards the left rather than in the centre. More than half of the people in Town A are older than the most commonly occurring age, *ie* most of the observations lie to the positive side of the peak. A data set with this sort of shape is said to be *positively skewed*.

The population in Town B is also skewed. However, for Town B, most of the observations lie to the negative side of the peak. A data set with this sort of shape is said to be *negatively skewed*.

These shapes are compared with a symmetric distribution in the diagram below:

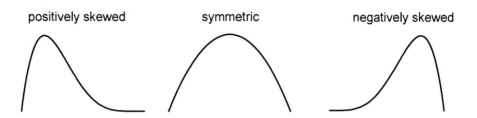

positively skewed   symmetric   negatively skewed

In Chapter 11, we will introduce a numerical measure of skewness.

Example 9.7

The diagrams below show boxplots for two different distributions:

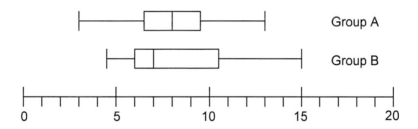

Compare the location, spread and skewness of these two distributions using the middle lines (the median), the boxes and the whole boxplot, respectively.

Solution

Using the middle line on each boxplot to compare the locations, we see that the middle value of Group A is 8 and the middle value of Group B is 7. So, on average, the values in Group A are higher than in Group B.

The differences between the largest and smallest values appear to be roughly the same for Group A and Group B. But looking at the boxes, we see that the central 50% of the observations in Group A are closer to one another that those in Group B. In this sense, Group A has a smaller spread than Group B.

Looking at the whole boxplot, we see that the data set for Group A is roughly symmetric whereas the data set for Group B is positively skewed (as most of the values are to the right of the midpoint).   ◆ ◆

Chapter 9 Practice Questions

◆ *Summarising data using statistical diagrams*

Question 9.1

The distances travelled by snails in 5 minutes were measured to the nearest centimetre. The results are shown in the table below:

Distance (cm)	Frequency
0 – 4	4
5 – 6	7
7 – 8	15
9 – 12	23
13 – 18	11

Calculate the frequency densities that you would use to draw a histogram of this data set.

Question 9.2

The mortality of males before the state retirement age is being investigated. The ages last birthday at death of 500 males were recorded and are summarised in the table below:

Age	5 – 19	20 – 29	30 – 39	40 – 49	50 – 54	55 – 59	60 – 64
Frequency	3	20	27	63	67	116	204

(i)   Draw a histogram to represent these data values.

Below is a histogram showing the deaths of 500 females in the same age range:

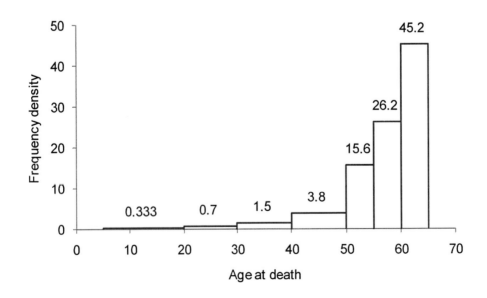

(ii)   Use the two histograms to compare the male and female mortality.

(iii)   Construct a grouped frequency distribution for the females.

Question 9.3

The following data values are the total number of hours spent processing some insurance claims:

| 8.02 | 5.11 | 5.04 | 3.88 | 4.76 | 3.26 | 4.41 | 5.19 | 4.48 | 6.28 |
| 9.12 | 6.53 | 5.14 | 2.57 | 6.80 | 7.31 | 5.71 | 6.16 | 7.51 | 8.58 |

(i)   Display this data set in a stem and leaf diagram by rounding to 1 decimal place.

(ii)   Comment on the shape of the distribution.

Question 9.4

The length of time (in minutes) for which calls to a helpline were put on hold are given in the following table:

Time (t)	Frequency
$0 < t \leq 0.5$	2
$0.5 < t \leq 1$	5
$1 < t \leq 2$	7
$2 < t \leq 5$	12
$5 < t \leq 10$	4

(i)   Construct a cumulative frequency curve for this data set.

(ii)   Use this graph to estimate:

(a)   how many calls were held for less than 3 minutes

(b)   the time for which more than 50% of the calls were on hold.

Question 9.5   (IFoA Past Examination Question)

The following table gives the ages of 100 men (in years) in the form of a grouped frequency distribution, where the ages are in groups of width five years, with the exception of the final group:

Age last birthday:	20-24	25-29	30-34	35-39	40-44	45-49	50-54	55-64
Number of men:	1	2	10	16	22	20	15	14

Draw a histogram of the data.

Question 9.6   **(IFoA Past Examination Question, adapted)**

As part of an investigation an insurance company collected data for the year 2000 on claims sizes for all claims on a certain type of motor insurance policy. The resulting data values are given below in the form of a grouped frequency distribution:

Claim size (£)	Frequency
≤ 100	862
> 100 and ≤ 200	608
> 200 and ≤ 300	1,253
> 300 and ≤ 400	1,066
> 400 and ≤ 500	558
> 500	1,290
Total	5,637

(i)   Calculate the cumulative frequencies and draw a graph of the claim size distribution function (*ie* the cumulative frequencies against claim size).

(ii)   Estimate the proportion of claim sizes that are less than £250.

◆ Using statistical diagrams to compare data sets

Question 9.7

The ages of employees in two departments are given below:

Marketing	24	25	27	27	28	28	28	29	29	32
Personnel	27	31	35	38	44	44	47	47	47	51

Draw dotplots for each department and use them to compare the ages of their employees.

Question 9.8   (IFoA Past Examination Question)

The following information on white blood cell count (WBCC) was collected from subjects one week after the start of chemotherapy treatment. One group of subjects (A) received steroids in addition to the chemotherapy treatment and the other group (B) received a placebo in addition to the chemotherapy. The subjects were assigned to the groups at random.

Group A — Steroid

WBCC (millions of cells per ml)

12.4	15.2	12.7	15.9	12.2	14.2	12.9	14.2	12.4	14.6
12.7	13.6	12.5	13.3	12.1	13.9	17.1	13.6	17.2	13.1

Group B — Placebo

WBCC (millions of cells per ml)

17.0	13.5	15.4	14.1	15.4	14.8	12.9	14.4	13.2	13.1
12.9	13.9	13.0	13.6	13.0	13.4	12.9	13.1	14.4	13.8

(i)   Construct stem and leaf diagrams for Group A and Group B separately.

(ii)   Comment on the results in the context of investigating an association between WBCC and the treatment with or without steroids.

10

Measures of location

Learning Objectives

The following learning objective is covered in this chapter:

- Describe the level/location of a set of data using the mean, median, mode, as appropriate.

- Explain how measures of location are affected when a linear transformation is applied to a data set.

10.1   *Mode*

In this chapter, we will introduce three measures of location of a numerical data set. These measures all reflect the size of the values in the data set. The first measure we will look at is the *mode*.

> ### Mode
>
> The mode of a data set is the value with the highest frequency, *ie* the value that occurs most often. The mode is also sometimes referred to as the *modal value*.

Example 10.1

Below are the numbers of new employees taken on in the last year by six companies:

> 8   5   19   3   6   5

Identify the modal value.

Solution

The modal value is 5 since 5 appears twice and all the other values appear only once.   ♦♦

The mode is very easy to identify and is not affected by extreme values (*eg* the presence of the large value of 19 in the above example does not affect the mode). There are, however, a few problems that limit its usefulness. These are illustrated in the next example.

Example 10.2

Identify the mode of each of the following data sets:

(i)   6   4   7   5   4   6

(ii)   1   2   3   4   5

Solution

(i)   Both 4 and 6 appear twice, so the mode is not unique. A data set with two modes is said to be *bimodal*.

(ii)   All the values appear once, so this data set does not have a mode.   ♦♦

◆ *Modal groups*

There may be situations where the exact value of each observation is not known, and all we do know about each observation is that it lies within a particular range. This is the case when we have a grouped frequency distribution. Without knowledge of the exact values, we cannot identify the mode. We can, however, identify the *modal group* from a grouped frequency distribution.

> ### Modal group
>
> For grouped data, the modal group is the group with the highest frequency.

Example 10.3

The grouped frequency distribution below summarises the ages last birthday at death for 30 male life assurance policyholders.

Age last birthday	40-49	50-59	60-69	70-79	80-89	90-99	100-109
Frequency	1	2	5	10	8	3	1

Identify the modal group.

Solution

The modal group is the 70-79 age group, as this has the highest frequency.   ◆◆

Below is a summary of the advantages and disadvantages of using the mode as a measure of location.

Advantages

- The mode is easy to calculate.
- The mode is not affected by extreme values in the data set.

Disadvantages

- The mode may not be unique.
- The mode may not exist.
- The mode focuses on a small number of data values.
- The mode does not have a simple algebraic formula and, as a result, it is not useful in further calculations.

10.2   Mean

The *mean* of a data set is obtained by summing the observations and dividing the total by the number of observations in the data set.

Example 10.4

The sizes of the last ten car insurance claims paid by an insurance company are:

£1,500	£1,820	£840	£260	£2,100
£790	£530	£1,360	£1,780	£1,650

Determine the mean of these observations.

Solution

The sum of the ten observations is:

$$1,500 + 1,820 + 840 + 260 + 2,100 + 790 + 530 + 1,360 + 1,780 + 1,650 = £12,630$$

So the mean is:

$$\frac{12,630}{10} = £1,263 \qquad \blacklozenge\blacklozenge$$

We normally use the symbol $\bar{x}$ to denote the mean of a data set.

Mean

The mean of the data set containing the values $x_1, x_2, \ldots, x_n$ is given by:

$$\bar{x} = \frac{x_1 + x_2 + \cdots + x_n}{n} = \frac{1}{n}\sum_{i=1}^{n} x_i$$

Unlike the mode, the mean uses all the values in a data set directly. As a result, the mean is affected by any extreme values. This is illustrated in Example 10.5 below. Despite this, the mean is still used as the main measure of location in statistics. This is mainly due to the fact that the mean has a number of properties that make it useful in further calculations.

Example 10.5

Below are the salaries (in £000s) of 8 individuals in a small company:

| 25 | 25 | 25 | 25 | 25 | 25 | 25 | 50 |

Calculate the mean salary earned by these 8 people.

Solution

The mean is:

$$\bar{x} = \frac{25 + 25 + 25 + 25 + 25 + 25 + 25 + 50}{8} = \frac{225}{8} = 28.125$$

ie £28,125.

Note that, without the large value of 50, the mean would be £25,000, but when we include the value of 50, the mean increases significantly (by £3,125). If we use the mean as a measure of average salary, 7 out of 8 employees could claim they were underpaid! ♦♦

◆ *Calculating the mean from a frequency distribution*

In Example 10.5, the value 25 is observed seven times and the value 50 is observed once. So the sum of the observations can be expressed as:

$$25 \times 7 + 50 \times 1$$

and the mean can be expressed as:

$$\frac{25 \times 7 + 50 \times 1}{7 + 1}$$

Now let's make this more general. Suppose we have a data set that contains m different values, $x_1, x_2, \ldots, x_m$, with frequencies $f_1, f_2, \ldots, f_m$ respectively.

The sum of these observations is:

$$x_1 f_1 + x_2 f_2 + \cdots + x_m f_m$$

and the total number of observations is:

$$f_1 + f_2 + \cdots + f_m$$

As always, the mean is obtained by dividing the sum of the observations by the number of observations.

Calculating the mean from a frequency distribution

$$\bar{x} = \frac{x_1 f_1 + x_2 f_2 + \cdots + x_m f_m}{f_1 + f_2 + \cdots + f_m} = \frac{\sum_{i=1}^{m} x_i f_i}{\sum_{i=1}^{m} f_i}$$

◆ *Estimating the mean from a grouped frequency distribution*

Suppose we want to calculate the mean of the data summarised in this grouped frequency distribution:

Claim amount, c	Frequency
$0 < c \leq £500$	6
$£500 < c \leq £1,000$	11
$£1,000 < c \leq £1,500$	49
$£1,500 < c \leq £2,000$	26
$£2,000 < c \leq £5,000$	8

We have a problem because we don't know the exact value of each observation. The best we can do is to *estimate* the mean. We can do this by assuming that each observation is equal to the midpoint of the group in which it lies.

We find the midpoint of a group by averaging the smallest and largest possible values in the group. The midpoint for the $0 < c \leq £500$ group is $\frac{0+500}{2} = £250$. Similarly, the midpoints for the other groups are $£750$, $£1,250$, $£1,750$, and $£3,500$.

So our estimate of the mean claim amount is:

$$\frac{(250 \times 6) + (750 \times 11) + (1,250 \times 49) + (1,750 \times 26) + (3,500 \times 8)}{6 + 11 + 49 + 26 + 8} = \frac{144,500}{100} = £1,445$$

When calculating the midpoint of groups constructed from rounded data, we need to make sure we correctly identify the smallest and largest possible values for each group.

Example 10.6

The grouped frequency distribution below summarises the ages last birthday at death for 30 male life assurance policyholders.

Age last birthday	40-49	50-59	60-69	70-79	80-89	90-99	100-109
Frequency	1	2	5	10	8	3	1

Estimate the mean of the exact ages at death for this group of people.

Solution

The midpoint of the 40-49 group is *not* $\dfrac{40+49}{2}$. As the 40-49 group ranges from exact age 40 to (just below) exact age 50, the midpoint is 45 years. Similarly, the midpoints (in years) for the other groups are:

$$55 \quad 65 \quad 75 \quad 85 \quad 95 \quad 105$$

Hence, our estimate of the mean of the exact ages at death is:

$$\frac{(45\times1)+(55\times2)+(65\times5)+(75\times10)+(85\times8)+(95\times3)+(105\times1)}{1+2+5+10+8+3+1}$$

$$=\frac{2,300}{30}=76.7 \text{ years}$$
♦♦

Below is a summary of the advantages and disadvantages of using the mean as a measure of location.

Advantages

- The mean uses all the data values.

- The mean has mathematical properties that make it useful in further calculations.

Disadvantages

- The mean can be distorted by extreme values.

10.3 Median

We will now introduce our third measure of location, the *median*.

Median

The median of a data set is the value that splits the set into two equal halves, so that half of the observations are below the median and half are above it.

When the exact value of each observation is known, the median is the middle value in the set when the observations are ordered from smallest to largest.

Example 10.7

Determine the median of the following observations:

125	75	25	20	50	25	50	15	30

Solution

We first arrange the observations in order, from smallest to largest:

15	20	25	25	30	50	50	75	125

We then identify the middle value:

15	20	25	25	(30)	50	50	75	125

So the median is 30.   ♦♦

If we have an even number of observations, the middle value will fall between two observations. In a situation like this, we define the median to be the average (or mean) of the middle two values.

Example 10.8

Determine the median of the following data set:

9	1	4	10	15	5	3	9

Solution

Arranged in increasing order the observations are:

1	3	4	5	9	9	10	15

The middle two values are 5 and 9:

1	3	4	(5	9)	9	10	15

The average of these is:

$$\frac{5+9}{2} = \frac{14}{2} = 7$$

So the median is 7.   ♦♦

In Example 10.7, there are 9 observations and the median is the 5th value when they are arranged in increasing order.

In Example 10.8, there are 8 observations and the median is the average of the 4th and 5th values when they are arranged in increasing order. We can think of this average as representing the 4.5th value.

Position of the median value in a list of ordered observations

If we have a list of n observations, arranged in order from smallest to largest, then the position of the median value is $\dfrac{n+1}{2}$.

If n is an even number, the median is defined to be the average of the middle two values, *ie* the average of the $\dfrac{n}{2}$ th and $\left(\dfrac{n}{2}+1\right)$ th values.

Like the mode, the median does not use all the data directly and is unaffected by extreme observations.

Example 10.9

Below are the salaries (in £000s) of 8 individuals in a small company:

      25   25   25   25   25   25   25   50

Determine the median salary earned by these 8 people.

Solution

The observations are already arranged in order from smallest to largest. The median is the average of the 4th and the 5th observations, which is £25,000.

If we compare this value with the mean of £28,125 that we calculated in Example 10.5, we see that the median is a much more sensible way of describing the average salary. Using this value as our benchmark, no-one can claim to be underpaid. ♦♦

◆▶ *Identifying the median from a frequency distribution*

Suppose we have the following frequency distribution and we want to identify the median.

Value, x	1	2	3	4	5
Frequency, f	3	4	6	5	2

This table tells us that the smallest observation is 1 and that it occurs 3 times, the next largest observation is 2 and it occurs 4 times, and so on. In the table, the observations are already listed in increasing order.

To identify the median, we first need to determine the total number of data points, n. This is the sum of the frequencies. So we have:

$$n = 3 + 4 + 6 + 5 + 2 = 20$$

Hence the position of the median is the $\dfrac{20+1}{2} = 10.5$ place. Since this is not a whole number, the median is defined to be the average of the 10th and 11th observations.

To find these, it is easiest to examine the cumulative frequencies. Including these in the table, we have:

Value, x	1	2	3	4	5
Frequency, f	3	4	6	5	2
Cumulative frequency	3	$3 + 4 = 7$	$7 + 6 = 13$	$13 + 5 = 18$	$18 + 2 = 20$

We can see from the table that the 8th, 9th, and so on up to the 13th values are all equal to 3. Hence both the 10th and 11th values are equal to 3, and so the median is also 3.

◆ *Estimating the median from a grouped frequency distribution*

In order to determine the median exactly, we need to know the exact value of each observation. When the data values are grouped, the best we can do is to *estimate* the median. Firstly, we will consider the case of *continuous* data values that have been grouped in some way.

The grouped frequency distribution below summarises the exact ages at death for 30 male life assurance policyholders.

Exact age at death, x	Frequency
$40 \leq x < 50$	1
$50 \leq x < 60$	2
$60 \leq x < 70$	5
$70 \leq x < 80$	10
$80 \leq x < 90$	8
$90 \leq x < 100$	3
$100 \leq x < 110$	1

To help us identify the group that contains the median, let's extend the frequency table to include cumulative frequencies:

Exact age at death, x	Frequency	Cumulative frequency
$40 \leq x < 50$	1	1
$50 \leq x < 60$	2	3
$60 \leq x < 70$	5	8
$70 \leq x < 80$	10	18
$80 \leq x < 90$	8	26
$90 \leq x < 100$	3	29
$100 \leq x < 110$	1	30

We have 30 observations in total so there are 15 observations less than the median and 15 observations greater than it. We can see from the table above that the median lies in the $70 \le x < 80$ class. In order to be more specific about the value of the median, we need to make a simplifying assumption. A convenient assumption is that the cumulative frequency increases linearly over each class.

Estimating the median

If we have a grouped frequency distribution involving a total of n observations, we:

- identify the interval in which the cumulative frequency reaches $\dfrac{n}{2}$

- use linear interpolation to estimate the median value.

When applying this method, we have to take care to identify the lower endpoint and the width of the median class correctly.

Returning to our death data, we see that there are 8 deaths before exact age 70 and 10 deaths between exact age 70 and exact age 80. Under the linearity assumption, the median is the point that is $\dfrac{15-8}{10} = \dfrac{7}{10}$ ths of the way through the interval $70 \le x < 80$. Since the lower endpoint of this interval is 70 and the width of the interval is 10, our estimate of the median is:

$$70 + \frac{7}{10} \times 10 = 77$$

This is illustrated in the diagram below.

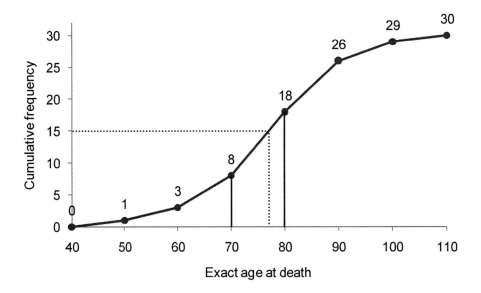

Now let's consider how we can estimate the median when we have *discrete* data values that have been grouped in some way. Suppose each data point is a whole number and the data set results in the following grouped frequency distribution:

Observation	Frequency
1-5	6
6-10	4
11-15	3
16-20	2

To help identify the median class, let's extend the table to show the cumulative frequencies:

Observation	Frequency	Cumulative frequency
1-5	6	6
6-10	4	10
11-15	3	13
16-20	2	15

The total number of observations is 15, so $\frac{n}{2} = 7.5$. We can see from the table that the cumulative frequency reaches 7.5 in the 6-10 class. There are 6 observations of 5 or less and 4 observations in the 6-10 class. Using the linearity assumption, the median is the point that is $\frac{7.5-6}{4} = \frac{3}{8}$ ths of the way through the 6-10 class.

When we use the linearity assumption, we should adjust the classes so that there are no spaces between them. In other words, we should apply a *continuity correction* to the classes. With this adjustment, the 6-10 class becomes 5.5-10.5. Similarly, the 11-15 class becomes 10.5-15.5.

The lower endpoint of the 5.5-10.5 class is 5.5 and its width is 5. So our estimate of the median is:

$$5.5 + \frac{3}{8} \times 5 = 7.375$$

◆ *Estimating the median using a cumulative frequency diagram*

If we are given a cumulative frequency diagram for n observations of continuous data, we can estimate the median by locating the value $\frac{n}{2}$ on the y-axis (*ie* the cumulative frequency axis) and reading off the corresponding value from the x-axis.

Example 10.10

A consumer watchdog measures the length of time (in minutes) for which 40 telephone calls to a helpline were put on hold. A cumulative frequency graph of the data is given below:

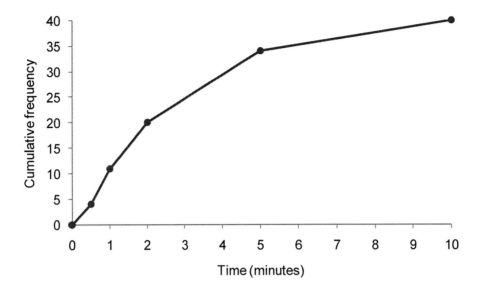

Estimate the median length of time that calls were placed on hold.

Solution

Since we have 40 observations, 20 of them will lie below the median and 20 of them will lie above the median. We can estimate the median by locating the value 20 on the *y*-axis and reading off the corresponding value from the *x*-axis.

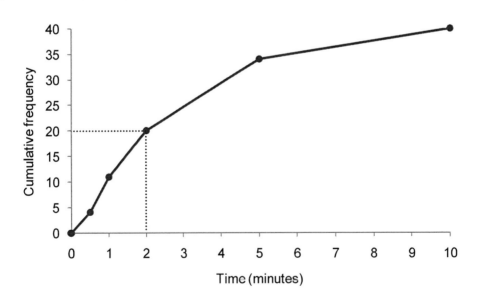

From the graph, we estimate the median to be 2 minutes.   ♦ ♦

Below is a summary of the advantages and disadvantages of using the median as a measure of location.

Advantages

- The median is not affected by extreme values.

Disadvantages

- The median does not use all the data values directly.

- The median does not have a simple algebraic formula and, as a result, it is not useful for further calculations.

10.4   *Transforming data sets*

In this section, we'll see how the mode, the mean and the median of a data set are affected when:

- a constant amount is added to each value in the data set

- each value in the data set is multiplied by the same amount.

Suppose we have the following data set:

$$1 \quad 2 \quad 5 \quad 6 \quad 8 \quad 8$$

The mode is 8, the mean is:

$$\bar{x} = \frac{1+2+5+6+8+8}{6} = \frac{30}{6} = 5$$

and the median is the 3.5th value (*ie* the average of the 3rd and 4th values), which is 5.5.

Now consider what happens to each of these measures if we *add* a constant amount, say 3, to each value in the data set.

The observations are now:

$$4 \quad 5 \quad 8 \quad 9 \quad 11 \quad 11$$

The new mode is 11, the new mean is:

$$\bar{x} = \frac{4+5+8+9+11+11}{6} = \frac{48}{6} = 8$$

and the new median is $\frac{8+9}{2} = 8.5$.

So we can see that adding 3 to each of the observations causes all three measures of location to increase by this amount.

Now consider what happens if we *multiply* each value in the data set by the same amount, *eg* 5. The values become:

$$5 \quad 10 \quad 25 \quad 30 \quad 40 \quad 40$$

The new mode is 40, the new mean is:

$$\bar{x} = \frac{5 + 10 + 25 + 30 + 40 + 40}{6} = \frac{150}{6} = 25$$

and the new median is $\dfrac{25 + 30}{2} = 27.5$.

So we can see that multiplying each of the observations by 5 means that the mode, the mean and the median are also all multiplied by 5.

In fact, we have the following general results:

Measures of location for a transformed data set

If each value in a data set is increased by a constant amount, a (which might be negative), then the mode, mean and median are also each increased by a.

If each value in a data set is multiplied by a constant, b, then the mode, mean and median are equal to their original values each multiplied by b.

10.5   *Shape of a data set*

In Chapter 9, we introduced the idea of skewness as a measure of the asymmetry of a data set. A reminder of the general (smoothed) shapes is shown below:

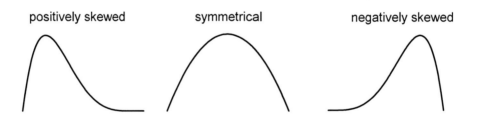

positively skewed   symmetrical   negatively skewed

Now let's consider the relative positions of the mode, median and mean of a data set in each of these situations.

First of all, consider the data set:

     1   2   2   3   3   3   3   4   4   5

A dotplot of these data values is shown below:

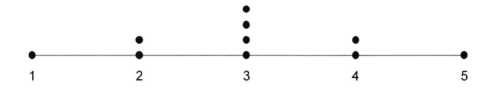

We can see from the dotplot that the data set is symmetrical about the value 3. The mode is 3, the mean is:

$$\frac{1+2+2+3+3+3+3+4+4+5}{10} = \frac{30}{10} = 3$$

and the median is the 5½th value, which is also 3. So, for this symmetrical data set, the mode, median and mean are all equal.

Next, let's consider the data set:

$$\begin{array}{cccccccccc} 1 & 2 & 2 & 2 & 2 & 3 & 3 & 3 & 4 & 5 \end{array}$$

A dotplot of these data values is shown below:

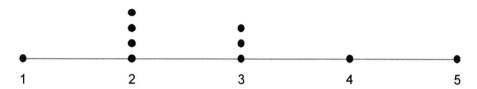

We can see from the dotplot that the data set is positively skewed. The mode is 2, the mean is:

$$\frac{1+2+2+2+2+3+3+3+4+5}{10} = \frac{27}{10} = 2.7$$

and the median is the 5½th value, which is 2.5 (the average of 2 and 3). So, for this positively skewed data set, the mode is less than the mean, and the median lies in between.

These two examples are what we might describe as 'well-behaved' data sets. By this we mean data sets for which the relative positions of the mode, median and mean for distributions of different shapes are as shown below.

Relative positions of mode, median and mean for _well-behaved_ data sets

mode = median = mean	for a symmetrical data set
mode < median < mean	for a positively skewed data set
mode > median > mean	for a negatively skewed data set

So, while most data sets will follow one of these patterns, not all of them do. Let's take the previous data set and simply change the '3's into '1's, and the '4' into a '2'. The ordered set now looks like:

$$\begin{array}{cccccccccc} 1 & 1 & 1 & 1 & 2 & 2 & 2 & 2 & 2 & 5 \end{array}$$

A dotplot of these data values is shown below:

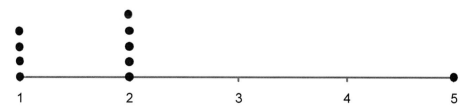

The data set is still positively skewed, as it still tails off to the right. The mode is still 2, the mean is now:

$$\frac{1+1+1+1+2+2+2+2+2+5}{10}=\frac{19}{10}=1.9$$

and the median is now 2 (as the 5th and 6th values are both 2). So, for this positively skewed data set, both the mode and median are greater than the mean, contrary to the 'standard' pattern we gave above.

So the relative positions of the mode, median and mean (for skewed data sets) cannot be used to identify the direction of skewness with certainty. To be certain of whether the skewness is positive or negative, we have to calculate its numerical value. This is covered in the next chapter.

Chapter 10 Practice Questions

◆ Mode

Question 10.1

The numbers of personal pension reviews completed by an analyst each day over the last four weeks are given below:

Reviews completed in a day	4	5	6	7	8
Frequency	5	7	4	3	1

Identify the mode of this data set.

Question 10.2

100 claims on car insurance policies has yielded the following results.

Claim amount, c	Number of claims
$0 < c \leq £500$	6
$£500 < c \leq £1,000$	11
$£1,000 < c \leq £1,500$	49
$£1,500 < c \leq £2,000$	26
$£2,000 < c \leq £5,000$	8

Identify the modal group.

◆ Mean

Question 10.3

Below are the numbers of new employees taken on in the last year by six companies:

      8   5   19   3   6   5

Calculate the mean number of these values.

Question 10.4

The mean age at death of 12 assurance policyholders was 72. Determine the total of the ages at death of these policyholders.

Question 10.5

The mean of the following list of investment returns is 4.2%:

      5%   4.75%   3.6%   x%   3.25%

Determine the value of x.

Question 10.6

A small company has ten employees. Their mean salary is £48,000. When an eleventh person joins the company the mean salary drops to £45,800. Determine the salary of the new employee.

Question 10.7

The mean sum assured on a group of 12 term assurance policies is £50,000 and the mean sum assured on a group of 8 endowment assurances policies is £30,000. Calculate the mean sum assured on the combined group of 20 policies.

Question 10.8

The journey times (in minutes) of 300 employees to a company's office are shown below:

Time (mins)	Frequency
$0 < t \leq 10$	50
$10 < t \leq 20$	70
$20 < t \leq 40$	80
$40 < t \leq 70$	75
$70 < t \leq 120$	25

Estimate the mean journey time.

Question 10.9   (IFoA Past Examination Question, adapted)

Sickness and absence records were kept on 30 employees in a company over a 91-day period. These data values are tabulated below:

Number of employees absent	0	1	2	3	4	5
Number of days	44	19	10	8	7	3

Calculate the mean of the number of employees absent per day.

Question 10.10   (IFoA Past Examination Question, adapted)

Consider a group of 47 white-collar workers and a group of 24 blue-collar workers, which have been randomly selected from the workforce of a large company. The mean salary for the group of white-collar workers is £28,470; whereas the mean salary for the group of blue-collar workers is £21,420.

Calculate the mean of the salaries in the combined group of 71 employees.

◆ Median

Question 10.11

The frequency table shows the number of claims (of a particular type) made each week in the last year.

Number of claims per week	0	1	2	3	4	5
Frequency	5	7	15	12	9	4

(i)   Calculate the median number of claims per week.

(ii)   In the first two weeks of the following year, 3 and 5 claims were made.   Add these values to the frequency distribution and find the new median of all 54 results.

Question 10.12

The heights, in centimetres, of thirty actuaries are recorded below.   Estimate the median height.

Heights, h	Frequency
$150 \leq h < 160$	4
$160 \leq h < 170$	6
$170 \leq h < 175$	11
$175 \leq h < 180$	7
$180 \leq h < 195$	2

Question 10.13   (IFoA Past Examination Question, adapted)

The values of 15 motor windscreen claim amounts (in £) are as follows:

121	107	139	72	123
114	215	156	100	136
169	89	115	153	111

Determine the median claim amount.

Question 10.14   (IFoA Past Examination Question)

Data values were collected on 100 consecutive days for the number of claims, x, arising from a group of policies.   This resulted in the following frequency distribution:

x	0	1	2	3	4	≥ 5
f	14	25	26	18	12	5

Calculate the median for these data values.

Question 10.15   (IFoA Past Examination Question)

The table below shows a grouped frequency distribution for 100 claim amounts on a certain class of insurance policy.

Claim amount	Frequency
under £100	4
£100 – 149.99	10
£150 – 199.99	25
£200 – 249.99	30
£250 – 299.99	15
£300 – 349.99	12
£350 – 399.99	4
£400 or over	0

Determine an approximate value for the median of these claim amounts.

Question 10.16   (IFoA Past Examination Question, adapted)

Fifty claim amounts (£) from a particular section of an insurance company's business are displayed below in a stem and leaf plot:

```
15 | 14678
16 | 0233368889
17 | 0000001233457888
18 | 3456779
19 | 0257
20 | 0
21 | 3
22 | 07
23 |
24 |
25 | 3
26 |
27 | 3
28 | 8
29 |
30 |
31 | 2
```

Stem unit = 100   Leaf unit = 10

The sum of the fifty amounts (before rounding) is £92,780.

Calculate the mean and median claim amounts.

11

Measures of spread and skewness

Learning Objectives

The following learning objectives are covered in this chapter:

- Describe the spread/variability of a set of data using the standard deviation, range, interquartile range, as appropriate.

- Calculate the moments of a data set.

- Explain what is meant by symmetry and skewness for the distribution of a set of data. Be familiar with the third central moment as a measure of skewness.

- Explain how measures of spread and skewness are affected when a linear transformation is applied to a data set.

11.1 Introduction

In the last chapter, we looked at measures of location of a data set. As well as location, we also want to be able to measure the spread of a data set. Comparing data sets on the basis of only their locations may be misleading, as illustrated by the following dotplots:

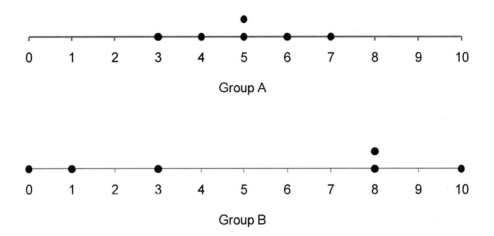

Group A

Group B

These are clearly very different data sets, but they both have a mean of 5. The observations in Group B are very spread out, whereas the observations in Group A are closer together.

In this chapter we will look at four measures of spread. These are the range, the interquartile range, the variance and the standard deviation.

11.2 Range

Range is a very simple measure of spread. It is defined as follows:

Range of a data set

The *range* of a data set is the difference between its largest value and its smallest value.

Example 11.1

Calculate the range of the following data set:

      8   5   19   3   6   5

Solution

The largest value in this data set is 19 and the smallest is 3. So its range is $19 - 3 = 16$.   ♦♦

Although the range of a data set is easy to calculate, it does have its disadvantages. The next example illustrates the problem with this measure.

Example 11.2

Below are the salaries of the employees of a small company:

Salary (£)	25,000	50,000
Frequency	7	1

Calculate the range of this data set.

Solution

The largest salary is £50,000 and the smallest is £25,000. So the range is $£50,000 - £25,000 = £25,000$.   ◆◆

The answer could be misleading because the £50,000 figure is an extreme value. The range of £25,000 suggests that the observations are widely spread. It does not take into account that 7 out of the 8 observations are identical.

The problem with the range is therefore that it uses the most extreme values (the maximum and minimum), which in many data sets are not representative values. We really need a better measure of the spread that does not rely solely on the extreme values. We will consider some alternatives later in this chapter.

◆ Estimating the range from a grouped frequency distribution

Suppose we want to calculate the range of the data summarised in this grouped frequency distribution:

Claim amount, c	Frequency
$0 < c \leq £500$	6
$£500 < c \leq £1,000$	11
$£1,000 < c \leq £1,500$	49
$£1,500 < c \leq £2,000$	26
$£2,000 < c \leq £5,000$	8

If we do not have the original list of data we will not be able to identify the largest and smallest values exactly. However, if we want to have some indication of the range, we could say that its *maximum possible* size is equal to the upper bound of the highest group minus the lower bound of the lowest group. For the grouped frequency distribution given above, this is $£5,000 - £100 = £4,900$.

Below is a summary of the advantages and disadvantages of using the range as a measure of spread.

Advantage

- The range is very easy to calculate.

Disadvantages

- The range is affected by extreme values.

- The range focuses on a small number of data values.

- The range does not have convenient mathematical properties and, as a result, is not useful.

11.3 *Interquartile range*

The *interquartile range* is a measure of spread that is not directly affected by the extreme values of a data set. It is defined to be the difference between the *lower quartile* and the *upper quartile*.

Lower and upper quartiles

The lower quartile of a data set is the point that is one quarter of the way through the data set when the values are arranged in increasing order. It is denoted by the symbol Q_1.

The upper quartile of a data set is the point that is three quarters of the way through the data set when the values are arranged in increasing order. It is denoted by the symbol Q_3.

Interquartile range

The interquartile range of a data set is:

$$Q_3 - Q_1$$

If the values in a data set are spread out, the upper and lower quartiles will usually be a long way apart and the interquartile range will have a high value.

In Chapter 10, we discussed the median (or middle value) of a data set. The median is sometimes denoted by the symbol Q_2. We saw that the median of a data set containing n observations is the $\left(\dfrac{n+1}{2}\right)$th value in the set, given that the observations have been arranged in order from smallest to largest. We have similar formulae for the positions of the lower and upper quartiles.

Positions of the lower and upper quartiles

For a data set that contains n observations, arranged in order from smallest to largest, the position of the lower quartile is:

$$\frac{n+1}{4}$$

and the position of the upper quartile is:

$$3\left(\frac{n+1}{4}\right)$$

However, there is no universal agreement about how the quartiles are best defined. An alternative pair of formulae for the positions of the lower and upper quartiles is:

$$\frac{n}{4}+\frac{1}{2} \quad \text{and} \quad \frac{3n}{4}+\frac{1}{2}$$

We will use the first pair of formulae in this textbook. To be able to work out the quartiles using these formulae, we need to have at least 3 values in the data set.

Example 11.3

Identify the lower quartile, median, upper quartile and interquartile range of the following data set:

£50	£120	£40	£30	£15	£50	£20

Solution

First we need to arrange the values in ascending order:

£15	£20	£30	£40	£50	£50	£120

There are 7 values, so $n = 7$.

The lower quartile is the $\dfrac{7+1}{4} = $ 2nd value:

£15	£20	£30	£40	£50	£50	£120

So $Q_1 = £20$.

The median is the $\dfrac{7+1}{2} = $ 4th value:

£15	£20	£30	£40	£50	£50	£120

So $Q_2 = £40$.

The upper quartile is the $3\left(\dfrac{7+1}{4}\right) = $ 6th value:

£15	£20	£30	£40	£50	£50	£120

So $Q_3 = £50$.

The interquartile range is:

$$Q_3 - Q_1 = £50 - £20 = £30$$

♦♦

It is easy to see from the above example how the lower quartile, median and upper quartile split the data set into 4 equal parts:

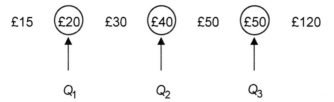

In this example, the positions of the lower quartile, median and upper quartile are all whole numbers, so the quartiles and the median all coincide with observed values. However, this is not the case for every data set. In such situations, we calculate the quartiles using linear interpolation.

Example 11.4

Calculate the lower quartile, upper quartile and interquartile range of the data set:

$$3 \quad 5 \quad 6 \quad 9 \quad 11 \quad 16$$

Solution

The data values are already arranged in ascending order and here we have $n = 6$.

The lower quartile is the $\dfrac{6+1}{4} = 1.75$th value. Using linear interpolation, this is 75% of the way between the 1st and 2nd observations. So the lower quartile is:

$$3 + 0.75(5 - 3) = 0.25 \times 3 + 0.75 \times 5 = 4.5$$

The upper quartile is the $3\left(\dfrac{6+1}{4}\right) = 5.25$th value. Using linear interpolation, this is 25% of the way between the 5th and 6th observations. So the upper quartile is:

$$11 + 0.25(16 - 11) = 0.75 \times 11 + 0.25 \times 16 = 12.25$$

Hence the interquartile range is:

$$12.25 - 4.5 = 7.75 \qquad\qquad\qquad\qquad\qquad\qquad\qquad ◆◆$$

◆ Calculating the quartiles from a frequency distribution

Suppose we want to determine the lower and upper quartiles of a data set that has the following frequency distribution:

Value, x	1	2	3	4	5
Frequency, f	3	4	6	5	2

To help us identify the quartiles, we will extend the table to include cumulative frequencies:

Value, x	1	2	3	4	5
Frequency, f	3	4	6	5	2
Cumulative frequency	3	7	13	18	20

We have 20 observations altogether. So $n = 20$.

The lower quartile is the $\dfrac{20 + 1}{4} = 5.25$th value. We can see from the cumulative frequencies that the 5th and 6th observations are both 2. So $Q_1 = 2$.

The upper quartile is the $3\left(\dfrac{20 + 1}{4}\right) = 15.75$th value. We can see from the cumulative frequencies that the 15th and 16th observations are both 4. So $Q_3 = 4$.

◆ *Estimating the quartiles from a grouped frequency distribution*

In order to determine the quartiles exactly, we need to know the exact value of each observation. When the data values are grouped, we are only able to *estimate* the quartiles. We can do this by assuming that the cumulative frequency increases linearly over each class. The procedure is outlined below:

Estimating the lower and upper quartiles

If we have a grouped frequency distribution involving a total of n observations, we estimate the lower quartile by:

- identifying the group in which the cumulative frequency reaches $\dfrac{n}{4}$

- using linear interpolation to estimate where in that group the lower quartile lies.

Likewise we estimate the upper quartile by:

- identifying the group in which the cumulative frequency reaches $\dfrac{3n}{4}$

- using linear interpolation to estimate where in that group the upper quartile lies.

This method is analogous to the one used to estimate the median of grouped data. Again we have to take care to identify the lower endpoints and the width of the classes correctly. Firstly, we will consider the case of *continuous* data values that have been grouped in some way.

The grouped frequency distribution below summarises the exact ages at death for 30 male life assurance policyholders.

Exact age at death, x	Frequency
$40 \leq x < 50$	1
$50 \leq x < 60$	2
$60 \leq x < 70$	5
$70 \leq x < 80$	10
$80 \leq x < 90$	8
$90 \leq x < 100$	3
$100 \leq x < 110$	1

To help us identify the groups that contain the quartiles, we extend the frequency table to include the cumulative frequencies:

Exact age at death, x	Frequency	Cumulative frequency
$40 \leq x < 50$	1	1
$50 \leq x < 60$	2	3
$60 \leq x < 70$	5	8
$70 \leq x < 80$	10	18
$80 \leq x < 90$	8	26
$90 \leq x < 100$	3	29
$100 \leq x < 110$	1	30

We have $n = 30$, so $\dfrac{n}{4} = 7.5$. We can see from the table that the cumulative frequency reaches 7.5 in the $60 \leq x < 70$ group. So the lower quartile lies somewhere within this group.

There are 3 deaths before exact age 60 and 5 deaths between exact age 60 and exact age 70. Under the linearity assumption, the lower quartile is the point that is $\dfrac{7.5 - 3}{5} = \dfrac{9}{10}$ ths of the way through the interval $60 \leq x < 70$. Since the lower endpoint of this interval is 60 and its width is 10, our estimate of the lower quartile is:

$$60 + \frac{9}{10} \times 10 = 69 \text{ years}$$

To estimate the upper quartile, we first identify the group in which the cumulative frequency reaches $\dfrac{3n}{4} = 22.5$. We can see from the table that this is somewhere in the $80 \leq x < 90$ group.

There are 18 deaths before exact age 80 and 8 deaths between exact age 80 and exact age 90. Under the linearity assumption, the upper quartile is the point that is $\dfrac{22.5 - 18}{8} = \dfrac{9}{16}$ ths of the way through the interval $80 \leq x < 90$. Since the lower endpoint of this interval is 80 and its width is 10, our estimate of the upper quartile is:

$$80 + \frac{9}{16} \times 10 = 85.625 \text{ years}$$

We will now show how to estimate the quartiles using the linearity assumption when we have *discrete* data values that have been grouped in some way.

Suppose that each data point is a whole number and the data set results in the following grouped frequency distribution:

Observation	Frequency
1-5	6
6-10	4
11-15	3
16-20	2

To help us identify the groups that contain the quartiles, we extend the table to show the cumulative frequencies:

Observation	Frequency	Cumulative frequency
1-5	6	6
6-10	4	10
11-15	3	13
16-20	2	15

The total number of observations is 15, so $\frac{n}{4} = 3.75$. We can see from the table that the cumulative frequency reaches 3.75 in the 1-5 class. Using the linearity assumption, the lower quartile is the point that is $\frac{3.75}{6} = \frac{5}{8}$ ths of the way through this class.

As we saw when estimating the median of grouped discrete data using the linearity assumption, we should apply a continuity correction, *ie* we should adjust the classes so that there are no spaces between them. Doing this, the 1-5 class becomes 0.5-5.5. The lower endpoint of this class is 0.5 and its width is 5. So our estimate of the lower quartile is:

$$0.5 + \frac{5}{8} \times 5 = 3.625$$

To estimate the upper quartile, we first identify the group in which the cumulative frequency reaches $\frac{3n}{4} = 11.25$. From the table above, we see that this is in the 11-15 class. There are 10 observations of 10 or less and 3 observations in the 11-15 class. Using the linearity assumption, the upper quartile is the point that is $\frac{11.25 - 10}{3} = \frac{5}{12}$ ths of the way through this class. Applying a continuity correction to the 11-15 class, it becomes 10.5-15.5. The lower endpoint of this class is 10.5 and its width is 5. So our estimate of the upper quartile is:

$$10.5 + \frac{5}{12} \times 5 = 12.583$$

◆ *Estimating the quartiles using a cumulative frequency diagram*

If we are given a cumulative frequency diagram based on n observations, we can estimate the lower quartile by locating the value $\frac{n}{4}$ on the *y*-axis (*ie* the cumulative frequency axis) and reading off the corresponding value from the *x*-axis. Similarly we can estimate the upper quartile by locating the value $\frac{3n}{4}$ on the *y*-axis and reading off the corresponding value from the *x*-axis.

Example 11.5

A consumer watchdog measures the length of time (in minutes) for which 40 telephone calls to a helpline were put on hold. A cumulative frequency graph of the data is given below:

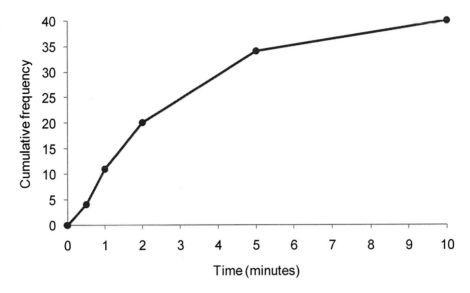

Estimate the lower quartile, upper quartile and interquartile range of the length of time that calls were placed on hold.

Solution

Here we have 40 observations. To estimate the lower quartile, we need to locate the point $40 / 4 = 10$ on the *y*-axis and read off the corresponding value from the *x*-axis:

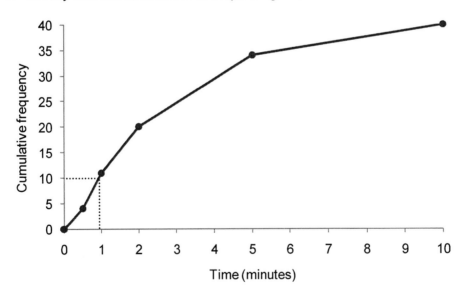

From the graph, we estimate the lower quartile to be 0.9 minutes.

To estimate the upper quartile, we need to locate the point $(3 \times 40) / 4 = 30$ on the *y*-axis and read off the corresponding value from the *x*-axis.

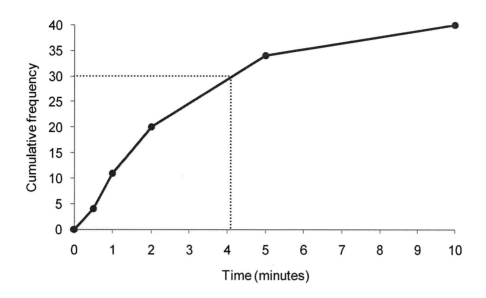

From the graph, we estimate the upper quartile to be 4.1 minutes.

Using these values, we estimate the interquartile range to be $4.1 - 0.9 = 3.2$ minutes.   ♦ ♦

◆ *Obtaining the quartiles from a boxplot*

Boxplots were introduced in Chapter 9 as a type of diagram that can be used to illustrate a data set. Recall that a boxplot looks like this:

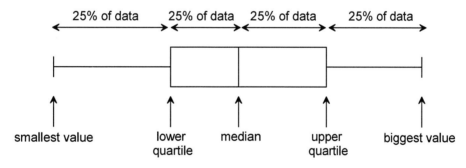

Given a boxplot with a scale, we can read off the values of the lower and upper quartiles directly.

Example 11.6

The boxplot below summarises the scores obtained by a group of students on a particular exam:

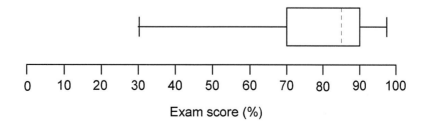

Calculate the interquartile range of the exam scores.

Solution

From the boxplot we see that the lower quartile is 70% and the upper quartile is 90%. So the interquartile range is 20%.   ◆◆

Below is a summary of the advantages and disadvantages of using the interquartile range as a measure of spread.

Advantage

- The interquartile range is not affected by extreme values of a data set.
- The interquartile range uses more data values than the range.

Disadvantages

- The interquartile range does not use all the data values.
- The interquartile range does not have convenient mathematical properties and, as a result, it is not useful for further calculations.

11.4 Variance and standard deviation

So far we have looked at the range and the interquartile range as measures of spread, and we have seen that both of these measures use only some of the values from a data set. Ideally, we would like a measure of spread that uses all of the data values. Two such measures are the *variance* and its square root, the *standard deviation*. Essentially, the standard deviation is a measure of the average distance between each observation and the mean – the bigger the average distance, the bigger the standard deviation and the bigger the spread.

To illustrate this, consider the following data set:

$$3 \quad 4 \quad 5 \quad 5 \quad 6 \quad 7$$

The mean of these observations is:

$$\overline{x} = \frac{3+4+5+5+6+7}{6} = 5$$

If we subtract the mean from each value, we obtain:

$$-2 \quad -1 \quad 0 \quad 0 \quad 1 \quad 2$$

These quantities are called *deviations*. The mean of these deviations is:

$$\frac{-2-1+0+0+1+2}{6} = 0$$

In fact, the mean of *any* set of deviations is 0. This is because some of the deviations are positive and some are negative and, when they are averaged, the positives and negatives cancel each other out. One way to avoid this problem is to square all of the deviations.

If we square each of the deviations listed above, we obtain:

$$4 \quad 1 \quad 0 \quad 0 \quad 1 \quad 4$$

The sum of these squared deviations is:

$$4 + 1 + 0 + 0 + 1 + 4 = 10$$

We then obtain the variance by dividing this total by n, the number of observations in the data set. So the variance of this data set is:

$$\frac{10}{6} = 1.667$$

Since the variance uses squared deviations, it is measured in squared units. For example, if the observations are claim amounts and are measured in £, then the variance is measured in $£^2$. This is not an intuitive unit of measurement, but we can avoid this problem by taking the square root of the variance. By doing so, we obtain the standard deviation, which is measured in the same units as the observations themselves. The variance is denoted by the symbol s^2 and the standard deviation is denoted by the symbol s.

How we calculate s^2 depends on how we are treating the data set. If the data set represents an entire population of values, then the formula we use is the one described above, where we have n in the denominator. This is the formula that we use in Module 0 of the CAA exams.

However in any other module, but especially Module 2 of the CAA exams (or if you are studying for the IFoA exams), then we use a different formula for s^2, which uses $n-1$ in the denominator of s^2, rather than n. This is because, in these cases, we are treating the data set not as an entire population of values, but as a random *sample* of a much larger (and possibly infinite) population of possible values. The mean and variance we calculate from these samples are then referred to as the *sample mean* and *sample variance* respectively. Their numerical values ($\bar{x}$ and s^2) are then used as estimates of (*ie* approximations for) the mean and the variance of the whole population. We have to use the $n-1$ denominator for the sample variance because, otherwise, it would not equal the true population variance, on average. The calculation of the mean, however, is the same whether we have the whole population or a sample.

Mathematical formulae for the variance and standard deviation are given below.

Formulae for variance and standard deviation

The variance of the data set containing the observations $x_1, x_2, ..., x_n$ is given by:

(1) $\qquad s^2 = \dfrac{1}{n}\displaystyle\sum_{i=1}^{n}(x_i - \bar{x})^2 \qquad$ if the data set is the total population of values

(2) $\qquad s^2 = \dfrac{1}{n-1}\displaystyle\sum_{i=1}^{n}(x_i - \bar{x})^2 \qquad$ if the data set is a random sample

The standard deviation of the data set containing the observations $x_1, x_2, ..., x_n$ is given by:

(1) $\qquad s = \sqrt{\dfrac{1}{n}\displaystyle\sum_{i=1}^{n}(x_i - \bar{x})^2} \qquad$ if the data set is the total population of values

(2) $\qquad s = \sqrt{\dfrac{1}{n-1}\displaystyle\sum_{i=1}^{n}(x_i - \bar{x})^2} \qquad$ if the data set is a random sample.

The statistics of random samples is not covered further in this textbook, and so we will be using formulae only of Type (1) in the rest of this course.

We can express these formulae in a different way by multiplying out the squared term inside the summation. Doing so, we see that:

$$s^2 = \frac{1}{n}\sum_{i=1}^{n}\left(x_i^2 - 2\overline{x}\,x_i + \overline{x}^2\right)$$

$$= \frac{1}{n}\left(\sum_{i=1}^{n}x_i^2 - 2\overline{x}\sum_{i=1}^{n}x_i + \sum_{i=1}^{n}\overline{x}^2\right)$$

$$= \frac{1}{n}\left(\sum_{i=1}^{n}x_i^2 - 2\overline{x}\sum_{i=1}^{n}x_i + n\overline{x}^2\right)$$

But:

$$\overline{x} = \frac{1}{n}\sum_{i=1}^{n}x_i \;\Rightarrow\; \sum_{i=1}^{n}x_i = n\overline{x}$$

So:

$$s^2 = \frac{1}{n}\left(\sum_{i=1}^{n}x_i^2 - 2\overline{x}.n\overline{x} + n\overline{x}^2\right) = \frac{1}{n}\left(\sum_{i=1}^{n}x_i^2 - n\overline{x}^2\right)$$

It is often quicker to calculate a variance using this alternative formula.

Alternative formulae for variance and standard deviation

The variance of the data set containing the observations $x_1, x_2, ..., x_n$ is given by:

$$s^2 = \frac{1}{n}\left(\sum_{i=1}^{n}x_i^2 - n\overline{x}^2\right)$$

The standard deviation of the data set containing the observations $x_1, x_2, ..., x_n$ is given by:

$$s = \sqrt{\frac{1}{n}\left(\sum_{i=1}^{n}x_i^2 - n\overline{x}^2\right)}$$

Example 11.7

Below are the salaries (in £000s) of eight individuals in a small company:

25	25	25	25	25	25	25	50

Calculate the standard deviation of the salaries of these eight people.

Solution

We have:

$$n = 8$$

$$\sum_{i=1}^{8} x_i^2 = 25^2 + 25^2 + 25^2 + 25^2 + 25^2 + 25^2 + 25^2 + 50^2 = 6,875$$

and:

$$\overline{x} = \frac{25 + 25 + 25 + 25 + 25 + 25 + 25 + 50}{8} = \frac{225}{8} = 28.125$$

So:

$$s = \sqrt{\frac{1}{8}\left(6,875 - 8 \times 28.125^2\right)} = \sqrt{68.359} = 8.268$$

ie £8,268.   ♦♦

◆ *Calculating the variance and standard deviation from a frequency distribution*

In **Error! Reference source not found.**, the value 25 is observed seven times and the value 50 is observed once. So the sum of the squared observations can be expressed as:

$$25^2 \times 7 + 50^2 \times 1$$

In general, if we have a data set that contains m different values, $x_1, x_2, \ldots, x_m$, with frequencies $f_1, f_2, \ldots, f_m$ respectively, then the sum of the squared observations is:

$$x_1^2 f_1 + x_2^2 f_2 + \cdots + x_m^2 f_m = \sum_{i=1}^{m} x_i^2 f_i$$

We saw in Chapter 10 that the mean of these observations is given by:

$$\overline{x} = \frac{x_1 f_1 + x_2 f_2 + \cdots + x_m f_m}{f_1 + f_2 + \cdots + f_m} = \frac{\sum\limits_{i=1}^{m} x_i f_i}{\sum\limits_{i=1}^{m} f_i}$$

These relationships give us the following formulae for calculating the variance from a frequency distribution.

Calculating the variance from a frequency distribution

If we have a data set that contains m different values, $x_1, x_2, \ldots, x_m$, with frequencies $f_1, f_2, \ldots, f_m$ respectively, then the variance of these observations is given by:

$$s^2 = \frac{1}{n}\sum_{i=1}^{m}(x_i - \bar{x})^2 f_i = \frac{1}{n}\left(\sum_{i=1}^{m}x_i^2 f_i - n\bar{x}^2\right)$$

where:

$$n = \sum_{i=1}^{m} f_i$$

and:

$$\bar{x} = \frac{\sum_{i=1}^{m}x_i f_i}{\sum_{i=1}^{m}f_i} = \frac{\sum_{i=1}^{m}x_i f_i}{n}$$

Example 11.8

The frequency table below shows the number of claims per policy made to a car insurance company in the last year:

Number of claims per policy	0	1	2	3
Frequency	74	19	5	2

Calculate the standard deviation of the number of claims per policy.

Solution

There are 4 distinct values, so:

$$m = 4$$

In addition:

$$n = \sum_{i=1}^{4} f_i = 74 + 19 + 5 + 2 = 100$$

$$\bar{x} = \frac{\sum_{i=1}^{4}x_i f_i}{\sum_{i=1}^{4}f_i} = \frac{(0\times 74) + (1\times 19) + (2\times 5) + (3\times 2)}{100} = 0.35$$

and:

$$\sum_{i=1}^{4}x_i^2 f_i = (0^2 \times 74) + (1^2 \times 19) + (2^2 \times 5) + (3^2 \times 2) = 57$$

So the variance is:

$$s^2 = \frac{1}{n}\left(\sum_{i=1}^{m} x_i^2 f_i - n\overline{x}^2\right) = \frac{1}{100}\left(57 - 100 \times 0.35^2\right) = 0.4475$$

Alternatively, we could use the formula:

$$s^2 = \frac{1}{n}\sum_{i=1}^{m}(x_i - \overline{x})^2 f_i$$

to obtain:

$$s^2 = \frac{1}{100}\left[(0-0.35)^2 \times 74 + (1-0.35)^2 \times 19 + (2-0.35)^2 \times 5 + (3-0.35)^2 \times 2\right]$$

$$= \frac{44.75}{100}$$

$$= 0.4475$$

Finally, taking the square root, we see that the standard deviation is:

$$s = \sqrt{0.4475} = 0.669$$ ◆◆

◆ *Estimating the variance and standard deviation from a grouped frequency distribution*

Suppose we want to calculate the standard deviation of the data summarised in the following grouped frequency distribution:

Claim amount, c	Frequency
£0 < c ≤ £500	6
£500 < c ≤ £1,000	11
£1,000 < c ≤ £1,500	49
£1,500 < c ≤ £2,000	26
£2,000 < c ≤ £5,000	8

There is a difficulty here because we do not know the exact value of each observation. The best we can do is to *estimate* the standard deviation. We can do this by assuming that each observation is equal to the midpoint of the group in which it lies.

The midpoint for the £0 < c ≤ £500 group is $\dfrac{0+500}{2} = £250$.

Similarly, the midpoints for the other groups are £750, £1,250, £1,750 and £3,500.

Using these midpoints in place of the observed values, we obtain:

$$\sum x_i^2 f_i = (250^2 \times 6) + (750^2 \times 11) + (1,250^2 \times 49) + (1,750^2 \times 26) + (3,500^2 \times 8)$$

$$= 260,750,000$$

and:

$$\sum x_i f_i = (250 \times 6) + (750 \times 11) + (1,250 \times 49) + (1,750 \times 26) + (3,500 \times 8) = 144,500$$

Since $n = \sum f_i = 100$, our estimate of the mean is:

$$\frac{144,500}{100} = £1,445$$

and our estimate of the standard deviation is:

$$\sqrt{\frac{1}{100}\left(260,750,000 - 100 \times 1,445^2\right)} = \sqrt{519,475} = £720.75$$

As always, when calculating the midpoint of groups constructed from rounded data, we need to make sure we correctly identify the largest and smallest possible values for each group.

Example 11.9

The grouped frequency distribution below summarises the ages last birthday at death for 30 male life assurance policyholders.

Age last birthday	40–49	50–59	60–69	70–79	80–89	90–99	100–109
Frequency	1	2	5	10	8	3	1

Estimate the standard deviation of the exact ages at death.

Solution

The 40–49 group ranges from exact age 40 to (just below) exact age 50, so the midpoint is 45 years.

Similarly, the midpoints (in years) for the other groups are:

$$55 \quad 65 \quad 75 \quad 85 \quad 95 \quad 105$$

Using these midpoints, we obtain:

$$\sum x_i^2 \, f_i = (45^2 \times 1) + (55^2 \times 2) + (65^2 \times 5) + (75^2 \times 10) + (85^2 \times 8) + (95^2 \times 3) + (105^2 \times 1)$$
$$= 181,350$$

and:

$$\sum x_i \, f_i = (45 \times 1) + (55 \times 2) + (65 \times 5) + (75 \times 10) + (85 \times 8) + (95 \times 3) + (105 \times 1) = 2,300$$

Since $n = 30$, our estimate of the mean is:

$$\frac{2,300}{30} \text{ years}$$

and our estimate of the standard deviation is:

$$\sqrt{\frac{1}{30}\left(181,350 - 30\left(\frac{2,300}{30}\right)^2\right)} = \sqrt{167.222} = 12.93 \text{ years} \qquad \blacklozenge\blacklozenge$$

Below is a summary of the advantages and disadvantages of using the variance and standard deviation as measures of spread.

Advantages

*   The variance and standard deviation use all the values in a data set.
*   The variance has mathematical properties that make it useful in further calculations.
*   The standard deviation has the same units as the data values.

Disadvantages

*   The variance and standard deviation are affected by extreme values (but to a lesser extent than the range).

11.5   *Moments of a data set*

The mean of the observations $x_1, x_2, \ldots, x_n$, *ie*:

$$\frac{1}{n}\sum_{i=1}^{n} x_i$$

is a member of a group of summary statistics called *moments*.

Non-central moments of a data set

The k th non-central moment of the observations $x_1, x_2, \ldots, x_n$ is defined to be:

$$\frac{1}{n}\sum_{i=1}^{n} x_i^k$$

The k th non-central moment is also sometimes called the k th moment about 0 or sometimes just the k th moment of a data set.

So the mean is the first non-central moment of a data set.

 ### *Example 11.10*

Calculate the second non-central moment of the following data set:

      6   13   15   20   22

Solution

The second non-central moment is:

$$\frac{1}{5}\left(6^2 + 13^2 + 15^2 + 20^2 + 22^2\right) = \frac{1,314}{5} = 262.8 \qquad\qquad \blacklozenge\blacklozenge$$

Central moments of a data set

The k th central moment of the observations $x_1, x_2, \ldots, x_n$ is defined to be:

$$\frac{1}{n}\sum_{i=1}^{n}(x_i - \overline{x})^k$$

The k th central moment is also sometimes called the k th moment about the mean.

So the variance is the second central moment of a data set.

Example 11.11

Calculate the second central moment of the following data set:

     6   13   15   20   22

Solution

The mean is:

$$\overline{x} = \frac{6 + 13 + 15 + 20 + 22}{5} = \frac{76}{5} = 15.2$$

So the second central moment is:

$$\frac{1}{5}\left[(6 - 15.2)^2 + (13 - 15.2)^2 + (15 - 15.2)^2 + (20 - 15.2)^2 + (22 - 15.2)^2\right]$$
$$= \frac{158.8}{5} = 31.76 \qquad\qquad \blacklozenge\blacklozenge$$

More generally, we can define moments about any point c.

Moments of a data set about the point c

The k th moment of the observations $x_1, x_2, \ldots, x_n$ about the point c is defined to be:

$$\frac{1}{n}\sum_{i=1}^{n}(x_i - c)^k$$

Example 11.12

Calculate the third moment of the following data set about the point 10:

     6   13   15   20   22

Solution

The third moment about the point 10 is:

$$\frac{1}{5}\left[(6 - 10)^3 + (13 - 10)^3 + (15 - 10)^3 + (20 - 10)^3 + (22 - 10)^3\right] = \frac{2,816}{5} = 563.2 \qquad \blacklozenge\blacklozenge$$

11.6   Shape of a data set

In Chapter 9, we introduced skewness as a measure of the asymmetry of a data set. Here is a reminder of the general shapes that occur:

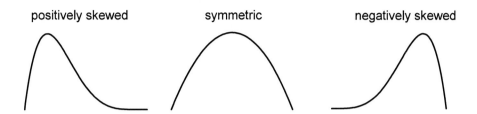

positively skewed   symmetric   negatively skewed

We now introduce a numerical measure of the skewness of a data set. This measure is the third central moment:

$$\frac{1}{n}\sum_{i=1}^{n}(x_i - \bar{x})^3$$

This has a positive value for a positively skewed data set, a negative value for a negatively skewed data set, and is equal to zero for a symmetrical data set. We will illustrate this using some numerical examples.

Firstly, consider the data set:

| 1 | 2 | 2 | 3 | 3 | 3 | 3 | 4 | 4 | 5 |

A dotplot of these data values is shown below:

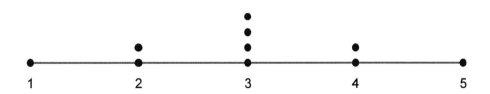

We can see from the dotplot that the data set is symmetric about the value 3 and we can check that the third central moment is zero:

$$\frac{1}{10}\left[(1-3)^3 + (2-3)^3 \times 2 + (3-3)^3 \times 3 + (4-3)^3 \times 2 + (5-3)^3\right]$$
$$= \frac{1}{10}\left[-8 - 2 + 0 + 2 + 8\right] = 0$$

Secondly, let's consider the data set:

    1   2   2   2   2   3   3   3   4   5

A dotplot of these data values is shown below:

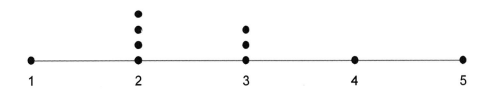

We can see from the dotplot that this data set is positively skewed. The mean is:

$$\frac{1+2\times4+3\times3+4+5}{10}=\frac{27}{10}=2.7$$

and the third central moment is:

$$\frac{1}{10}\left[(1-2.7)^3+(2-2.7)^3\times4+(3-2.7)^3\times3+(4-2.7)^3+(5-2.7)^3\right]$$
$$=\frac{1}{10}\left[-4.913-1.372+0.081+2.197+12.167\right]=0.816$$

As expected, this value is positive.

11.7 *Transforming data sets*

In this section, we consider how the range, interquartile range, standard deviation, variance and skewness (as measured by the third central moment) are affected when:

- a constant amount is added to each value in the data set
- each value in the data set is multiplied by a constant amount.

Suppose we have the following data set:

    2   4   9

This data set is illustrated in the diagram below:

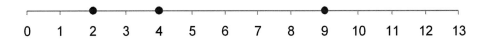

The range of this data set is $9-2=7$.

Now consider what happens when we *add* a constant amount, say 3, to each value in the data set. The transformed observations are:

    5   7   12

The transformed data set is illustrated in the diagram below:

The range of the transformed data set is $12 - 5 = 7$. This is the same as the range of the original data set because adding a constant to each value *changes the location of the data set but does not change its spread.* For the same reason, the interquartile range, standard deviation and variance do not change when the same constant is added to each observation in the data set.

The skewness is calculated using the deviations from the mean, $x_i - \bar{x}$, which are unaffected by adding a constant. So the skewness does not change either.

Now consider what happens if we *multiply* each observation by a constant amount, *eg* 4. Doing this, the observations become:

$$8 \qquad 16 \qquad 36$$

The new range is $36 - 8 = 28$, which is 4 times the original range. Similarly, the interquartile range of the transformed data is 4 times that of the original data set.

Next, consider how the variance and standard deviation are affected by this multiplicative transformation. We will firstly need the mean of the original data set. This is:

$$\frac{2 + 4 + 9}{3} = 5$$

and its variance is:

$$\frac{1}{3}\left[(2-5)^2 + (4-5)^2 + (9-5)^2\right] = \frac{1}{3}\left[3^2 + 1^2 + 4^2\right] = 8.667$$

The mean of the transformed data set is:

$$\frac{8 + 16 + 36}{3} = 20$$

which is 4 times the original mean.

However, the variance is:

$$\frac{1}{3}\left[(8-20)^2 + (16-20)^2 + (36-20)^2\right] = \frac{1}{3}\left[144 + 16 + 256\right] = 138.667$$

which is 4^2 times the original variance.

This is because each of the deviations from the mean (3, 1 and 4) in the variance formula is multiplied by 4 and *then* squared, which gives:

$$\frac{1}{3}\left[(3\times4)^2 + (1\times4)^2 + (4\times4)^2\right] = 8.667 \times 4^2$$

The standard deviation, on the other hand, is only multiplied by a factor of 4. We can see this by comparing the standard deviation of the original data set:

$$\sqrt{8.667} = 2.944$$

With that of the transformed data set:

$$\sqrt{138.667} = 11.776 = 4 \times 2.944$$

These results reflect the *units* in which the various measures are measured. Since the variance is a squared measure, it has been increased by a factor of 4^2. The standard deviation is measured in normal units (not squared units), so it only increases by a factor of 4.

Similarly, since the third central moment is a cubed measure, multiplying each data point by 4 means that the third central moment is multiplied by 4^3.

Below is a summary of how measures of spread and skewness are affected by linear transformations.

Measures of spread and skewness for a transformed data set

If each value in a data set is transformed by *adding* a constant, a (which might be negative), then the range, interquartile range, standard deviation, variance and third central moment are unaffected.

If each value in a data set is *multiplied* by a constant, b, then:

- the range, interquartile range and standard deviation are also multiplied by a factor of b

- the variance is multiplied by a factor of b^2

- the third central moment (skewness) is multiplied by a factor of b^3.

Chapter 11 Practice Questions

Interquartile range

Question 11.1   (IFoA Past Examination Question)

The following amounts are the sizes of claims (in £) on house insurance policies for a certain type of repair.

198	221	215	209	224
210	223	215	203	210
220	200	208	212	216

Determine the lower quartile, median, upper quartile and interquartile range of these claim amounts.

Question 11.2   (IFoA Past Examination Question)

Data values were collected on 100 consecutive days for the number of claims, x, arising from a group of policies. This resulted in the following frequency distribution:

x	0	1	2	3	4	≥ 5
f	14	25	26	18	12	5

Calculate the interquartile range for this data set.

Question 11.3   (IFoA Past Examination Question)

The table below shows a grouped frequency distribution for 100 claim amounts on a certain class of insurance policy.

Claim amount	Frequency
under £100	4
£100 – 149.99	10
£150 – 199.99	25
£200 – 249.99	30
£250 – 299.99	15
£300 – 349.99	12
£350 – 399.99	4
£400 or over	0

Determine an approximate value for the interquartile range of these claim amounts.

Question 11.4   (IFoA Past Examination Question)

A set of claim amounts (£) is given below:

192	136	253	138	87
112	221	176	336	203
159	55	308	165	254

Present these data values graphically using a boxplot.

◆ *Variance and standard deviation*

Question 11.5

Calculate the variance of the following data set:

    3   8   0   2   4

Question 11.6

A life insurance company has recorded 10 male deaths and 8 female deaths over the last week. The ages at death of the males have a mean of 72 years and a standard deviation of 7 years. The ages at death of the females have a mean of 78 years and a standard deviation of 9 years.

The data values for males and females are combined into a single group.   Calculate the standard deviation of the ages at death for this group.

Hint: You first need to calculate $\sum x_i$ and $\sum x_i^2$ for each sex.

Question 11.7   (IFoA Past Examination Question, adapted)

Sickness and absence records were kept on 30 employees in a company over a 91-day period. The data values are tabulated below:

Number of employees absent	0	1	2	3	4	5
Number of days	44	19	10	8	7	3

Calculate the standard deviation of the number of employees absent per day.

Question 11.8

The table below shows the journey times (in minutes) of employees to reach their place of work:

Time (mins), t	Number of employees
$0 < t \le 10$	4
$10 < t \le 20$	13
$20 < t \le 40$	21
$40 < t \le 60$	9
$60 < t \le 120$	3

Estimate the standard deviation of these times.

Question 11.9   (IFoA Past Examination Question, adapted)

Shortly before close of business on a particular day an insurance office has sold 8 new policies. The mean and standard deviation of the sums assured have been calculated, in units of £000s, as 31.5 and 34.83174, respectively.   Another policy for £60,000 is then sold just before the close.

Calculate the mean and standard deviation of the full set of 9 sums assured.

Question 11.10   (IFoA Past Examination Question, adapted)

Consider a group of 47 white-collar workers and a group of 24 blue-collar workers from the workforce of a large company. The mean salary for the group of white-collar workers is £28,470 and the standard deviation is £4,270; whereas the mean salary for the group of blue-collar workers is £21,420 and the standard deviation is £3,020.

Calculate the mean and the standard deviation of the salaries in the combined group of 71 employees.

Skewness

Question 11.11

Calculate the third central moment of the following data set and comment on its skewness:

$$0 \quad 2 \quad 3 \quad 3 \quad 4 \quad 4 \quad 4 \quad 5$$

Transforming data sets

Question 11.12   (IFoA Past Examination Question, adapted)

The marks (in %) of a group of 20 students from a large class in a recent examination have a mean of 43 and a standard deviation of 6. Each mark is then adjusted by multiplying it by 1.3 and adding 10.

Calculate the standard deviation of the adjusted marks.

12

Probability

Learning Objectives

The following learning objectives are covered in this chapter:

- Define basic properties satisfied by the probability of occurrence of an event, and calculate probabilities of events in simple situations.

- Define the addition rule for the probability of the union of two events, and use the rule to calculate probabilities, including the use of Venn diagrams.

- Define independence for two events, and calculate probabilities in situations involving independence.

- Define the conditional probability of one event given the occurrence of another event, and calculate probabilities in situations involving dependence.

- Define the unconditional probability of a dependent event, and calculate such probabilities.

12.1 Basic probability

Probability theory is used to explain and predict the outcomes of future uncertain events. Examples in actuarial science include the uncertainties involved in finance and insurance.

 ## Terminology

The *sample space* is defined as the complete set of possible outcomes that can occur. For example, for one roll of a die (where 'die' is the singular of 'dice'), the possible outcomes are 1, 2, 3, 4, 5 and 6, and this is therefore the relevant sample space.

 ### Example 12.1

A 10p and a 50p coin are both tossed, and their outcomes (head or tail) recorded. List all the possible outcomes (*ie* give the sample space).

Solution

The outcomes that could occur (*ie* the sample space) are:

10p coin	50p coin
Head	Head
Head	Tail
Tail	Head
Tail	Tail

♦♦

An *event* is the group of possible outcomes that we are interested in. For example, when rolling a die we might be interested in any of the following events:

'rolling a 2', 'rolling an odd number', 'rolling a number greater than 3'.

The *probability* of an event is a measure of how likely it is that the event happens (*ie* the chance of the event occurring). All probabilities must lie between 0 and 1 inclusive, where impossible events have a probability of 0 and certain events have a probability of 1.

We use the notation $P(A)$ to stand for the probability of event A occurring.

Basic properties satisfied by the probability of occurrence of an event

(1) $0 \le P(A) \le 1$

(2) $P(A) = 0$ if A is an impossible event

(3) $P(A) = 1$ if A is a certain event

◆ *Calculating probabilities*

Suppose we wish to calculate the probability of rolling a 3 on a die.

To do this we make the assumption that each of the outcomes is equally likely. As rolling a 3 is one of the six possible (equally likely) outcomes, then the probability is $\frac{1}{6}$.

Example 12.2

A die is rolled. Calculate the probability that the outcome is a number greater than 4.

Solution

Of the six outcomes (1, 2, 3, 4, 5 and 6) two of them (5 and 6) are greater than 4. So:

$$P(\text{roll more than } 4) = \frac{2}{6} = \frac{1}{3}$$ ◆◆

Probability of an event occurring

The probability that event A occurs is given by:

$$P(A) = \frac{\text{number of equally likely outcomes in which event } A \text{ can happen}}{\text{total number of equally likely outcomes}}$$

We will now look at an example where several of the equally likely outcomes are considered to be the same.

Suppose that in a tutorial class there are 8 male and 4 female students. What is the probability that a student picked at *random* is male?

Let M be the event 'a male student is picked'. Since there are 8 individual male students, there are 8 equally likely outcomes in which event M would occur. There are 12 individual students altogether so there are 12 equally likely outcomes in total. So:

$$P(M) = \frac{8}{12} = \frac{2}{3}$$

Example 12.3

A pile of 15 examination scripts contains 2 Mathematics (Pure), 3 Mathematics (Applied), 4 English and 6 Chemistry papers. A marker selects a script from the pile at *random*.

Calculate the probability that the selected script is for a Mathematics subject.

Solution

There are 5 (individual) Mathematics scripts out of 15 scripts altogether. Hence:

$$P(\text{choose Mathematics script}) = \frac{5}{15} = \frac{1}{3}$$ ◆◆

◆ *Complementary events*

If we have an event A then the complementary event is defined as the event that A does *not* happen. For example, when rolling a die:

$$P(4) = \frac{1}{6} \qquad \text{and} \qquad P(\text{not } 4) = \frac{5}{6}$$

These probabilities must sum to 1, so that the probability of the complementary event can be found from:

$$P(\text{not } 4) = 1 - P(4)$$

Example 12.4

The probability that any motor insurance claim payment exceeds £1,000 is 0.6. Calculate the probability that the claim payment does not exceed £1,000.

Solution

$P(\text{does not exceed } £1{,}000) = 1 - P(\text{exceeds } £1{,}000) = 1 - 0.6 = 0.4$ ♦♦

The notation A' (or $\overline{A}$) is used to denote the complementary event of event A.

Probability of a complementary event

$$P(A') = P(\overline{A}) = 1 - P(A)$$

where A' (or $\overline{A}$) is the complementary event of event A.

12.2 Addition rule for mutually exclusive events

We are now going to calculate the probability of two or more events happening.

First we will consider the case for *mutually exclusive* events. Two events are said to be mutually exclusive if *only* one event *or* the other can occur – *ie* it is impossible for *both* events to occur together.

For example, on a single roll of a die the outcome can be a 3 *or* a 4, but we cannot observe *both* numbers on a single roll. So the events 'roll a 3' and 'roll a 4' are mutually exclusive.

Similarly, the event that a claim occurs on an insurance policy and the event that a claim does not occur on the policy are mutually exclusive.

Example 12.5

State which of the following pairs of events are mutually exclusive:

(i)   win a football match or lose a football match

(ii)   wear a red tie or wear black shoes

(iii)   a card picked from a pack of playing cards is a diamond or an ace

(iv)   to obtain an even number or an odd number on one roll of a die

(v)   to obtain an even number or a prime number on one roll of a die.

Solution

(i)   mutually exclusive (it is impossible both to win *and* lose a football match)

(ii)   not mutually exclusive (it is possible to wear both a red tie *and* black shoes)

(iii)   not mutually exclusive (since we could choose the ace of diamonds)

(iv)   mutually exclusive (a number cannot be both odd *and* even)

(v)   not mutually exclusive (since 2 is both an even number *and* a prime number).   ◆◆

This idea can be extended to more than two events. For example, all the six possible outcomes (1, 2, 3, ..., 6) that can occur on one roll of a die constitute six mutually exclusive events.

Now we will consider the *probability* that one or more mutually exclusive events occur. For example, consider the probability of rolling a 3 or a 4 on one roll of a die. This can be directly calculated to be $\frac{2}{6}$ (by thinking about the numbers of equally likely outcomes that could occur, in the usual way). However, we can also think of this, in terms of the separate events, as follows:

Event	Outcome	Probability
'roll a 3'	3	$\frac{1}{6}$
'roll a 4'	4	$\frac{1}{6}$
'roll a 3 *or* a 4'	3, 4	$\frac{2}{6}$

So we can see that:

$$P(3 \text{ or } 4) = P(3) + P(4) = \frac{1}{6} + \frac{1}{6} = \frac{2}{6}$$

Example 12.6

Consider again the situation described in Example 12.3, where a pile of 15 exam scripts contains 2 Mathematics (Pure), 3 Mathematics (Applied), 4 English and 6 Chemistry papers, and a script is selected from the pile at *random*.

Calculate the probability that the selected script is for any mathematics or science subject.

Solution

The probabilities are:

Event	Outcomes	Probability
'selects a mathematics script'	2×Pure, 3×Applied	$\frac{5}{15}$
'selects a science script'	6×Chemistry	$\frac{6}{15}$
'selects a mathematics or a science script'	2×Pure, 3×Applied, 6×Chemistry	$\frac{11}{15}$

We can see that:

$$P(\text{Mathematics or Science}) = P(\text{Mathematics}) + P(\text{Science}) = \frac{5}{15} + \frac{6}{15} = \frac{11}{15}$$ ◆◆

Addition rule for mutually exclusive events

For any two *mutually exclusive* events A and B:

$$P(A \text{ or } B) = P(A) + P(B)$$

The mathematical notation used to denote the event 'A or B occurs (or both)' is $A \cup B$. Using this notation, for mutually exclusive events A and B, we have:

$$P(A \cup B) = P(A) + P(B)$$

The addition rule can be easily extended to more than two mutually exclusive events. For example, if events A, B and C are mutually exclusive then:

$$P(A \text{ or } B \text{ or } C) = P(A \cup B \cup C) = P(A) + P(B) + P(C)$$

Example 12.7

In a traffic survey the probabilities of observing various types of cars are given below:

Feature	Probability
blue	0.25
white	0.3
silver	0.15
Ford	0.3
Renault	0.2

(i)   Calculate the probability that the next car:

   (a)   is a Ford or a Renault

   (b)   is blue, white or silver.

(ii)   Explain why the probability that the next car is a Ford or blue is *not* equal to $0.3 + 0.25$.

Solution

(i)   (a) $P(\text{Ford or Renault}) = 0.3 + 0.2 = 0.5$

        (b) $P(\text{blue, white or silver}) = 0.25 + 0.3 + 0.15 = 0.7$.

(ii)   This is not the correct probability because the events 'Ford' and 'blue' are not mutually exclusive, and so Ford cars that are also blue are included in both probabilities. Hence this basic addition rule cannot be used for non-mutually exclusive events.   ◆◆

12.3 *Addition rule for non-mutually exclusive events*

In part (ii) of Example 12.7 the simple addition rule broke down. This was because the events were *not* mutually exclusive, ie they could *both* happen at the same time.

We are now going to extend our addition rule to cover non-mutually exclusive events, which are events that *can* occur at the same time. So, in general, when we consider the probability of events *A or B* occurring, we mean the probability that events *A, B,* or *both A and B,* occur.

Suppose we want to calculate the probability of rolling an odd number or a number greater than 4 on one roll of a die. We can first calculate the probability by considering the *outcomes*:

Event	Outcomes	Probability
'roll an odd number'	1, 3, 5	$\frac{3}{6}$
'roll a number greater than 4'	5, 6	$\frac{2}{6}$
'roll an odd number *or* a number greater than 4'	1, 3, 5, 6	$\frac{4}{6}$

We can see that the simple addition rule does not work:

$$P(\text{odd } or \text{ greater than } 4) \neq P(\text{odd}) + P(\text{greater than } 4)$$

ie:

$$\frac{3}{6} + \frac{2}{6} \neq \frac{4}{6}$$

The reason for the error is that the outcome 'roll a 5' is counted in both events, *ie* it is included twice whereas it should only be included once. So we need to adjust the calculation by deducting the probability of rolling a 5:

$$P(\text{odd } or \text{ greater than } 4) = P(\text{odd}) + P(\text{greater than } 4) - P(5) = \frac{3}{6} + \frac{2}{6} - \frac{1}{6} = \frac{4}{6}$$

In general, outcomes will be double counted only when they occur in both events. So we can more generally write:

$$P(\text{odd } or \text{ greater than } 4) = P(\text{odd}) + P(\text{greater than } 4) - P(\text{odd } and \text{ greater than } 4)$$

This leads us to a general rule:

Addition rule

For *any* two events A and B:

$$P(A \text{ } or \text{ } B) = P(A) + P(B) - P(A \text{ } and \text{ } B)$$

The notation $A \cap B$ is used to denote the event that both A and B occur. Recalling that $A \cup B$ indicates the event that A or B (or both) occur, we have:

$$P(A \cup B) = P(A) + P(B) - P(A \cap B)$$

The addition rule for *mutually exclusive* events is a special version of this more general rule. This is because if events A and B are mutually exclusive then:

$$P(A \text{ } and \text{ } B) = P(A \cap B) = 0$$

◆ *Use of Venn diagrams*

Calculating probabilities such as these can be made easier with the aid of *Venn diagrams*. The following Venn diagram depicts the non-mutually exclusive events defined above:

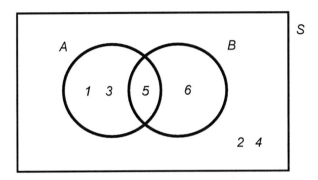

The rectangle shape represents all the possible outcomes of the experiment, that is the sample space, which in the case of rolling a die would be the outcomes 1, 2, 3, 4, 5, 6. This is denoted by *S*.

The two circles within the rectangle represent the specified events, labelled as events *A* and *B*. So in our example, Event *A* is the event that an odd number is obtained, while Event *B* is the event that a number greater than 4 is obtained, on one roll of a die.

The overlap of the two circles indicates that the two events are not mutually exclusive, and the area of overlap contains the events that are common to both Events *A* and *B*, *ie* the outcome 5, which is both an odd number *and* a number greater than 4.

Replacing the events in each segment with their corresponding probability, we obtain the following:

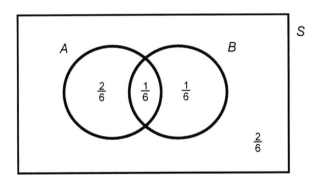

Now we can calculate the required probability using these values:

$$P(A \text{ or } B) = \frac{2}{6} + \frac{1}{6} + \frac{1}{6} = \frac{4}{6} = \frac{2}{3}$$

Example 12.8

In a group of students it is known that 45% watch *Alias*, 50% watch *West Wing* and 30% watch *Alias* and *West Wing* on television.

Calculate the probability that a student watches *Alias* or *West Wing*.

Solution

Watching *Alias* and *West Wing* are not mutually exclusive events (since 30% of students watch both), therefore using the general addition rule:

$$P(Alias\ or\ West\ Wing) = P(Alias) + P(West\ Wing) - P(Alias\ and\ West\ Wing)$$
$$= 0.45 + 0.50 - 0.30$$
$$= 0.65 \qquad\qquad\qquad ♦♦$$

12.4 Multiplication rule for independent events

We are now going to calculate the probability of two events *both* happening, *ie* a probability of the form $P(A\ and\ B)$, where the two events are *independent*.

Two events are said to be *independent* if they do not affect each other's probability of occurring. So if events A and B are independent, then event A has no influence whatsoever on event B and vice versa.

For example, rolling a die and then tossing a coin will not affect each other in any way, and so the outcomes of the two events are independent of each other.

On the other hand, a person obtaining a high grade in a Mathematics exam and the same person obtaining a high grade in a Physics exam are not independent events, because that person is likely to have a similar ability in both subjects.

Example 12.9

State, with brief reasons, which of the following pairs of events are independent:

(i)   arriving in time to catch the early bus and getting to work on time

(ii)   one policyholder dying and a second policyholder dying

(iii)   rolling a 6 on one die and rolling a 6 on a second die

(iv)   Team A winning a football match and Team B winning the same football match.

Solution

(i)   *not* independent (catching the early bus increases the probability of getting to work on time)

(ii)   we can normally assume that these events would be independent, although there is a possibility that the two people will be killed in the same accident or in a natural disaster affecting many people, for example

(iii)   independent (the dice do not affect each other)

(iv)   *not* independent (because if A wins this would prevent B from winning, and vice versa).

$$♦♦$$

The idea of independence extends to any number of events. For example, the outcomes obtained from rolling three separate dice are all independent events.

Now we consider the *probabilities* of two (or more) *independent* events occurring together. For example, a coin is tossed and a die is rolled: calculate the probability of the coin landing heads *and* obtaining an even number on the die.

We can first calculate this by considering outcomes. There are twelve (2×6) total possible pairs of outcomes from one toss of a coin and one roll of a die, of which three satisfy the specified event (H2, H4, and H6). So the required probability would be $\frac{3}{12} = \frac{1}{4}$.

However, we can see that:

$$\frac{3}{12} = \frac{1}{2} \times \frac{3}{6}$$

where $\frac{1}{2}$ is the probability of landing a head on the coin, and $\frac{3}{6}$ is the probability of rolling an even number on the die. In other words, when events are independent, the probability of *both* events occurring is the product of their individual (independent) probabilities.

 ### Example 12.10

A coin is tossed and a die is rolled. Calculate the probability of the coin landing tails *and* obtaining a number greater than 4 on the die.

Solution

The independent probabilities are:

$$P(\text{tails}) = \frac{1}{2}$$
$$P(\text{greater than 4}) = \frac{2}{6} = \frac{1}{3}$$

As the two events are independent, then:

$$P(\text{tails and greater than 4}) = P(\text{tails}) \times P(\text{greater than 4}) = \frac{1}{2} \times \frac{1}{3} = \frac{1}{6}$$

Alternatively we could have calculated this by considering outcomes: there are twelve (2×6) total possible pairs of outcomes from one toss of a coin and one roll of a die, of which two satisfy the specified event ('land a tail and roll a 5', and 'land a tail and roll a 6'). So the required probability would be $\frac{2}{12} = \frac{1}{6}$.   ♦♦

Multiplication rule for independent events

For any two *independent* events A and B:

$$P(A \text{ and } B) = P(A) \times P(B)$$

Recalling that the notation $A \cap B$ is used to denote the event that both A and B occur, we can also write this rule (for independent events) as:

$$P(A \cap B) = P(A) \times P(B)$$

 ### Example 12.11

A gaming machine has two wheels. Each wheel spins and then stops to reveal a picture. The probability that the picture on the first wheel is a cherry is $\frac{3}{10}$, whereas for the second wheel the probability is $\frac{2}{5}$. The two wheels operate independently.

Calculate the probability of obtaining:

(i)   a cherry on the first wheel and on the second wheel

(ii)   a cherry on the second wheel but not on the first wheel

(iii)   no cherries on either of the two wheels.

Solution

Since the wheels are independent we obtain:

(i) $P(\text{cherry on 1st } and \text{ cherry on 2nd}) = \frac{3}{10} \times \frac{2}{5} = \frac{6}{50} = \frac{3}{25}$

(ii) $P(\text{no cherry on 1st } and \text{ cherry on 2nd}) = \frac{7}{10} \times \frac{2}{5} = \frac{14}{50} = \frac{7}{25}$

(iii) $P(\text{no cherry on 1st } and \text{ no cherry on 2nd}) = \frac{7}{10} \times \frac{3}{5} = \frac{21}{50}$.   ◆◆

The multiplication rule easily extends to more than two independent events. For example, if events A, B and C are independent then:

$$P(A \text{ and } B \text{ and } C) = P(A) \times P(B) \times P(C)$$

In Example 12.12 below, we use the multiplication rule to calculate the number of repetitions required to produce a specified probability for an event.

Example 12.12

The probability that an arrow misses a target is 3%. Calculate the smallest number of arrows that would need to be shot at a target to ensure that the probability of missing the target altogether is less than 1 in a million. You can assume that all arrow shootings are independent.

Solution

If we shoot n arrows, the probability of them all missing the target is:

$$P(\text{all } n \text{ arrows miss}) = P(\text{1st arrow misses}) \times P(\text{2nd arrow misses}) \times \ldots$$
$$\times P(n\text{th arrow misses})$$
$$= (0.03)^n$$

So we need the smallest value of n such that:

$$P(\text{all } n \text{ arrows miss}) < \frac{1}{1,000,000} = 0.000001$$

or:

$$0.03^n < 0.000001$$

Now since $0.03^3 = 0.000027$ and $0.03^4 = 0.00000081$, the smallest number of arrows that need to be shot is 4.

Alternatively we could take logs to obtain:

$$n \ln 0.03 < \ln 0.000001 \quad \Rightarrow \quad -3.506n < -13.816 \quad \Rightarrow \quad n > \frac{13.816}{3.506} = 3.940$$

which again means that n cannot be smaller than 4.   ◆◆

12.5 *Multiplication rule for dependent events*

A *dependent* event is one that is affected by the outcome of another event or events.

For example, when going outside the probability of taking an umbrella is likely to be affected by whether it is currently raining. So we might have the following:

> P(takes umbrella if raining) $= 0.8$
>
> P(takes umbrella if not raining) $= 0.1$

The probability of taking an umbrella is therefore *dependent* on (*ie conditional* on) whether or not it is currently raining. We use the notation $P(B \mid A)$ to denote the probability of B happening *conditional* on A happening. This is known as a *conditional probability,* which can be more briefly defined as 'the probability of B *given* A'. So, in the case of our umbrella example, we would write:

> P(takes umbrella | raining) $= 0.8$
>
> P(takes umbrella | not raining) $= 0.1$

Example 12.13

A regular theatre-goer likes to sit in a particular seat in the auditorium. If she books her theatre ticket early, the probability that she gets her favourite seat is 0.8. If she books her theatre ticket late, the probability that she gets her favourite seat is 0.3. Write down the following probabilities:

(i) P(gets favourite seat | early booking)

(ii) P(does not get favourite seat | late booking) .

Solution

(i) P(gets favourite seat | early booking) $= 0.8$

(ii) P(does not get favourite seat | late booking)

> $= 1 - P$(gets favourite seat | late booking)
>
> $= 1 - 0.3 = 0.7$ ♦♦

In this question the conditional probabilities were given, but often they will need to be calculated. For example, suppose there are 2 lemon and 3 strawberry sweets in a bag. A boy chooses a sweet and eats it, and then chooses another sweet at random and eats that as well.

Now consider the conditional probability that the second sweet is lemon. If the first sweet is lemon, then there are 1 lemon and 3 strawberry sweets left in the bag.

So:

> P(2nd sweet is lemon | 1st sweet is lemon) $= \frac{1}{4}$

Similarly, if the first sweet is strawberry, then there are 2 lemon and 2 strawberry sweets left in the bag, and so:

> P(2nd sweet is lemon | 1st sweet is strawberry) $= \frac{2}{4} = \frac{1}{2}$

Example 12.14

There are 3 jam doughnuts and 4 apple doughnuts for sale in a baker's shop, but the baker cannot remember which is which. They all look the same from the outside. A customer buys a doughnut, and leaves the shop before eating it. Later, another customer arrives and wants to buy a second doughnut. Find:

(i) P(2nd doughnut is apple | 1st doughnut was jam)

(ii) P(2nd doughnut is apple | 1st doughnut was apple).

Solution

(i)   If the first doughnut was jam then there are 2 jam and 4 apple doughnuts left in the shop. Hence:

$$P\text{(2nd doughnut is apple | 1st doughnut was jam)} = \frac{4}{6} = \frac{2}{3}$$

(ii)   If the first doughnut was apple then there are 3 jam and 3 apple doughnuts left in the shop. Hence:

$$P\text{(2nd doughnut is apple | 1st doughnut was apple)} = \frac{3}{6} = \frac{1}{2}$$ ♦♦

Now we will consider how we can calculate probabilities of the form $P(A \text{ and } B)$ when the two events are not independent.

Returning to the umbrella example, we are now given the additional information that the probability of it raining on any day is 0.2. As before, the probability that a man takes his umbrella when it is raining is 0.8, and the probability that he takes his umbrella when it is not raining is 0.1. Suppose we wish to find the probability that it rains *and* the man takes his umbrella, that is P(raining *and* takes umbrella).

As with independent events, the probability of *both* events happening is the probability of the first event occurring multiplied by the probability of the second event occurring. However, because the second event (taking the umbrella) is conditional on the first event (whether it is raining or not), then we have to use the *relevant conditional probability* for this purpose.

So:

$$P\text{(raining and takes umbrella)} = P\text{(raining)} \times P\text{(takes umbrella | raining)}$$
$$= 0.2 \times 0.8$$
$$= 0.16$$

Example 12.15

William's sock drawer contains 4 blue socks and 4 black socks.

(i)   William takes two socks from the drawer at random. Calculate the probability that:

   (a)   he chooses a blue sock followed by a black sock

   (b)   he chooses a pair of black socks.

(ii)   To be sure that he gets a matching pair of socks, William decides to take three socks (chosen at random) from the drawer. Calculate the probability that:

   (a)   he chooses 3 blue socks

   (b)   he chooses a blue sock followed by 2 black socks.

Solution

(i)   (a)   If William chooses a blue sock then there are 3 blue and 4 black socks remaining. So we have:

$$P(\text{1st sock blue } and \text{ 2nd sock black})$$
$$= P(\text{1st sock blue}) \times P(\text{2nd sock black} \mid \text{1st sock blue})$$
$$= \frac{4}{8} \times \frac{4}{7}$$
$$= \frac{16}{56} = \frac{2}{7}$$

(b)   If William chooses a black sock then there are 4 blue and 3 black socks remaining. So:

$$P(\text{1st sock black } and \text{ 2nd sock black})$$
$$= P(\text{1st sock black}) \times P(\text{2nd sock black} \mid \text{1st sock black})$$
$$= \frac{4}{8} \times \frac{3}{7}$$
$$= \frac{12}{56} = \frac{3}{14}$$

(ii)   Extending this in a similar way to three socks, we have:

(a) $P(\text{1st sock blue } and \text{ 2nd sock blue } and \text{ 3rd sock blue})$
$$= \frac{4}{8} \times \frac{3}{7} \times \frac{2}{6} = \frac{1}{14}$$

(b) $P(\text{1st sock blue } and \text{ 2nd sock black } and \text{ 3rd sock black})$
$$= \frac{4}{8} \times \frac{4}{7} \times \frac{3}{6} = \frac{1}{7} \qquad \blacklozenge\blacklozenge$$

Multiplication rule

For *any* two events A and B:

$$P(A \text{ and } B) = P(A) \times P(B \mid A)$$

Recalling that $A \cap B$ denotes the event A *and* B, we can also write this as:

$$P(A \cap B) = P(A) \times P(B \mid A)$$

The multiplication rule for independent events is a special case of this more general rule.

If events A and B are independent then the probability of B happening will be the same whether or not A happens, that is:

$$P(B \mid A) = P(B)$$

Hence, if A and B are independent, we obtain the multiplication rule for independent events that we had earlier:

$$P(A \cap B) = P(A) \times P(B \mid A) = P(A) \times P(B)$$

12.6 *Unconditional probability of a dependent event*

We are now going to consider the overall probability of a dependent event occurring.

Suppose a country is divided into four geographical regions: North, South, East and West. The conditional probabilities of a person who is born in each region receiving a university education are as follows:

P(Go to university | North) = 0.7

P(Go to university | South) = 0.25

P(Go to university | East) = 0.5

P(Go to university | West) = 0.6

The probability that a person is born in each of the four regions is:

P(North) = 0.2

P(South) = 0.4

P(East) = 0.1

P(West) = 0.3

Because $P(\text{North}) + P(\text{South}) + P(\text{East}) + P(\text{West}) = 1$, we describe our list of dependent probabilities is being *exhaustive*, because there are *no other* possibilities that could occur. We can also see that the four different possibilities are all mutually exclusive.

Now suppose all we know about a particular individual is that he or she was born in that country, without knowing the region. To calculate the overall probability of that person receiving a university education, we add up all the mutually exclusive and exhaustive possibilities:

P(Go to university) = P(North)$\times P$(Go to university | North)

$+ P$(South)$\times P$(Go to university | South)

$+ P$(East)$\times P$(Go to university | East)

$+ P$(West)$\times P$(Go to university | West)

$= 0.2\times0.7 + 0.4\times0.25 + 0.1\times0.5 + 0.3\times0.6$

$= 0.47$

This is referred to as calculating the *unconditional* probability of the dependent event occurring.

Unconditional probability of a dependent event occurring

For an event B, which is dependent on mutually exclusive and exhaustive events $A_1, A_2, ..., A_n$:

$$P(B) = P(A_1)\times P(B\,|\,A_1) + P(A_2)\times P(B\,|\,A_2) + ... + P(A_n)\times P(B\,|\,A_n)$$

We will explore and extend these ideas more fully in the next chapter.

 ### *Example 12.16*

Kate catches the bus to work. The probability that the bus is late on any day is 0.6. If the bus is late, the probability that Kate is late for work is 0.8, otherwise it is 0.3. Calculate:

(i)   the probability that the bus is late and Kate is late for work

(ii)   the probability that the bus is early and Kate is late for work

(iii)   the probability that Kate is late for work.

Solution

(i)   P(bus late and Kate late for work) $= P$(bus late) $\times P$(Kate late for work | bus late)
$$= 0.6 \times 0.8$$
$$= 0.48$$

(ii)   P(bus early and Kate late for work) $= P$(bus early) $\times P$(Kate late for work | bus early)
$$= 0.4 \times 0.3$$
$$= 0.12$$

(iii)   The two ways in which Kate can be late for work (bus late or bus early) are mutually exclusive and exhaustive events. The unconditional probability for Kate being late for work is therefore just the sum of the probabilities we calculated in parts (i) and (ii). This gives:

$$P(\text{Kate late to work}) = 0.48 + 0.12 = 0.6 \qquad \blacklozenge \blacklozenge$$

We have now covered all of the types of events and the probability rules.

Chapter 12 Practice Questions

◆ Basic probability

Question 12.1

A bag has 4 blackcurrant, 3 orange and 2 strawberry sweets left in it. A sweet is picked at random from the bag. Calculate the probability that:

(i)   a blackcurrant sweet is picked

(ii)   an orange sweet is picked.

Question 12.2

When Allstars play their next match they could win, lose or draw. The probability of them winning is 0.5 and the probability of them losing is 0.3. Calculate the probability that Allstars:

(i)   draw in the next match

(ii)   do not win the next match.

◆ Addition rule

Question 12.3

The probability of a student obtaining each grade on a particular examination is shown below:

Grade	A	B	C	D	E
Probability	0.4	0.3	0.15	0.1	0.05

Calculate the probability that a student obtains:

(i)   Grade A, B or C

(ii)   Grade B, C, D, or E.

Question 12.4

A chocolate factory produces milk and plain chocolates, either of which may have a caramel filling. On average, 25% of the chocolates produced by the factory are plain, and 15% have a caramel filling.

A chocolate made in the factory is chosen at random. Explain why the probability of this being a plain chocolate or a caramel-filled chocolate is *not* $0.25 + 0.15 = 0.40$.

Question 12.5

In a group of home insurance policies, 30% of claims arise from burglaries and 60% pay out more than £2,000. Given that claims from burglaries or claims for more than £2,000 account for 80% of all claims, calculate the probability that the claim is from a burglary paying out more than £2,000.

◆ *Multiplication rule*

Question 12.6

In a typical hour at work the probability that Robert receives an email is 0.9 and the probability that he receives a phone call is 0.4. Calculate the probability that, during a typical hour:

(i)   Robert receives both an email and a phone call

(ii)   Robert receives neither an email nor a phone call.

Question 12.7

A particular insurance company expects 35% of all its car insurance claims to be caused by cars reversing. Calculate the probability that:

(i)   the next three claims are all due to reversing

(ii)   none of the next four claims are due to reversing

(iii)   of the next 5 claims, the second, third and fourth claims (only) are due to reversing.

Question 12.8

The probability that a student revises for their General Studies exam is 0.6. If a student revises, the probability that they pass is 0.7, otherwise it is only 0.1. If a student is selected at random, find the probability that:

(i)   they revised and they passed the exam

(ii)   they did not revise and they failed the exam.

Question 12.9

Two male and four female candidates are waiting in a room to be called for interview. They are to be called randomly one after the other. Calculate the probability that:

(i)   a male and then a female candidate are called

(ii)   the next three candidates called are all female.

Question 12.10   (IFoA Past Examination Question, adapted)

The portfolio of a private investor includes investments in 12 unit trusts, 8 of which are UK trusts and 4 of which are overseas trusts. Suppose the investor decides to check the prices of units in 3 of the 12 trusts selected at random.

Calculate the probability that the 3 selected trusts are all UK trusts.

Question 12.11   (IFoA Past Examination Question)

The probability that a component in a rocket motor will fail when the motor is fired is 0.02. To achieve a greater reliability several similar components are to be fitted in parallel; the motor will then fail only if all the individual components fail simultaneously.

Determine the minimum number of components required to ensure that the probability the motor fails is less than one in a billion (*ie* less than 10^{-9}), assuming that components fail independently.

◆ *Calculating the unconditional probability of a dependent event*

Question 12.12

Calculate the unconditional probability that the student in Question 12.8 passes their General Studies exam.

13

Advanced probability

Learning Objectives

The following learning objectives are covered in this chapter:

- Use techniques such as listing outcomes and tree diagrams to assist in the calculation of probabilities, including those relating to sampling without replacement from finite populations.

- State the formula for the conditional probability of one event given the occurrence of another event, in terms of unconditional probabilities, and use the formula to calculate such probabilities.

- Apply Bayes' theorem to calculate conditional probabilities.

13.1 Introduction

In this chapter we consider some useful techniques that can help in calculating probabilities, most importantly the use of tree diagrams. We then describe how these techniques can be used when sampling from finite populations, and for calculating conditional probabilities using Bayes' Theorem.

13.2 Calculation techniques

 ### Listing outcomes

Consider the following example.

The probability that a particular train is late on any day is 0.15, and this is independent of what happens to the train on any other day. Calculate the probability that the train is late on exactly one of the next two days.

A good way of calculating probabilities in a question like this is to list all the possible outcomes along with their associated probabilities. The possible outcomes for the train over the next two days are listed in the following table, where L means 'late' and N means 'not late'. (Instead of N we could have used the notation L′, indicating the *complementary event* of event L, as defined in the previous chapter.)

Outcome	1st day	2nd day
1	L	L
2	L	N
3	N	L
4	N	N

Because the outcomes on the two days are independent of each other, we can obtain the probabilities of each *pair* of outcomes by multiplying the individual probabilities together, as shown below:

Outcome	1st day	2nd day	Probability
1	L	L	$0.15 \times 0.15 = 0.0225$
2	L	N	$0.15 \times 0.85 = 0.1275$
3	N	L	$0.85 \times 0.15 = 0.1275$
4	N	N	$0.85 \times 0.85 = 0.7225$

These probabilities sum to 1, since we have included all of the (mutually exclusive) possibilities. Since outcomes 2 and 3 lead to the train being late on *exactly* one of the two days, the required probability is:

$$P(\text{train late on exactly one day}) = P(\text{LN or NL})$$
$$= P(\text{LN}) + P(\text{NL})$$
$$= 0.1275 + 0.1275$$
$$= 0.255$$

Example 13.1

For the late train example above, calculate the probability that the train is late *on at least one* of the next two days.

Solution

We can see that outcomes 1, 2 and 3 involve the train being late on at least one (that is, on one or more) of the two days. So the required probability is:

$$P(\text{train late on at least one day}) = P(\text{LL or LN or NL})$$
$$= P(\text{LL}) + P(\text{LN}) + P(\text{NL})$$
$$= 0.0225 + 0.1275 + 0.1275$$
$$= 0.2775 \qquad \qquad ◆◆$$

We could alternatively (and more easily) calculate the probability in Example 13.1 as:

$$P(\text{train late on at least one day}) = 1 - P(\text{NN})$$
$$= 1 - 0.7225$$
$$= 0.2775$$

In this case, 'NN' is the complementary event to the event we are interested in, and deducting its probability from 1 provides us with a quicker way of solving the problem.

So, listing all possible outcomes and their probabilities can help to ensure that:

- no possibilities are missed
- the calculation is accurate
- the simplest calculation route is followed.

Example 13.2

In a darts tournament, the probability that a player hits (and therefore scores) a triple twenty with a single dart is $\frac{5}{8}$, independently of his other throws. The player throws three darts in succession.

(i)   List all the possible outcomes together with their probabilities.

(ii)   Calculate the probability that the player obtains the following scores:

      (a)   exactly two scores of triple twenty

      (b)   at least one score of triple twenty.

Solution

(i)   The possible outcomes, along with their probabilities, are shown in the table below. We use T to represent a score of 'triple twenty' and N to represent any score *except* 'triple twenty':

1st dart	2nd dart	3rd dart	Probability
T	T	T	$\frac{5}{8} \times \frac{5}{8} \times \frac{5}{8} = \frac{125}{512}$
T	T	N	$\frac{5}{8} \times \frac{5}{8} \times \frac{3}{8} = \frac{75}{512}$
T	N	T	$\frac{5}{8} \times \frac{3}{8} \times \frac{5}{8} = \frac{75}{512}$
T	N	N	$\frac{5}{8} \times \frac{3}{8} \times \frac{3}{8} = \frac{45}{512}$
N	T	T	$\frac{3}{8} \times \frac{5}{8} \times \frac{5}{8} = \frac{75}{512}$
N	T	N	$\frac{3}{8} \times \frac{5}{8} \times \frac{3}{8} = \frac{45}{512}$
N	N	T	$\frac{3}{8} \times \frac{3}{8} \times \frac{5}{8} = \frac{45}{512}$
N	N	N	$\frac{3}{8} \times \frac{3}{8} \times \frac{3}{8} = \frac{27}{512}$

(ii)   (a) $P(\text{exactly 2 scores of triple twenty}) = P(\text{TTN or TNT or NTT})$

$$= P(\text{TTN}) + P(\text{TNT}) + P(\text{NTT})$$

$$= \frac{75}{512} + \frac{75}{512} + \frac{75}{512} = \frac{225}{512}$$

(b)   Here it is easiest to deduct the probability of the complementary event occurring from 1. So we have:

$$P(\text{at least 1 score of triple twenty}) = 1 - P(\text{no score of triple twenty})$$

$$= 1 - P(\text{NNN})$$

$$= 1 - \frac{27}{512} = \frac{485}{512} \qquad \blacklozenge\blacklozenge$$

◆ Tree diagrams

We now consider the use of tree diagrams as an alternative (and often quicker) way of listing the outcomes and finding probabilities.

Consider the train example again. Instead of considering the outcomes in a table, we can draw them as branches on a tree diagram. So we first draw two branches, leading to the two possible outcomes (train late or train not late) on Day 1. Then from *each* of these possibilities we draw a further set of branches for the outcomes on Day 2. The complete set of outcomes can be obtained by following the various possible routes through the tree.

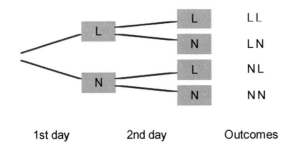

| 1st day | 2nd day | Outcomes |

The probabilities are usually written along the branches. The probabilities for the final outcomes can then be obtained by multiplying the probabilities along the routes through the tree.

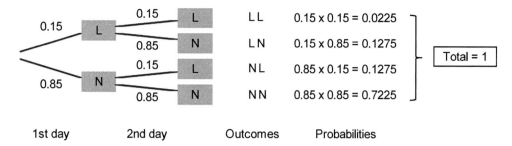

| 1st day | 2nd day | Outcomes | Probabilities |

We have now obtained the same set of possible outcomes and probabilities that we listed earlier.

Example 13.3

The probability that a car insurance claim involves another vehicle is 0.6. If a claim involves another vehicle, the probability that the claim is in excess of £2,000 is 0.95, otherwise this probability is only 0.25.

(i)   Draw a tree diagram showing all the possible outcomes together with their probabilities.

(ii)   Hence, calculate the probability that:

    (a)   a claim does not involve another vehicle and is for less than £2,000

    (b)   a claim is for more than £2,000.

Solution

(i)   We will use V and N to represent 'involves another vehicle' and 'does not involve another vehicle', respectively, and M and L to represent 'more than £2,000' and 'less than £2,000', respectively.

The tree diagram is then as follows:

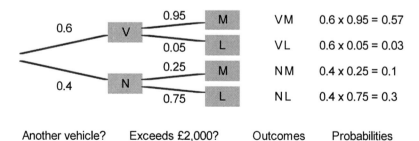

Another vehicle?   Exceeds £2,000?   Outcomes   Probabilities

(ii)   (a)   The probability that the claim does not involve another vehicle and is for less than £2,000 is found directly as:

$$P(\text{NL}) = 0.3$$

    (b)   For the total probability of a claim being for more than £2,000, we need to sum over all the possible outcomes in which this occurs. So we have:

$$P(\text{M}) = P(\text{VM or NM})$$
$$= P(\text{VM}) + P(\text{NM})$$
$$= 0.57 + 0.1 = 0.67$$

♦♦

Example 13.3 differs from the other examples covered so far in this chapter, in that the outcomes of the two events are not independent.

Tree diagrams can be easily adapted to a variety of problems involving independent and/or dependent events. The particular tree design constructed will vary according to the problem, as we show in this next example.

Example 13.4

A triple bypass heart operation has a success rate of 70%. If the operation is unsuccessful it can be repeated once, but the probability that the second operation is a success is only 45%. Calculate the probability that the treatment is ultimately successful.

Solution

Using S to represent a successful operation and F to represent a failure, the first branch of the tree diagram is:

1st operation

The second operation is only needed if the first one is a failure. Hence, we need to continue the tree for this branch only:

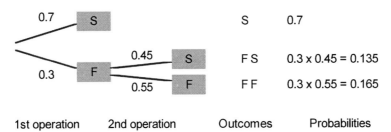

| 1st operation | 2nd operation | Outcomes | Probabilities |

S   0.7

F S   0.3 x 0.45 = 0.135

F F   0.3 x 0.55 = 0.165

The treatment is successful if either of the S or FS outcomes occur. Hence, the probability that the treatment is successful is:

$$0.7 + 0.135 = 0.835$$

or, alternatively:

$$1 - 0.165 = 0.835$$ ◆◆

Example 13.5

A man aged exactly 70 has a policy with a life insurance company, which will pay an amount of £50,000 if he dies in the next two years.

The following is an extract from a mortality table used by the insurance company:

x	q_x
70	0.025
71	0.028

where q_x is the probability that a man, who is alive at exact age x, dies in the next year of age (*ie* between exact ages x and $x+1$).

Assuming that the insurance company's mortality table is correct, calculate the probability that the policy pays out the £50,000.

Solution

The policy pays out the £50,000 only if the man dies in either of the next two years, so we need to calculate the probability of this occurring. Using D to represent 'dies' and N for 'does not die' we obtain:

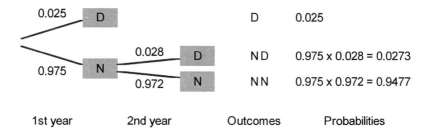

So the probability that the man dies within the next 2 years is given by:

$$P(\text{dies in 1st year}) + P(\text{dies in 2nd year}) = P(D) + P(ND)$$
$$= 0.025 + 0.0273$$
$$= 0.0523$$

Alternatively, we could calculate this as:

$$1 - P(\text{does not die in 1st year and does not die in 2nd year}) = 1 - P(NN)$$
$$= 1 - 0.9477$$
$$= 0.0523 \qquad \blacklozenge \blacklozenge$$

13.3 Sampling from finite populations

We can also use tree diagrams to calculate probabilities where we are selecting items (sampling) from known, finite, populations, as shown in the following example.

Example 13.6

A firm of consultants has 12 partners. 8 are accountants (A) and 4 are lawyers (L). None of the partners are members of both professions. Two different partners are chosen at random, one after the other. Calculate the probability that both are members of the same profession.

Solution

The probability that the second partner chosen is an accountant (A) or a lawyer (L) is *dependent* upon the outcome of the first selection. For example, using the notation for conditional probabilities:

$$P(2\text{nd} = A|1\text{st} = A) = \tfrac{7}{11}$$
$$P(2\text{nd} = A|1\text{st} = L) = \tfrac{8}{11}$$

according to how many accountants are still left in the group after the first selection has been made.

The resulting tree diagram is as follows:

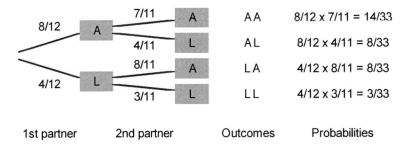

	7/11 A	A A	8/12 x 7/11 = 14/33
8/12 A	4/11 L	A L	8/12 x 4/11 = 8/33
	8/11 A	L A	4/12 x 8/11 = 8/33
4/12 L	3/11 L	L L	4/12 x 3/11 = 3/33

| 1st partner | 2nd partner | Outcomes | Probabilities |

Therefore, as both partners belong to the same profession in outcomes AA and LL, the probability of this event is:

$$\tfrac{14}{33} + \tfrac{3}{33} = \tfrac{17}{33}$$

♦♦

Example 13.7

For the firm of consultants described in Example 13.6 above, three partners are now chosen at random, one after the other.

Calculate the probability that:

(a)   exactly two of the partners chosen are accountants

(b)   at least one of the partners chosen is an accountant.

Solution

The probability tree is now:

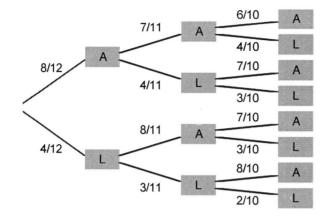

A A A	8/12 x 7/11 x 6/10	= 42/165
A A L	8/12 x 7/11 x 4/10	= 28/165
A L A	8/12 x 4/11 x 7/10	= 28/165
A L L	8/12 x 4/11 x 3/10	= 12/165
L A A	4/12 x 8/11 x 7/10	= 28/165
L A L	4/12 x 8/11 x 3/10	= 12/165
L L A	4/12 x 3/11 x 8/10	= 12/165
L L L	4/12 x 3/11 x 2/10	= 3/165

(a) P(exactly 2 partners are accountants) $= P$(AAL or ALA or LAA)

$$= P(\text{AAL}) + P(\text{ALA}) + P(\text{LAA})$$

$$= \frac{28}{165} + \frac{28}{165} + \frac{28}{165}$$

$$= \frac{84}{165}$$

(b) P(at least 1 partner is an accountant) $= 1 - P$(no partner is an accountant)

$$= 1 - P(\text{LLL})$$

$$= 1 - \frac{3}{165}$$

$$= \frac{162}{165}$$

♦♦

13.4 *Conditional probabilities and Bayes' Theorem*

In the previous chapter, we used the following formula for the probability of any two events, A and B, both occurring:

$$P(A \text{ and } B) = P(A) \times P(B \mid A)$$

where $P(B \mid A)$ is the conditional probability of event B occurring given that event A has already occurred. This multiplication rule applies equally when event A is conditional on event B:

$$P(A \text{ and } B) = P(B) \times P(A \mid B)$$

We can rearrange this equation to obtain a formula for *calculating* a conditional probability:

Conditional probabilities

For any two events A and B, the probability of event A happening *given* that event B happens is:

$$P(A \mid B) = \frac{P(A \text{ and } B)}{P(B)}$$

This formula does not apply when $P(B) = 0$ (as it would involve dividing by 0).

As we have seen already in this chapter, tree diagrams are useful in solving problems where conditional probabilities are involved. However, we can also use them to calculate the conditional probabilities themselves. We will illustrate this using the following example.

Example 13.8

The probability that a student revises for an exam is 0.4. If the student revises, the probability of passing the exam is 0.7, otherwise the probability of passing is only 0.1. Given that the student passes the exam, calculate the probability that the student revised.

Solution

Using R for 'revise', N for 'not revise', P for 'pass' and F for 'fail' we obtain the following tree diagram:

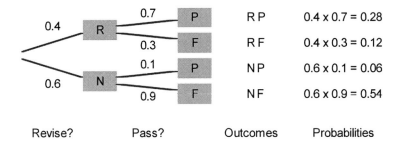

0.7	P	R P	0.4 x 0.7 = 0.28
0.3	F	R F	0.4 x 0.3 = 0.12
0.1	P	N P	0.6 x 0.1 = 0.06
0.9	F	N F	0.6 x 0.9 = 0.54

Revise?　　　　Pass?　　　　Outcomes　　　Probabilities

We need to find the conditional probability that the student revised *given* that they passed. The formula is:

$$P(\text{revised} \mid \text{passed}) = \frac{P(\text{revised and passed})}{P(\text{passed})}$$

The numerator is the probability of the RP outcome:

$$P(\text{revised and passed}) = P(\text{RP}) = 0.28$$

For the denominator, we need the *unconditional* probability of passing. Probabilities of this type were covered in the previous chapter. We need:

$$P(\text{passed}) = P(\text{R}) \times P(\text{P}|\text{R}) + P(\text{N}) \times P(\text{P}|\text{N})$$

So we need to sum the probabilities of the two 'pass' outcomes shown on the diagram, that is RP and NP. Hence, the probability is:

$$P(\text{passed}) = P(\text{RP or NP}) = 0.28 + 0.06 = 0.34$$

So the required conditional probability is:

$$P(\text{revised} \mid \text{passed}) = \frac{0.28}{0.34} = 0.824$$

♦♦

Example 13.9

Assume that, in the example above, the student has failed the exam. Calculate the probability that the student revised.

Solution

The required probability is:

$$P(\text{revised} \mid \text{failed}) = \frac{P(\text{revised and failed})}{P(\text{failed})}$$

The numerator is:

$$P(\text{revised and failed}) = P(RF) = 0.12$$

The denominator is:

$$P(\text{failed}) = P(RF) + P(NF) = 0.12 + 0.54 = 0.66$$

So the required probability is:

$$P(\text{revised} \mid \text{failed}) = \frac{0.12}{0.66} = 0.182$$ ♦♦

The formula we are using for calculating these conditional probabilities is known as Bayes' Theorem.

Bayes' Theorem

Bayes' Theorem for the calculation of a conditional probability is:

$$P(E_i \mid A) = \frac{P(E_i) \times P(A \mid E_i)}{\displaystyle\sum_{j=1}^{n} P(E_j) \times P(A \mid E_j)}$$

where

- event A is conditional on possible events $E_1, E_2, ..., E_n$

- $P(E_i)$ is the unconditional probability of event E_i occurring, and

- $P(E_i \mid A)$ is the conditional probability of event E_i occurring, incorporating the fact that event A is known to have occurred.

Using a tree diagram is usually by far the easiest way of using Bayes' Theorem in practice.

So, in Example 13.8 and Example 13.9, we have two events of interest:

$$E_1 = N = \text{not revised}$$

$$E_2 = R = \text{revised}$$

The unconditional probability of revising for the exam is:

$$P(E_2) = 0.4$$

However, if we know that the student has passed the exam, we calculate the (conditional) probability of having revised as:

$$P(E_2 \mid P) = 0.824$$

as in Example 13.8.

However, if we know that the student has failed the exam, the conditional probability of having revised is:

$$P(E_2 \mid F) = 0.182$$

as in Example 13.9.

So we can see that the probability, or our *belief*, in whether the student revised for the exam, has been changed according to the additional information that we have:

- from 0.4 to 0.824 if we know the student passed

- from 0.4 to 0.182 if we know the student failed.

This approach, in which unconditional probabilities or beliefs are improved by knowing the outcomes of particular dependent events, is a technique frequently used by statisticians.

Example 13.10

A blood test for a particular type of cancer is 95% accurate for a patient with the cancer and 98% accurate for a healthy patient. 6% of patients taking the test have the cancer.

(i)   Calculate the probability of a patient having the cancer given that:

     (a)   the test result is positive

     (b)   the test result is negative.

(ii)   Comment on the usefulness of the test in terms of identifying whether or not the patient has the cancer.

Solution

(i)   Using C for 'has the cancer', H for 'healthy', P for 'test result is positive' and N for 'test result is negative', we can produce the following tree diagram:

0.06 C	0.95 → P	C P	0.06 x 0.95 = 0.057
	0.05 → N	C N	0.06 x 0.05 = 0.003
0.94 H	0.02 → P	H P	0.94 x 0.02 = 0.0188
	0.98 → N	H N	0.94 x 0.98 = 0.9212

     (a)   Here we need the conditional probability:

$$P(\text{have cancer} \mid \text{test result is positive}) = P(C \mid P)$$

$$= \frac{P(CP)}{P(CP) + P(HP)}$$

$$= \frac{0.057}{0.057 + 0.0188}$$

$$= \frac{0.057}{0.07588}$$

$$= 0.752$$

(b)   Here we need the conditional probability:

$$P(\text{have cancer}|\text{test result is negative}) = P(C|N)$$

$$= \frac{P(CN)}{P(CN) + P(HN)}$$

$$= \frac{0.003}{0.003 + 0.9212}$$

$$= \frac{0.003}{0.9242}$$

$$= 0.00325$$

(ii)   Result (a) indicates that 25% of patients testing positive will not actually have the cancer. These people could then be subjected in error to further medical procedures and caused unnecessary anxiety. This is not a very good feature of the test.

Result (b) shows that, if a person has a negative test result, then they can be highly confident that they do not have the cancer. This is a good feature of the test.   ♦ ♦

Chapter 13 Practice Questions

◆ Calculation techniques – tree diagrams

Question 13.1

65% of the policyholders of a general insurance company are male. Of these male policyholders, 85% are aged over 55. The percentage of female policyholders that are aged over 55 is 68%. Calculate the probability that a randomly selected policyholder is:

(i)   male and aged under 55

(ii)   aged over 55.

Question 13.2

The probability of Peter passing an exam on his first attempt is 50%. If he fails on his first attempt, the probability that he passes on his second attempt is 60%. Calculate the probability that:

(i)   he fails on both attempts

(ii)   he passes on either his first or second attempt.

Question 13.3

A new motorist takes out a motor insurance policy with an insurance company. For the first year of cover the full annual premium for the policy is payable.

In subsequent years, the premium may be subject to a discount, depending on the claims that the policyholder makes each year. Specifically:

*   there are three discount levels: 30%, 20% and 0% (where 0% discount implies that the full premium would be paid)

*   a policyholder at the 0% discount level who makes no claim during a year, will progress to the 20% discount level in the next year; otherwise the discount level remains at 0%

*   a policyholder at the 20% discount level who makes no claim during the year, will progress to the 30% discount level in the following year; otherwise the discount level reverts to 0%.

The probability that the motorist makes a claim in any year is 0.2. Calculate the probability that after two years the discount level for this motorist is:

(i)   30%

(ii)   20%

(iii)   0%.

Sampling from finite populations

Question 13.4

Two male and four female candidates are waiting in a room to be called for interview. Before lunch two candidates are called randomly one after the other. Calculate the probability that:

(i)   two candidates of the same sex are called

(ii)   at least one male candidate is called.

Conditional probabilities and Bayes' Theorem

Question 13.5

The allocation of theatre seats for a particular performance depends on when an order to buy tickets is received. If the order is received early, the probability that the applicant obtains their first choice of seats is 0.8. If the order is received late, the probability that the applicant obtains their first choice of seats is 0.3. The probability of an order being received early is 0.45.

(i)   Calculate the probability that an applicant, selected at random, does not obtain their first choice of seats.

(ii)   Given that the applicant obtained their first choice of seats, calculate the probability that their order was received early.

Question 13.6

On the way to work, I pass one set of traffic lights. The probability that these lights are red is $\frac{3}{5}$. If the lights are red, the probability that I will be late for work is $\frac{3}{8}$; otherwise the probability that I will be late for work is $\frac{1}{5}$. Calculate the probability that the lights were red given that I was not late for work.

Question 13.7   (IFoA Past Examination Question, adapted)

In a certain territory, 30% of voters have a genetic trait called 'broad-nosed', of whom 46% voted for the Considerate Party at the last parliamentary election. Of the remaining voters, 36% voted for the Considerate Party.

Consider a voter selected at random from those who voted for the Considerate Party in this territory. Calculate the probability that this voter has the 'broad-nosed' trait.

Question 13.8   (IFoA Past Examination Question, adapted)

Two students are selected at random, one after the other and without replacement, from a group of ten students of whom six are men and four are women.

Calculate the probability that the first student selected is a man, given that the second student selected is a man.

Question 13.9   (IFoA Past Examination Question)

The probability that a car accident is due to faulty brakes is 0.02, the probability that a car accident is correctly attributed to faulty brakes is 0.95, and the probability that a car accident is incorrectly attributed to faulty brakes is 0.01.

Calculate the probability that a car accident, which is attributed to faulty brakes, was due to faulty brakes.

Question 13.10   (IFoA Past Examination Question, adapted)

The probability that a life currently aged 40 survives 10 years is 0.95. For lives currently aged 50 and 60 this probability reduces to 0.85 and 0.70 respectively.

(i)   Determine the probability that exactly one of these three lives survives ten years.

(ii)   Determine the probability that it is the youngest life that survives, given that exactly one life survives ten years.

14

Permutations and combinations

Learning Objectives

The following learning objectives are covered in this chapter:

- Calculate the number of permutations of a group of objects, including cases where some of the objects are the same and where only some of the group is selected.

- Calculate the number of combinations of selecting a group of objects from a larger group.

- Define the multinomial coefficient, and the binomial coefficient in particular, and use them to calculate permutations.

- Apply permutations and combinations in the calculation of probabilities.

14.1   Introduction

In this chapter we will describe the calculation of permutations and combinations in a range of circumstances. We will then go on to show some of the various ways in which these calculation techniques can be helpful when calculating probabilities.

14.2   *Simple choosing*

Consider two spinners:

Spinning each of them once we will produce one of the following six possible outcomes:

1st spinner	2nd spinner
A	1
A	2
A	3
B	1
B	2
B	3

We have 2 possible outcomes from the first spinner, and each of these can be associated with each of the 3 possible outcomes from the second spinner. Hence, the total number of combinations of outcomes can be calculated as:

$$2 \times 3 = 6$$

So, we simply multiply together the number of possible outcomes from each activity, in order to obtain the total number of combinations of outcomes that can occur.

Simple choosing

If we have to make r different choices and there are n_1 options for the first choice, n_2 options for the second choice, and so on, then the total number of different choices that can be made is:

$$n_1 \times n_2 \times ... \times n_r$$

Example 14.1

At a restaurant the menu has:

- 2 starters (soup or prawn cocktail)
- 4 main courses (chicken, pasta, fish or risotto)
- 3 desserts (chocolate cake, crepes or ice-cream)

Calculate the number of different meals that can be ordered.

Solution

Multiplying the numbers of choices together for the starters, main courses and desserts, the number of different meals is:

$$2 \times 4 \times 3 = 24$$

♦♦

14.3 Permutations

 ### Permutations of all objects in a group

We will now extend this simple choosing to the case where choosing an option reduces the number of subsequent choices remaining. This process is sometimes referred to as *sampling without replacement*.

Consider a race between 3 runners: Abdul (A), Belinda (B) and Charlie (C). We wish to calculate the number of ways in which the 1st, 2nd and 3rd prizes can be awarded.

We could list all of the different outcomes:

1st	2nd	3rd
A	B	C
A	C	B
B	A	C
B	C	A
C	A	B
C	B	A

From this table we can see that the total number of possible arrangements is 6. However, it is quicker to calculate this by multiplying together the number of choices that can be made on each selection.

There are 3 choices for the first position in the race. If Belinda is in first place, there are now only two choices remaining for the second position (Abdul or Charlie). So the total number of ways in which the three people can occupy the first two positions is 3×2. Actually, with the first two positions decided, the remaining person *has* to take third position in the race.

Hence the total number of arrangements is:

$$3 \times 2 \times 1 = 6$$

Each different arrangement (or order) is called a *permutation*, and in this example there are $3 \times 2 \times 1$ permutations. The notation 3! (pronounced '3 factorial') is used to represent this number.

Permutations of all objects in a group

The number of ways of ordering *n* different objects is:

$$n! = n \times (n-1) \times \cdots \times 3 \times 2 \times 1$$

This (factorial) function is also available on most calculators.

Example 14.2

I need to put the following coins into a meter:

| £2 | £1 | 50p | 20p | 10p |

Calculate the number of different orders in which this can be done.

Solution

There are five different coins, so the number of different orders is:

$$5! = 5 \times 4 \times 3 \times 2 \times 1 = 120$$

This is because there are 5 choices for the 1st coin, then 4 choices for the 2nd coin, and so on.

♦ ♦

Permutations when only some of the objects are selected

We now consider the case in which we only select *some* of the objects, rather than all of them. Consider the following example.

A race has 8 competitors. There are gold, silver and bronze medals for the first three places. We wish to calculate the number of different ways in which these medals can be allocated to the competitors.

The gold medal can be won by any of the eight competitors. Once the gold has been won, the silver is available to any of the remaining seven competitors. Once this has also been won, the bronze is available to any of the last six competitors.

Hence, the total number of ways in which three different medals can be distributed when there are 8 competitors is:

$$8 \times 7 \times 6 = 336$$

This calculation can also be written:

$$8 \times 7 \times 6 = \frac{8 \times 7 \times 6 \times 5 \times 4 \times 3 \times 2 \times 1}{5 \times 4 \times 3 \times 2 \times 1} = \frac{8!}{5!} = \frac{8!}{(8-3)!}$$

So, in general, if:

- we have *n* different objects

- we choose *r* of the objects one at a time without replacement

then the number of different sequences (*ie* permutations) of *r* objects that can be obtained is:

$$\frac{n!}{(n-r)!}$$

This is given the symbol ^nP_r. This function is available on many calculators and it is perfectly acceptable to use this as a shortcut in calculations.

The number of permutations of *all n* objects is ^nP_n, but as this must equal $n!$, we have:

$$n! = {^nP_n} = \frac{n!}{(n-n)!} = \frac{n!}{0!}$$

So we need to define:

$$0! = 1$$

Permutations of some of the objects selected from a group

The number of ways in which *r* objects, chosen from *n* different objects, can be ordered is:

$$^nP_r = \frac{n!}{(n-r)!}$$

Example 14.3

Thirty people buy one raffle ticket each, to win one of four prizes. The prizes are a car, a holiday, a bicycle and some wine. Calculate the number of different ways in which the prizes can be allocated.

Solution

There are 30 ways of allocating the car, then 29 (remaining) ways of allocating the holiday, 28 ways for allocating the bicycle, and 27 ways for the wine.

The number of different ways of allocating the 4 prizes amongst 30 people is therefore:

$$30 \times 29 \times 28 \times 27 = 657,720$$

Alternatively, the number of ways of arranging 4 objects from a group of 30 is $^{30}P_4$, which can either be calculated directly using the ^nP_r function on a calculator, or by using factorials:

$$^{30}P_4 = \frac{30!}{(30-4)!} = \frac{30!}{26!} = 657,720 \qquad\qquad \blacklozenge\blacklozenge$$

14.4 Combinations

So far we have been calculating the number of ways in which a group of objects can be chosen (from a larger group) and then *ordered* (within the subgroup). In this section we will only be concerned with the first part of this process, that is, calculating the number of ways in which a group of objects can be *chosen* from a larger group, when the *order* in which the objects are selected in not important.

Consider again the following example, which we first met in the previous section.

A race has 8 competitors, in which gold, silver and bronze medals are to be awarded for the first three places, as before. All three medal winners are now to be invited to a special dinner reception held after the race. Calculate the number of different groups of people who could be invited to the dinner.

Suppose that Abdul wins gold, Belinda wins silver, and Charlie wins Bronze. All three will go to the dinner. However, the same three will go to the dinner if, for example, Belinda wins gold, Abdul wins silver and Charlie wins bronze. Hence, in this case, the order in which the medals are allocated within the selected group makes no difference to which people are invited to the dinner.

Now, for every combination of three runners who get medals, there are $3 \times 2 \times 1 = 3!$ ways in which the medals could be allocated between them.

Given (from earlier) that the number of different *orders* of medal winners was:

$$^8P_3 = \frac{8!}{5!} = 8 \times 7 \times 6 = 336$$

then the number of different *combinations* of competitors going to the dinner (*ie* ignoring the order) is:

$$\frac{336}{6} = 56$$

This calculation can be written as:

$$\frac{^8P_3}{3!} = \frac{8!}{(8-3)! \times 3!}$$

So, in general, if:

- we have n different objects

- we choose r of the objects

then the number of different groups (*ie* combinations) of r objects that can be obtained is:

$$\frac{n!}{(n-r)! \times r!}$$

This is given the symbol ^nC_r, or alternatively $\binom{n}{r}$.

Combinations

The number of ways of choosing r objects from n different objects, when the order is not important, is:

$$^nC_r = \binom{n}{r} = \frac{n!}{(n-r)! \times r!}$$

Example 14.4

A football team manager has a squad of 20 players and needs to pick a team of 11 for Saturday's game. Calculate the number of different teams that can be selected.

Solution

The number of different combinations of 11 players that can be chosen from 20 is:

$$^{20}C_{11} = \frac{20!}{(20-11)!11!} = 167,960$$

The ^nC_r function is also available on many calculators, in which case it is again perfectly acceptable to use this as a shortcut in calculations.   ♦♦

Example 14.5

A lottery machine selects 6 balls from 49 different balls numbered 1, 2, 3,..., 49.

To play the lottery, a person buys a lottery ticket showing 6 numbers chosen (from the same 49 numbers) by the player. The jackpot (first prize) is won by anyone who has chosen exactly the same 6 numbers as the machine.

(i)   Calculate the number of combinations of 6 numbers that the machine can select.

(ii)   A person buys one lottery ticket. Calculate the probability that this person wins the jackpot.

Solution

(i)   The number of combinations of 6 numbers that can be chosen from a total of 49 different numbers is:

$$^{49}C_6 = \frac{49!}{43! \times 6!} = 13,983,816$$

(ii)   Only one of the 13,983,816 combinations will win the jackpot. Assuming that the machine is equally likely to choose any one of these combinations, then the probability of this being the same as on the lottery ticket (and hence the probability of this person winning the jackpot) is:

$$\frac{1}{13,983,816}$$ ♦♦

◆ Choosing from several groups

So far we have only considered the number of ways of choosing a subgroup from one, larger, group. Now we will extend this to choosing from several groups. Consider the following example.

A committee has to consist of 3 women and 2 men, chosen from a group of 5 women and 8 men. Calculate the number of different committees that can be constructed.

Firstly, there are $^5C_3 = 10$ different combinations of 3 women that can be selected from the 5 women available.

Secondly, there are $^8C_2 = 28$ different combinations of 2 men that can be selected from the 8 men available.

Hence there are $^5C_3 \times ^8C_2 = 10 \times 28 = 280$ different committees that can be chosen altogether.

Example 14.6

A student research group of 6 people must contain equal numbers of each sex. This group is to be selected from a total of 10 male and 8 female students. Calculate the number of different ways in which the research group can be chosen.

Solution

We require 3 men from the 10 available and 3 women from the 8 available.

There are $^{10}C_3 = 120$ ways of selecting 3 men from 10.

There are $^{8}C_3 = 56$ ways of selecting 3 women from 8.

Hence, the total number of different possible research groups that contain exactly 3 men and 3 women is:

$$^{10}C_3 \times {}^{8}C_3 = 120 \times 56 = 6,720$$ ◆ ◆

Example 14.7

In the lottery described in Example 14.5 above, a lottery ticket that includes exactly 3 of the numbers selected by the machine will win its owner £10.

(i)   Calculate the number of ways of matching exactly 3 numbers chosen by the machine, when a person chooses 6 numbers from 49.

(ii)   Calculate the probability that a person who buys one lottery ticket will win a £10 prize.

    Hint: You will need to use your answer from Example 14.5(i).

Solution

(i)   We will refer to the numbers chosen by the machine as the 'winning' numbers. This means there are 6 winning numbers and 43 'non-winning' numbers.

To win £10, the numbers selected by the person must include exactly 3 of the 6 winning numbers and exactly 3 of the 43 non-winning numbers. The total number of ways of doing this is:

$$^{6}C_3 \times {}^{43}C_3 = \frac{6!}{3! \times 3!} \times \frac{43!}{40! \times 3!} = 20 \times 12,341 = 246,820$$

(ii)   We will assume that the machine is equally likely to choose any of the possible 6-number combinations. From Example 14.5(i) we know that the total number of (equally likely) ways is:

$$^{49}C_6 = 13,983,816$$

We know that 246,820 of these combinations lead to the £10 prize, and because each choice is equally likely, the probability that one selected lottery ticket wins a £10 prize is:

$$\frac{246,820}{13,983,816} = 1.765\%$$ ◆ ◆

 ## *Using combinations to calculate probabilities*

In Chapter 12 we defined the probability of an event A occurring as:

$$P(A) = \frac{\text{number of equally likely outcomes in which event } A \text{ can happen}}{\text{total number of equally likely outcomes}}$$

We have essentially been using this formula to calculate the probabilities of winning the lottery prizes in Example 14.5 and Example 14.7.

Example 14.8

In Example 14.6 above, a male student (Robert) and a female student (Aaisha) are both keen to be selected in the student research group. Assuming that students are selected from the 10 male and 8 female students at random, calculate the probability that both Robert and Aaisha are chosen for the research group.

Solution

From Example 14.6, there are $^{10}C_3 \times {}^8C_3 = 120 \times 56 = 6,720$ (equally likely) ways of choosing the research group.

We now need to calculate the number of these groups that contain both Robert and Aaisha. The 3 males would need to include Robert plus any combination of two other males from the 9 available. The number of different combinations of 3 males that include Robert is therefore:

$$1 \times {}^9C_2 = 1 \times \frac{9!}{7!\,2!} = 36$$

Similarly, the number of different combinations of 3 females that include Aaisha is:

$$1 \times {}^7C_2 = 1 \times \frac{7!}{5!\,2!} = 21$$

So, the number of different (equally likely) outcomes in which both Robert and Aaisha are included is:

$$36 \times 21 = 756$$

Hence, the probability that both Robert and Aaisha are chosen is:

$$\frac{756}{6,720} = 11.25\% \qquad\qquad \blacklozenge\blacklozenge$$

14.5 Permutations of all objects when some are identical

Suppose we have six numbers:

1, 2, 3, 4, 5, 6

We will call these Group A. The number of permutations of these six numbers is $6! = 720$.

Now consider Group B, consisting of the six numbers:

1, 1, 3, 4, 5, 6

Group B is the same as Group A except that the value 2 has been replaced by the value 1 in Group B. Now both of the Group A permutations 123456 and 213456, for example, correspond to the same permutation 113456 in Group B. So there are half as many permutations of the six Group B numbers compared to the six Group A numbers. So, where we have six numbers of which two are the same, the number of possible permutations is:

$$\frac{6!}{2!} = \frac{720}{2} = 360$$

Now consider Group C, which consists of the six numbers:

1, 1, 1, 4, 5, 6

If all the numbers were different, there would be $6! = 720$ permutations (as before, for Group A). However, three of the numbers in Group C are the same. So, for each permutation such as 111456 of group C, there would be $3! = 6$ different permutations of group A, *ie*:

123456 132456 213456 231456 312456 321456

So the total number of different permutations of Group C is:

$$\frac{6!}{3!} = \frac{720}{6} = 120$$

Now consider Group D, consisting of the six numbers:

1, 1, 2, 2, 2, 3

In this group we have two numbers both equal to 1, three numbers equal to 2, and one number equal to 3. Applying the same logic as in the previous examples, the number of different ways of ordering these (*ie* the number of permutations) is:

$$\frac{6!}{2! \times 3!} = \frac{6 \times 5 \times 4}{2 \times 1} = 60$$

This is an example of a *multinomial coefficient*. In general, if we have n objects, of which n_1 are of Type 1, n_2 are of Type 2, and so on, and we have r *different types* of object in the group, then the number of permutations is:

$$\frac{n!}{n_1! \times n_2! \times \cdots \times n_r!}$$

Permutations of all objects when some are identical

The number of distinct orderings of n objects of which n_1 are identical and of Type 1, n_2 are identical and of Type 2, ..., n_r are identical and are of Type r, is equal to the multinomial coefficient:

$$\frac{n!}{n_1! \times n_2! \times \cdots \times n_r!}$$

Example 14.9

Calculate the number of possible anagrams of the word 'REINSURER'.

Solution

There are nine letters in total, of which three are the letter R, two are the letter E, and all the other letters are different (I, N, S and U). So the total number of different anagrams is:

$$\frac{9!}{3! \times 2!} = 30,240 \qquad\qquad \blacklozenge\blacklozenge$$

Now consider the special case in which there are only two types of object. Going back to our 6-number example, let's define Group E to be the six numbers:

1, 1, 2, 2, 2, 2

Using the multinomial coefficient, the number of permutations of this is:

$$\frac{6!}{2! \times 4!} = 15$$

This is a binomial coefficient, which is the same as the formula for $^6C_4$ that we defined earlier.

Binomial coefficient

The number of permutations of a group of n objects of which r objects are of Type 1 and $n-r$ objects are of Type 2, is:

$$^nC_r = \frac{n!}{(n-r)! \times n!}$$

It should be noted that, in this application, we are still using ^nC_r to calculate the number of *permutations*, not combinations, as the ordering is important here.

14.6   *Using permutations to help calculate probabilities*

◆ *Independent events*

We will first show some examples where permutations can be used to help calculate probabilities involving *independent* events. Consider the following example.

On the way to work I pass through 4 sets of traffic lights. The probability that each set is green when I reach it is 0.6. Calculate the probability that exactly 2 sets of traffic lights are green when I reach them.

The probability tree for this question is shown on the next page, where G stands for 'green light' and N stands for 'not green light'.

The outcomes in which 'exactly two sets of traffic lights are green', along with their probabilities, are:

GGNN	$0.6 \times 0.6 \times 0.4 \times 0.4 = 0.0576$
GNGN	$0.6 \times 0.4 \times 0.6 \times 0.4 = 0.0576$
GNNG	$0.6 \times 0.4 \times 0.4 \times 0.6 = 0.0576$
NGGN	$0.4 \times 0.6 \times 0.6 \times 0.4 = 0.0576$
NGNG	$0.4 \times 0.6 \times 0.4 \times 0.6 = 0.0576$
NNGG	$0.4 \times 0.4 \times 0.6 \times 0.6 = 0.0576$

Hence the total probability is $6 \times 0.0576 = 0.3456$.

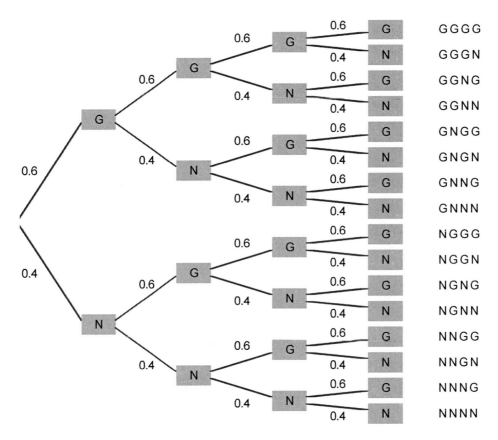

However, a much quicker way of obtaining this answer is first to note that each outcome has the same probability, since each has 2 'green light' and 2 'not green light' outcomes, which is:

$$0.6^2 \times 0.4^2 = 0.0576$$

Then we need to calculate the number of different ways (*ie* orderings) in which I could encounter 2 green and 2 not-green sets of traffic lights on my way to work. This is:

$$\frac{4!}{2! \times 2!} = 6$$

(which is the binomial coefficient $^4C_2$).

Hence the probability is given by:

$$^4C_2 \times 0.6^2 \times 0.4^2 = 6 \times 0.0576 = 0.3456$$

This is actually an example of a *binomial probability*.

Binomial probability

If there are:

-      *n* independent identical trials

-      at each trial there are only two possible outcomes ('success' and 'failure'), and

-      the probability of success at each trial is a constant *p*

then the probability of observing exactly *r* successes in the *n* trials is:

$$P(r) = {}^nC_r \times p^r \times (1-p)^{n-r}$$

So, in our traffic light example, each trial is represented by each set of traffic lights (so $n = 4$); a success is a 'green light', a failure is a 'not green' light; and the probabilities of success and failure are respectively $p = 0.6$ and $1 - p = 0.4$.

Example 14.10

In a portfolio of 30 life assurance policies, the probability that any one of them leads to a claim in the next year is 0.02. Assuming that claims on the different policies occur independently of each other, calculate the probability that:

(i)   there is exactly 1 claim in the next year

(ii)   there are at least 2 claims in the next year.

Solution

(i)   We have 30 policies (trials), each having an identical probability of 0.02 of producing a claim in a year, and a probability of 0.98 of not producing a claim. Using the binomial probability formula, the probability of exactly one claim occurring is:

$$P(1) = {}^{30}C_1 \times 0.02 \times 0.98^{29} = 30 \times 0.02 \times 0.98^{29} = 0.33397$$

(ii)   The probability that at least 2 policies out of 30 have claims is:

$$P(\text{at least 2}) = 1 - P(0) - P(1)$$

Now $P(0)$, the probability of no claims occurring in 30 policies is:

$$P(0) = {}^{30}C_0 \times 0.02^0 \times 0.98^{30} = 1 \times 1 \times 0.98^{30} = 0.54548$$

and from part (i) we know that $P(1) = 0.33397$.

Hence, the probability of at least two claims is given by:

$$P(\text{at least 2}) = 1 - 0.54548 - 0.33397 = 0.12055$$ ♦♦

Example 14.11

Applicants for new life insurance policies are received from people living in any of three territories: Goodland, Averageland, and Badland. The probabilities of any randomly selected applicant living in each of these territories are 0.3, 0.5 and 0.2 respectively.

Calculate the probability that, out of a randomly selected group of 10 applicants, 2 are from Goodland, 3 are from Averageland, and 5 are from Badland.

Solution

Using obvious notation, the outcome:

     GGAAABBBBB

has probability:

$$0.3^2 \times 0.5^3 \times 0.2^5$$

The number of different ways in which this outcome can be ordered is:

$$\frac{10!}{2! \times 3! \times 5!} = 2,520$$

Hence the required probability is:

$$2{,}520 \times 0.3^2 \times 0.5^3 \times 0.2^5 = 0.009072$$

◆◆

Example 14.11 is an example of a *multinomial probability*.

◆ *Sampling without replacement*

We will now look at questions that involve sampling without replacement, which we first encountered at the start of Section 14.3. Consider the following example.

A box of chocolates contains 6 milk and 4 plain chocolates. Three chocolates are selected at random from the box. Calculate the probability that exactly 2 of them are milk chocolates.

Using obvious notation, the probability tree for this question is:

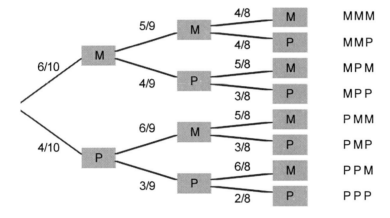

The three nodes represent the 1st, 2nd and 3rd chocolate selected respectively.

It can be seen that the probabilities change every time a chocolate is selected. The outcomes that lead to exactly 2 milk chocolates being chosen, and their probabilities, are:

MMP $\qquad \frac{6}{10} \times \frac{5}{9} \times \frac{4}{8} = \frac{1}{6}$

MPM $\qquad \frac{6}{10} \times \frac{4}{9} \times \frac{5}{8} = \frac{1}{6}$

PMM $\qquad \frac{4}{10} \times \frac{6}{9} \times \frac{5}{8} = \frac{1}{6}$

Hence the required probability is:

$$3 \times \frac{1}{6} = \frac{1}{2}$$

However, it can be seen that each outcome has the same probability irrespective of the order in which the chocolates are selected. So a simpler technique for calculating the probability is to:

•   calculate the probability of one sequence occurring (*eg* MMP)

•   multiply this by the number of permutations of the sequence.

So we have:

$$P(\text{MMP}) = \frac{1}{6}$$

The number of different permutations of MMP is:

$$\frac{3!}{2! \times 1!} = 3$$

Hence, the required probability is:

$$3 \times \frac{1}{6} = \frac{1}{2}$$

as before. This is an example of a *hypergeometric probability*.

Example 14.12

I own 15 shares in different companies. 9 are ordinary shares and 6 are preference shares.

I select 5 shares at random. Calculate the probability that the selection includes exactly 3 preference shares.

Solution

The selection must include exactly 3 preference shares and 2 ordinary shares. The probability of selecting these in any one particular order will be the same as:

$$P(\text{PPPOO}) = \frac{6}{15} \times \frac{5}{14} \times \frac{4}{13} \times \frac{9}{12} \times \frac{8}{11} = \frac{24}{1,001}$$

The number of different orders in which 3 preference shares and 2 ordinary shares can be chosen is:

$$\frac{5!}{3! \times 2!} = 10$$

Hence the total probability is:

$$10 \times \frac{24}{1,001} = \frac{240}{1,001} = 0.23976 \qquad\qquad\qquad \blacklozenge\blacklozenge$$

Example 14.13

30 schoolchildren arrive at school on a cold morning, each wearing a scarf. Six of the scarves are red, 10 are blue, and 14 are green. The teacher gathers them in at the start of the day and puts them in a box. At break time, 6 of the children ask to go outside to play. The teacher takes out 6 scarves at random and hands them to the children to wear.

Calculate the probability that 2 scarves of each colour are selected.

Solution

The selection of 6 scarves must include exactly 2 red, 2 blue, and 2 green scarves. The probability of selecting these in any one particular order will be the same as:

$$P(\text{RRBBGG}) = \frac{6}{30} \times \frac{5}{29} \times \frac{10}{28} \times \frac{9}{27} \times \frac{14}{26} \times \frac{13}{25} = \frac{1}{870}$$

The number of different ways in which this combination of six scarves can be ordered is:

$$\frac{6!}{2! \times 2! \times 2!} = \frac{720}{8} = 90$$

Hence the required probability is:

$$90 \times \frac{1}{870} = \frac{3}{29} \qquad\qquad\qquad \blacklozenge\blacklozenge$$

Chapter 14 Practice Questions

◆ *Simple choosing*

Question 14.1

A drinks machine contains:

                coffee   tea   water   cola   orange   soup

(i)   Two people each select one drink from the machine, one after the other.

            Calculate the number of different sequences of drinks produced by the machine (*eg* orange followed by coffee is one possible sequence).

(ii)   Assuming each person is equally likely to choose any drink, calculate the probability that the two people choose the same drink.

◆ *Permutations when all objects are different*

Question 14.2

A competition involves ranking 10 features of a car from the most important to the least important. Anyone who ranks the features in the 'correct' order (as determined by the competition judges) wins a prize.

              economical   reliable   central locking   power steering

              5 speed gearbox   electric windows   air bag   boot space

              value for money   alarm

(i)   Calculate the number of different ways in which these features can be ranked.

(ii)   Someone ranks the features at random. Calculate the probability that they win a prize.

Question 14.3

Ten employees (Alan, Bob and eight others) apply for 2 jobs (manager and floor supervisor). The jobs are allocated randomly to two of the employees.

(i)   Calculate the number of different ways in which the two jobs can be allocated.

(ii)   Calculate the probability that Bob is the manager and Alan is the floor supervisor.

(iii)   Calculate the number of ways of allocating the two jobs that include Alan as the manager. Hence calculate the probability that Alan is the manager.

◆ *Combinations*

Question 14.4

A committee of fourteen people needs to select a sub-committee of three people to represent it. Calculate the number of different sub-committees that can be selected.

Question 14.5

A football team manager has a squad of 20 players that includes 2 goalkeepers, 5 defenders, 6 midfielders and 7 strikers. He wishes to pick a team of 11 players for Saturday's game consisting of 1 goalkeeper, 3 defenders, 4 midfielders and 3 strikers. Calculate the number of different teams that he can choose.

◆▶ Using permutations and combinations to calculate probabilities

Question 14.6

A factory produces electrical components, and the probability that any one component is faulty is 0.01. Assuming that faulty components arise independently, calculate the probability that, in a box of 500 components from the factory, exactly three of the components are faulty.

Question 14.7

In a chess match Alicia plays 5 games against Baldeep and 5 games against Charlotte. The probability that Alicia wins a game against Baldeep is $\frac{3}{5}$ and the probability that she wins a game against Charlotte is $\frac{2}{3}$. Calculate the probability that Alicia wins exactly 2 of the games against Baldeep and 3 of the games against Charlotte.

Question 14.8

In a bag of 30 sweets, 6 are blackcurrant flavour. I choose 5 sweets at random from the bag. Calculate the probability that exactly 2 of these sweets are blackcurrant flavour.

Question 14.9   (IFoA Past Examination Question, adapted)

In a simple lottery the organiser chooses three numbers at random without replacement from the numbers 1 to 5. Players also choose three numbers without replacement from the numbers 1 to 5.

Calculate the probability that a player matches two or three of the organiser's numbers.

Question 14.10   (IFoA Past Examination Question, adapted)

The probability of suffering a side effect from a certain flu vaccine is 0.005. If 1,000 people are inoculated, calculate the probability that at most one person suffers a side effect.

Question 14.11   (IFoA Past Examination Question, adapted)

Five students are selected at random, one after the other and without replacement, from a group of twenty students of whom twelve are men and eight are women.

Calculate the probability that the fifth student selected is a man.

15

Discrete random variables

Learning Objectives

The following learning objectives are covered in this chapter:

- Explain what is meant by a discrete random variable, define the distribution function and the probability function of such a variable, and use these functions to calculate probabilities.

- Define the expected value of a function of a discrete random variable, the mean, the variance, the standard deviation, the coefficient of skewness and the moments of a discrete random variable, and calculate such quantities.

15.1   Introduction

In earlier chapters we introduced measures of location, spread and skewness of a data set. A data set is a collection of values that has already been observed.

Now we want to consider what might happen in the future, *eg* we might be interested in the number of claims that arise in the next year from a particular group of insurance policies. This is an example of a *random variable* because its value is uncertain and it depends on which random events happen over the next year. One thing we do know is that the number of claims in the next year must be a whole number, and this means it is a *discrete* random variable.

If we are able to assign probabilities to each possible value of a random variable, we will have a theoretical model of the future. We can use such a model to obtain theoretical measures of location, spread and skewness.

15.2   Random variables

Let's start with the definition of a random variable.

Random variables

A random variable is a quantity whose value is uncertain and is subject to variations that are due to chance.

Examples of random variables include:

- the score obtained when a die (the singular of dice) is rolled

- the total number of hurricanes in the Caribbean in the next year

- the number of deaths in a population in the next month

- the total amount that an insurance company has to pay in claims in the next quarter.

The sample space of a random variable is the set of all possible values that the random variable can take. Random variables are usually denoted by capital letters, *eg* X. As an example, suppose that X is the score obtained when a die is rolled. The possible values of X are 1, 2, 3, 4, 5 and 6. So the sample space of X is the set of values $\{1,2,3,4,5,6\}$. Observed values of the random variable are usually denoted by the corresponding lower case letter, *ie* x in this case.

In this chapter we will restrict our attention to discrete random variables.

Discrete random variables

A random variable is said to be discrete if its sample space is:

- a finite set, *eg* $\{1,2,3,4\}$, or

- a *countably infinite* set, *eg* the set of non-negative integers $\{0,1,2,3,...\}$.

Countably infinite means that we can count all the elements in the set in such a way that, even though counting the whole set will take forever, we will get to any particular element in a finite amount of time.

Example 15.1

Consider the following list of items:

I   the number of months in a year

II   the number of candidates who pass Module 0 at the next sitting

III   the number of fountains currently in Trafalgar Square in London

IV   the number of claims received tomorrow by a particular insurance company.

Which pair of items are discrete random variables?

Solution

To be a discrete random variable, the item must *randomly* take a discrete value. We know that:

I   the number of months in a year is fixed

II   the number of candidates who pass is uncertain but must take one of the values 0, 1, 2, ..., n, where n is the number of candidates sitting the exam

III   the number of fountains currently in Trafalgar Square is fixed

IV   the number of claims received tomorrow is uncertain but must be a whole number.

So II and IV are discrete random variables.   ♦ ♦

15.3   Probability functions

Every discrete random variable has a *probability function* associated with it. We use the notation $P(X = x)$ to denote the probability that the random variable X will take the value x.

For example, if X is the score obtained when a fair die is rolled, then:

$$P(X = x) = \frac{1}{6} \quad \text{for } x = 1, 2, 3, 4, 5, 6$$

We could also present these probabilities in the form of a table as shown below:

Number rolled on a fair die, x	1	2	3	4	5	6
$P(X = x)$	$\frac{1}{6}$	$\frac{1}{6}$	$\frac{1}{6}$	$\frac{1}{6}$	$\frac{1}{6}$	$\frac{1}{6}$

This table is called a *probability distribution* as it shows the distribution of the probabilities over the values in the sample space, *ie* it shows how the total probability (of 1) is shared out amongst the possible values of the random variable.

Recall that a frequency distribution for a data set shows the number of times that each value has been observed. The key difference between a probability distribution and a frequency distribution is that a probability distribution shows the likelihood of each value occurring in the future, whereas a frequency distribution shows an actual set of observations.

A third way to represent this probability distribution is with a graph, as shown below.

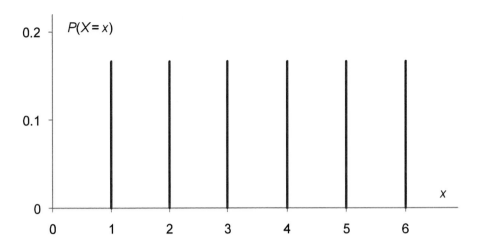

 ## Example 15.2

Determine the probability distribution of the number of heads obtained when a fair coin is tossed twice.

Solution

We can draw a tree diagram to illustrate the possible outcomes:

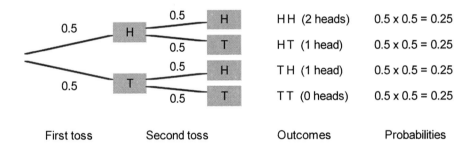

So the probability distribution is as follows:

Number of heads	0	1	2
Probability	0.25	0.5	0.25

♦♦

We know from Chapter 12 that probabilities must always lie between 0 and 1 and that, when we consider all the possible outcomes of a random variable, the probabilities must sum to 1. These conditions give us the formal definition of a probability function.

Probability functions

$P(X = x)$ is a probability function if both of the following conditions hold:

(i) $P(X = x) \geq 0$

(ii) $\sum\limits_{x} P(X = x) = 1$

Technically, a probability function is defined for *all* values of x, with $P(X = x) = 0$ for the values of x that are impossible. For convenience, we tend to state the probability function only for values of x for which it is non-zero.

Example 15.3

Show that the following function *is* a probability function:

$$P(X = x) = \frac{1}{12}(8 - x) \qquad x = 2, 4 \text{ or } 6$$

Solution

Substituting $x = 2, 4$ and 6 into the formula above, we see that:

$$P(X = 2) = \tfrac{1}{12}(8 - 2) = \tfrac{6}{12}$$

$$P(X = 4) = \tfrac{1}{12}(8 - 4) = \tfrac{4}{12}$$

$$P(X = 6) = \tfrac{1}{12}(8 - 6) = \tfrac{2}{12}$$

So $P(X = x) \geq 0$ for each value of x.

Now summing the probabilities, we obtain:

$$P(X = 2) + P(X = 4) + P(X = 6) = \tfrac{6}{12} + \tfrac{4}{12} + \tfrac{2}{12} = 1$$

Hence the function above is a probability function.   ◆◆

Example 15.4

The probability function of a random variable Y is given by:

$$P(Y = y) = cy^2 \qquad y = 1, 2, 3 \text{ or } 4$$

Determine the value of c.

Solution

The probability distribution of Y is:

y	1	2	3	4
$P(Y = y)$	c	$4c$	$9c$	$16c$

Since the sum of the probabilities must be 1, we have:

$$c + 4c + 9c + 16c = 30c = 1$$

So:

$$c = \frac{1}{30}$$ ♦♦

We can use probability functions to calculate cumulative (*ie* less than or equal to) probabilities. To do this, we sum the probability function over an appropriate range of values.

Example 15.5

The probability function of a random variable W is given by:

$$P(W = w) = \frac{1}{4}\left(\frac{3}{4}\right)^{w} \qquad\qquad w = 0, 1, 2, 3, \ldots$$

Calculate $P(W \le 2)$.

Solution

Since W can only take whole number values:

$$P(W \le 2) = P(W = 0, 1 \text{ or } 2)$$

A random variable can only take one value at a time, so its values are mutually exclusive. Hence:

$$P(W \le 2) = P(W = 0) + P(W = 1) + P(W = 2)$$

Using the probability function, we see that:

$$P(W = 0) = \frac{1}{4}\left(\frac{3}{4}\right)^{0} = \frac{1}{4}$$

$$P(W = 1) = \frac{1}{4}\left(\frac{3}{4}\right)^{1} = \frac{3}{16}$$

$$P(W = 2) = \frac{1}{4}\left(\frac{3}{4}\right)^{2} = \frac{9}{64}$$

So:

$$P(W \le 2) = \frac{1}{4} + \frac{3}{16} + \frac{9}{64} = \frac{37}{64}$$ ♦♦

15.4   Cumulative distribution functions

The probability function of a random variable X is the function that assigns probabilities to each of the possible values of X (and gives zero for all other values). The *cumulative distribution function* (or *CDF*) gives the cumulative probability for all values of x (*ie* the total probability so far). The cumulative distribution function is sometimes just called the *distribution function*.

Cumulative distribution functions

The cumulative distribution function of a random variable X is denoted by $F_X(x)$, or sometimes just $F(x)$. It is defined as follows:

$$F_X(x) = P(X \le x) \quad \text{for each } x$$

Let's see how this works by going back to the situation where X denotes the score obtained when a fair die is rolled. We have:

x	1	2	3	4	5	6
$P(X = x)$	$\frac{1}{6}$	$\frac{1}{6}$	$\frac{1}{6}$	$\frac{1}{6}$	$\frac{1}{6}$	$\frac{1}{6}$
$P(X \le x)$	$\frac{1}{6}$	$\frac{2}{6}$	$\frac{3}{6}$	$\frac{4}{6}$	$\frac{5}{6}$	1

This table shows the value at which the cumulative probability increases. However, the CDF is defined for *all* values of x. So we have to work out the values of the CDF for values of x that don't belong to the set $\{1, 2, 3, 4, 5, 6\}$.

If $x < 1$, we haven't yet reached any of the possible values of X. So:

$$F_X(x) = P(X \le x) = 0 \quad \text{for } x < 1$$

If $x > 6$, we have already exceeded all the possible values of X. So:

$$F_X(x) = P(X \le x) = 1 \quad \text{for } x > 6$$

If $1 < x < 2$, $P(X = x) = 0$ so:

$$F_X(x) = P(X \le x) = P(X \le 1) = F_X(1) \quad \text{for } 1 < x < 2$$

In other words, $F_X(x)$ is constant over the interval $1 \le x < 2$. Similarly, $F_X(x)$ is constant over each of the intervals $2 \le x < 3$, $3 \le x < 4$, $4 \le x < 5$ and $5 \le x < 6$ and we have:

$$F_X(x) = \begin{cases} 0 & x < 1 \\ 1/6 & 1 \le x < 2 \\ 2/6 & 2 \le x < 3 \\ 3/6 & 3 \le x < 4 \\ 4/6 & 4 \le x < 5 \\ 5/6 & 5 \le x < 6 \\ 1 & x \ge 6 \end{cases}$$

A graph of this CDF is shown below:

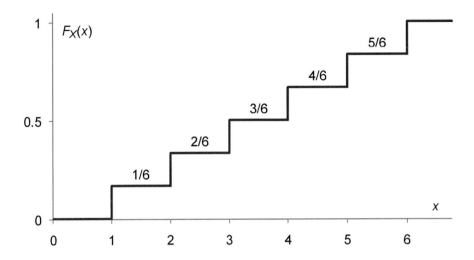

The CDF starts at 0 and stays there until the smallest possible value of X is reached. At that point, the CDF increases. It then stays constant until the next possible value of X is reached. At that point, it increases again. This process continues until all the possible values of X have been included. At that point the CDF reaches its maximum value, which is 1.

Functions that produce this kind of stepped graph are called *step functions*.

The CDF of a discrete random variable

If X is a discrete random variable, its CDF, which is defined for all x, is given by:

$$F_X(x) = \sum_{k \le x} P(X = k)$$

This a step function that increases at each value in the sample space of X.

Example 15.6

The random variable W has the following probability distribution:

w	2	4	5
$P(W = w)$	0.2	0.5	0.3

(i)   Sketch the graph of the CDF of W.

(ii)   Give a formula for the CDF of W.

(iii) State the values of $F_W(1)$, $F_W(4.5)$ and $F_W(10)$.

Solution

(i)   The graph is:

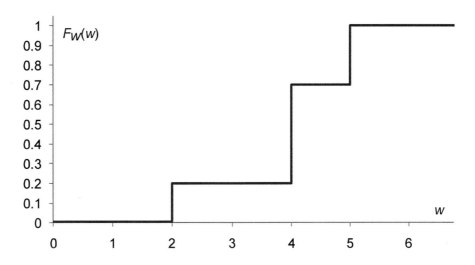

(ii)   The CDF of W is:

$$F_W(w) = \begin{cases} 0 & w < 2 \\ 0.2 & 2 \le w < 4 \\ 0.7 & 4 \le w < 5 \\ 1 & w \ge 5 \end{cases}$$

(iii)   Either reading off the graph or using the CDF we see that:

$$F_W(1) = 0$$
$$F_W(4.5) = 0.7$$
$$F_W(10) = 1$$

♦♦

◆ Calculating probabilities using a CDF

Suppose the random variable X has CDF:

$$F_X(x) = \begin{cases} 0 & x < 0 \\ 0.15 & 0 \le x < 1 \\ 0.5 & 1 \le x < 2 \\ 0.8 & 2 \le x < 3 \\ 1 & x \ge 3 \end{cases}$$

We can determine the probability function of X by subtracting adjacent cumulative probabilities. For example:

$$P(X = 2) = P(X \le 2) - P(X \le 1) = F_X(2) - F_X(1) = 0.8 - 0.5 = 0.3$$

Using the same process for $P(X = 0)$, $P(X = 1)$ and $P(X = 3)$, we find that the probability distribution of X is:

x	0	1	2	3
$P(X = x)$	0.15	0.35	0.3	0.2

Now suppose we want to determine $P(X \geq 2)$. We can do this using the probability function of X as follows:

$$P(X \geq 2) = P(X = 2) + P(X = 3) = 0.3 + 0.2 = 0.5$$

Alternatively, we could calculate $P(X \geq 2)$ directly from the CDF of X:

$$P(X \geq 2) = 1 - P(X < 2) = 1 - P(X \leq 1) = 1 - F_X(1) = 1 - 0.5 = 0.5$$

This method is often quicker.

Example 15.7

The CDF of the random variable V is given by:

$$F_V(v) = \begin{cases} 0 & v < 1 \\ 0.216 & 1 \leq v < 2 \\ 0.648 & 2 \leq v < 3 \\ 0.936 & 3 \leq v < 4 \\ 1 & 4 \leq v \end{cases}$$

Determine:

(i) $P(V = 2)$

(ii) $P(V > 1)$

(iii) $P(V < 3)$

Solution

(i) $P(V = 2) = F_V(2) - F_V(1) = 0.648 - 0.216 = 0.432$

(ii) $P(V > 1) = 1 - P(V \leq 1) = 1 - F_V(1) = 1 - 0.216 = 0.784$

(iii) $P(V < 3) = P(V \leq 2) = 0.648$ ◆◆

15.5 *Measures of location*

In this section we will define the mean, median and mode of a discrete random variable.

 ## *Mean*

In Chapter 10 we saw how to calculate the mean of a data set. Given a set of values, $x_1, x_2, ..., x_m$, with frequencies $f_1, f_2, ..., f_m$ respectively, the mean is given by:

$$\bar{x} = \frac{\sum_{i=1}^{m} x_i f_i}{\sum_{i=1}^{m} f_i}$$

We now consider the mean of a random variable (rather than a data set). The mean (or expected value or expectation) of a random variable X is usually written as $E(X)$.

If X is a discrete random variable, $E(X)$ is a weighted average of the possible values of X. The weights are the probabilities. So:

$$E(X) = \frac{\sum\limits_{x} x\,P(X = x)}{\sum\limits_{x} P(X = x)}$$

This is similar to the formula for $\bar{x}$ – the only difference is that the frequencies are replaced by probabilities.

However, since $\sum\limits_{x} P(X = x) = 1$, the formula for $E(X)$ can be simplified.

Mean (or expected value) of a discrete random variable

$$E(X) = \sum\limits_{x} x\,P(X = x)$$

The mean of a random variable is also often denoted by the Greek letter μ. Throughout statistics we use Greek letters for quantities associated with random variables and English (Roman) letters for quantities associated with observations.

The units of measurement of $E(X)$ are the same as the units of measurement of X. For example, if X denotes the amount, in £, of an insurance claim, then $E(X)$ is also measured in £.

Example 15.8

The random variable X has the following probability distribution:

x	0	1	2	3
$P(X = x)$	0.1	0.2	0.4	0.3

Calculate $E(X)$.

Solution

The expected value of X is:

$$E(X) = (0 \times 0.1) + (1 \times 0.2) + (2 \times 0.4) + (3 \times 0.3) = 1.9 \qquad \blacklozenge\blacklozenge$$

Since $E(X)$ is a weighted average, its value must lie between the smallest possible value and the largest possible value of X. We see in this example that $E(X)$ lies between 0 and 3.

◆ Median

The median of a data set is the value that splits the data set into two equal halves, so that half the observations lie below the median and half lie above it. The median of the random variable X is a value m such that:

$$P(X < m) \le 0.5 \le P(X \le m)$$

This looks quite complicated, but it is easy to determine the median of a random variable from the graph of its CDF. As we will see, in some cases there may be more than one possible value for m.

Median of a discrete random variable

To identify the median of a discrete random variable:

- draw a graph of the CDF

- locate the value 0.5 on the cumulative probability axis (*ie* the y-axis)

- read off the corresponding value from the x-axis – this is the median.

Example 15.9

The random variable W has the following probability distribution:

w	2	4	5
$P(W = w)$	0.2	0.5	0.3

Determine the median of W.

Solution

The CDF of W is:

$$F_W(w) = \begin{cases} 0 & w < 2 \\ 0.2 & 2 \leq w < 4 \\ 0.7 & 4 \leq w < 5 \\ 1 & w \geq 5 \end{cases}$$

From the graph of the CDF, we see that $F_W(w) = 0.5$ when $w = 4$. So the median of W is 4.

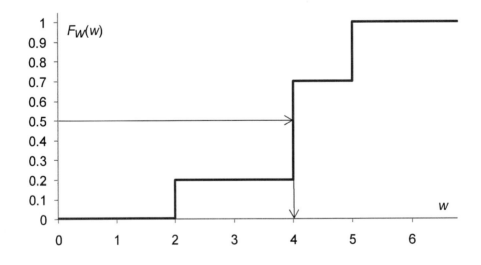

♦♦

Example 15.10

The random variable Z has the following probability distribution:

z	2	4	5
$P(Z = z)$	0.2	0.3	0.5

Determine the median of Z.

Solution

The CDF of Z is:

$$F_Z(z) = \begin{cases} 0 & z < 2 \\ 0.2 & 2 \le z < 4 \\ 0.5 & 4 \le z < 5 \\ 1 & z \ge 5 \end{cases}$$

From the graph of the CDF, we see that $F_Z(z) = 0.5$ for all values of z in the interval $[4,5)$.

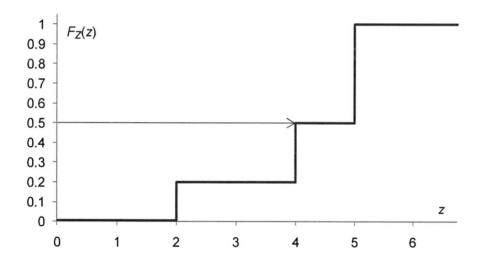

So Z does not have a unique median.   ♦♦

 Mode

We saw in Chapter 10 that the mode of a data set is the value with the highest frequency. The mode of a random variable is defined in an analogous way.

Mode of a discrete random variable

The mode of a discrete random variable is the value with the highest probability.

Example 15.11

The random variable X has the following probability distribution:

x	0	1	2	3
$P(X = x)$	0.1	0.2	0.4	0.3

Identify the mode of X.

Solution

The mode of X is 2 as this value has the highest probability.   ♦ ♦

Some random variables have no mode (*eg* the score obtained when a fair die is rolled), and some random variables do not have a unique mode.

Example 15.12

The random variable X has the following probability distribution:

x	0	1	2	3
$P(X = x)$	0.15	0.35	0.15	0.35

Identify the mode of X.

Solution

The values 1 and 3 both have the highest probability, so they are both modes. Since this random variable has two modes, it is *bimodal*.   ♦ ♦

15.6   *The expected value of a function of a discrete random variable*

Consider once again the random variable X from Example 15.8, which has the probability distribution shown below:

x	0	1	2	3
$P(X = x)$	0.1	0.2	0.4	0.3

We saw in the previous section that:

$$E(X) = (0 \times 0.1) + (1 \times 0.2) + (2 \times 0.4) + (3 \times 0.3) = 1.9$$

Now let's consider the random variable X^2. To work out the possible values of this random variable, we square each of the possible values of X:

$$x = 0 \Rightarrow x^2 = 0^2 = 0$$
$$x = 1 \Rightarrow x^2 = 1^2 = 1$$
$$x = 2 \Rightarrow x^2 = 2^2 = 4$$
$$x = 3 \Rightarrow x^2 = 3^2 = 9$$

So the possible values of X^2 are 0, 1, 4 and 9.

Now the only way that X^2 can take the value 0 is if X takes the value 0. So:

$$P(X^2 = 0) = 0.1$$

Likewise, the only way that X^2 can take the value 1 is if X takes the value 1. So:

$$P(X^2 = 1) = 0.2$$

Continuing in this way, we obtain the following probability distribution for X^2:

k	0	1	4	9
$P(X^2 = k)$	0.1	0.2	0.4	0.3

We can now calculate $E(X^2)$ in the usual way (*ie* by multiplying each possible value of the random variable X^2 by its probability and then summing):

$$E(X^2) = (0 \times 0.1) + (1 \times 0.2) + (4 \times 0.4) + (9 \times 0.3) = 4.5$$

In fact, for any discrete random variable, X:

$$E(X^2) = \sum_x x^2 \, P(X = x)$$

Note that, in general, $E(X^2) \neq [E(X)]^2$. We can see this from the figures above (since $4.5 \neq 1.9^2$).

We can deal with other functions of X in a similar way, *eg*:

$$E(X^3) = \sum_x x^3 \, P(X = x)$$

$$E(4X - 1) = \sum_x (4x - 1) P(X = x)$$

$$E(e^{2X}) = \sum_x e^{2x} \, P(X = x)$$

The same process works for any function of X. This can be summarised as follows:

Expected value of a function of a discrete random variable

If X is a discrete random variable and $g(X)$ is a function of that random variable, then:

$$E[g(X)] = \sum_x g(x)P(X = x)$$

 Example 15.13

The random variable W has the following probability distribution:

w	2	4	5
$P(W = w)$	0.2	0.5	0.3

Calculate:

(i) $E(W)$

(ii) $E(5W - 2)$

(ii) $E\left(\frac{1}{W}\right)$

Solution

(i) $E(W) = \sum_w wP(W = w) = (2 \times 0.2) + (4 \times 0.5) + (5 \times 0.3) = 3.9$

(ii) $E(5W - 2) = \sum_z (5w - 2)P(W = w) = (8 \times 0.2) + (18 \times 0.5) + (23 \times 0.3) = 17.5$

(iii) $E\left(\frac{1}{W}\right) = \sum_w \frac{1}{w}P(W = w) = \left(\frac{1}{2} \times 0.2\right) + \left(\frac{1}{4} \times 0.5\right) + \left(\frac{1}{5} \times 0.3\right) = 0.285$ ◆◆

◆ *Linear functions*

In the example above, we can see that:

$$E(5W - 2) = 5E(W) - 2$$

since:

$$17.5 = 5 \times 3.9 - 2$$

But:

$$E\left(\frac{1}{W}\right) \neq \frac{1}{E(W)}$$

since:

$$0.285 \neq \frac{1}{3.9}$$

Recall that $g(W)$ is a linear function of W if it is of the form $aW + b$ for some constants a and b. So $5W - 2$ is a linear function of W, but $\dfrac{1}{W}$ is not. We have the following important result concerning linear functions of random variables:

Expected value of a linear function of a random variable

Suppose that X is a random variable and that a and b are constants. Then:

$$E(aX + b) = aE(X) + b$$

Using the general formula for the expected value of a function of a random variable, it's easy to see why this is the case. If X is a discrete random variable, then:

$$E(aX + b) = \sum_x (ax + b)P(X = x)$$

$$= \sum_x ax\, P(X = x) + \sum_x b\, P(X = x)$$

$$= a\sum_x x\, P(X = x) + b\sum_x P(X = x)$$

Since:

$$\sum_x x\, P(X = x) = E(X) \quad \text{and} \quad \sum_x P(X = x) = 1$$

it follows that:

$$E(aX + b) = aE(X) + b$$

Setting $a = 0$ in the formula above, we can also see that $E(b) = b$ for any constant b.

Example 15.14

Given that $E(Y) = 6$, calculate:

(i) $E(4Y)$

(ii) $E\left(\dfrac{1 - 3Y}{5}\right)$

Solution

(i) $E(4Y) = 4E(Y) = 4 \times 6 = 24$

(ii) $E\left(\dfrac{1 - 3Y}{5}\right) = E\left(\dfrac{1}{5} - \dfrac{3}{5}Y\right) = \dfrac{1}{5} - \dfrac{3}{5}E(Y) = \dfrac{1}{5} - \dfrac{3}{5} \times 6 = -3.4$ ♦♦

◇ Linear combinations

Suppose that X is a discrete random variable and consider the function $g(X) = 3X^2 - 4X + 9$. Using the general formula for the expected value of a function of a discrete random variable, we have:

$$E(3X^2 - 4X + 9) = \sum_x (3x^2 - 4x + 9)P(X = x)$$

$$= \sum_x 3x^2 P(X = x) + \sum_x (-4x)P(X = x) + \sum_x 9P(X = x)$$

$$= 3\sum_x x^2 P(X = x) - 4\sum_x x P(X = x) + 9$$

We have already seen that:

$$\sum_x x^2 P(X = x) = E(X^2)$$

$$\sum_x x P(X = x) = E(X)$$

and: $$\sum_x P(X = x) = 1$$

So:

$$E(3X^2 - 4X + 9) = 3E(X^2) - 4E(X) + 9$$

This technique of breaking down the expected value into smaller parts is often a helpful way of calculating the expected value of expressions involving random variables.

Example 15.15

Given that $E(Y) = 6$ and $E(Y^2) = 100$, calculate $E\left[(Y + 1)^2\right]$.

Solution

$$E\left[(Y + 1)^2\right] = E(Y^2 + 2Y + 1) = E(Y^2) + 2E(Y) + 1 = 100 + 12 + 1 = 113$$ ◆◆

15.7 Measures of spread

In this section we will define the variance and standard deviation of a discrete random variable. The variance of the random variable X is usually denoted by $\text{var}(X)$.

◇ Variance

In Chapter 11 we saw how to calculate the variance of a data set. Given a set of values, $x_1, x_2, ..., x_m$, with frequencies $f_1, f_2, ..., f_m$ respectively, the variance is given by:

$$s^2 = \frac{1}{n}\sum_{i=1}^{m}(x_i - \bar{x})^2 f_i \quad \text{where} \quad n = \sum_{i=1}^{m} f_i$$

This is a measure of the average squared distance between each data point and the sample mean, $\bar{x}$.

We now consider the variance of a random variable (rather than a data set). The variance of a random variable X is usually written as $\text{var}(X)$.

If X is a discrete random variable, $\text{var}(X)$ is a weighted average of the possible values of $(x - \mu)^2$. The weights are the probabilities, so:

$$\text{var}(X) = \frac{\sum_x (x - \mu)^2 P(X = x)}{\sum_x P(X = x)}$$

However, since $\sum_x P(X = x) = 1$, the formula for $\text{var}(X)$ can be simplified.

Variance of a random variable

$$\text{var}(X) = \sum_x (x - \mu)^2 P(X = x) = E\left[(X - \mu)^2\right] = E\left[(X - E(X))^2\right]$$

As it is the square of the standard deviation, which we will meet below, the variance of a random variable is also often denoted by σ^2. This notation emphasises the fact that the variance is always positive (or zero).

We can express the formula for $\text{var}(X)$ in a different way by multiplying out the squared term inside the expected value. Doing so, we see that:

$$\text{var}(X) = E(X^2 - 2\mu X + \mu^2) = E(X^2) - 2\mu E(X) + \mu^2$$

Since $\mu = E(X)$, this simplifies further to give:

$$\text{var}(X) = E(X^2) - 2\mu^2 + \mu^2 = E(X^2) - \mu^2 = E(X^2) - [E(X)]^2$$

It is often quicker to calculate the variance of a random variable using this formula.

Alternative formula for the variance of a random variable

$$\sigma^2 = \text{var}(X) = E(X^2) - [E(X)]^2$$

Example 15.16

The random variable X has the following probability distribution:

x	0	1	2	3
$P(X = x)$	0.1	0.2	0.4	0.3

Calculate $\text{var}(X)$.

Solution

We have:

$$\mu = E(X) = (0 \times 0.1) + (1 \times 0.2) + (2 \times 0.4) + (3 \times 0.3) = 1.9$$

So:

$$var(X) = E\left[(X - 1.9)^2\right]$$
$$= (0 - 1.9)^2 \times 0.1 + (1 - 1.9)^2 \times 0.2 + (2 - 1.9)^2 \times 0.4 + (3 - 1.9)^2 \times 0.3$$
$$= 0.89$$

Using the alternative formula:

$$E(X^2) = (0^2 \times 0.1) + (1^2 \times 0.2) + (2^2 \times 0.4) + (3^2 \times 0.3) = 4.5$$

and once again we find that:

$$var(X) = 4.5 - 1.9^2 = 0.89$$ ♦♦

The variance of a random variable is measured in units squared. For example, if X denotes the amount, in £, of an insurance claim, then the units of measurement of $var(X)$ are $£^2$. This is not an intuitive quantity but we can avoid this problem by taking the square root of the variance as our measure of spread.

◆ *Standard deviation*

The standard deviation of a random variable is the square root of its variance. It is denoted by the Greek letter σ. The standard deviation is measured in the same units as the random variable itself. For example, if X denotes the amount, in £, of an insurance claim, then the units of measurement of the standard deviation are also £. In the previous example, we calculated the variance of X to be 0.89. So the standard deviation of X is $\sqrt{0.89} = 0.9434$.

15.8   *The variance of a function of a discrete random variable*

In Section 15.6, we considered the expected value of a linear function of a random variable. Now let's consider the variance.

Variance of a linear function of a random variable

Suppose that X is a random variable and that a and b are constants. Then:

$$var(aX + b) = a^2 \, var(X)$$

A derivation of this result now follows. Suppose that $Y = aX + b$. Then:

$$E(Y) = aE(X) + b$$

$$E(Y^2) = E\left[(aX + b)^2\right] = E(a^2 X^2 + 2abX + b^2) = a^2 E(X^2) + 2abE(X) + b^2$$

and:

$$\begin{aligned}
\operatorname{var}(Y) &= E(Y^2) - \left[E(Y)\right]^2 \\
&= a^2 E(X^2) + 2abE(X) + b^2 - \left[aE(X) + b\right]^2 \\
&= a^2 E(X^2) + 2abE(X) + b^2 - \left[a^2 [E(X)]^2 + 2abE(X) + b^2\right] \\
&= a^2 E(X^2) - a^2 [E(X)]^2 \\
&= a^2 \left[E(X^2) - [E(X)]^2\right] \\
&= a^2 \operatorname{var}(X)
\end{aligned}$$

It is worth noting the following important points.

*   Adding a constant, b, to a random variable *does not* change its variance. This is to be expected since adding b will change the possible values of the random variable and will increase the mean by b, but it will not change the spread of the values around the mean.

*   Multiplying a random variable by a constant a *does* change its variance (unless $|a| = 1$). Since variance is a squared measure, multiplying a random variable by a causes its variance to be multiplied by a^2.

*   Taking the square root of both sides of the equation $\operatorname{var}(aX + b) = a^2 \operatorname{var}(X)$, we see that the standard deviation of $aX + b$ is equal to a times the standard deviation of X.

*   Setting $a = 0$ in the equation $\operatorname{var}(aX + b) = a^2 \operatorname{var}(X)$ tells us that $\operatorname{var}(b) = 0$ for any constant b. This makes sense because, if the value is always b, there is no spread or deviation in the values we observe.

Example 15.17

Given that $\operatorname{var}(Z) = 4$, calculate:

(i) $\operatorname{var}(9 - 4Z)$

(ii) $\operatorname{var}\left(\dfrac{3Z + 1}{8}\right)$

Solution

(i) $\operatorname{var}(9 - 4Z) = (-4)^2 \operatorname{var}(Z) = 16 \times 4 = 64$

(ii) $\operatorname{var}\left(\dfrac{3Z + 1}{8}\right) = \left(\dfrac{3}{8}\right)^2 \operatorname{var}(Z) = \dfrac{9}{64} \times 4 = \dfrac{9}{16} = 0.5625$ ◆◆

15.9   Measures of skewness

In Chapter 11 we introduced the third central moment as a measure of skewness (or asymmetry) of a data set. Recall that the third central moment of the data set $x_1, x_2, ..., x_n$ is:

$$\frac{1}{n}\sum_{i=1}^{n}(x_i - \bar{x})^3$$

We will now define the skewness of a random variable.

Skewness

The skewness of the random variable X is given by:

$$skew(X) = E[(X - \mu)^3]$$

There are no restrictions on the value of $skew(X)$ – it could be positive, negative or zero. The skewness of a discrete random variable is:

- positive if the probability distribution has a tail to the right (*ie* the positive side)

- negative if the probability distribution has a tail to the left (*ie* the negative side)

- zero if the probability distribution is symmetric.

Example 15.18

The random variable X has the following probability distribution:

x	0	1	2	3
$P(X = x)$	0.1	0.2	0.4	0.3

Calculate $skew(X)$.

Solution

We have:

$$\mu = E(X) = (0 \times 0.1) + (1 \times 0.2) + (2 \times 0.4) + (3 \times 0.3) = 1.9$$

So:

$$skew(X) = E\left[(X - 1.9)^3\right]$$
$$= (0 - 1.9)^3 \times 0.1 + (1 - 1.9)^3 \times 0.2 + (2 - 1.9)^3 \times 0.4 + (3 - 1.9)^3 \times 0.3$$
$$= -0.432$$

A graph of this probability distribution is shown below:

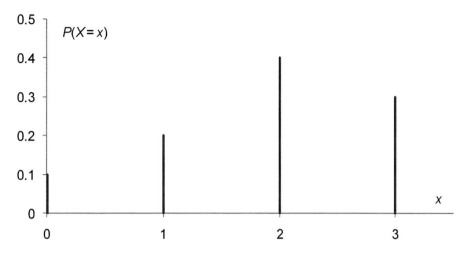

We can see from the graph that the distribution has a tail to the left and so it is negatively skewed. The negative value of $skew(X)$ is consistent with this.   ♦♦

We can obtain an alternative formula for $skew(X)$ by multiplying out the cubed term in the expected value. Using the properties of expected value (and remembering that $\mu = E(X)$ is a constant), we see that:

$$skew(X) = E\left[(X - \mu)^3\right]$$
$$= E(X^3 - 3\mu X^2 + 3\mu^2 X - \mu^3)$$
$$= E(X^3) - 3\mu E(X^2) + 3\mu^2 E(X) - \mu^3$$
$$= E(X^3) - 3\mu E(X^2) + 3\mu^3 - \mu^3$$
$$= E(X^3) - 3\mu E(X^2) + 2\mu^3$$

It may sometimes be quicker to calculate the skewness of a random variable using this version of the formula.

Alternative formula for skewness

$skew(X) = E(X^3) - 3\mu E(X^2) + 2\mu^3$

The skewness of a random variable is measured in units cubed. For example, if X denotes the amount, in £, of an insurance claim, then the units of measurement of $skew(X)$ are $£^3$. Once again, this measure is not intuitive. We can avoid this problem by using the *coefficient of skewness* as our measure of asymmetry.

Coefficient of skewness

The coefficient of skewness of the random variable X is given by:

$$\frac{skew(X)}{[var(X)]^{3/2}}$$

This is a dimensionless measure since the units in the numerator cancel with the units in the denominator. There are no restrictions on the value of the coefficient of skewness – it could be positive, negative or zero. Coefficients of skewness can be used to compare the asymmetry of probability distributions – the larger the *magnitude* of the coefficient of skewness, the more asymmetric the distribution.

Example 15.19

Claims arising from a particular group of insurance policies can be divided into two types, Type A and Type B. The amount paid by the insurer on a Type A claim is £500 and the amount paid by the insurer on a Type B claim is £800. 60% of claims are of Type A and 40% of claims are of Type B.

Let X denote the amount paid by the insurer on a randomly selected claim. Calculate the coefficient of skewness of X.

Solution

The probability distribution of X is as follows:

x	£500	£800
$P(X = x)$	0.6	0.4

So:

$$E(X) = 500 \times 0.6 + 800 \times 0.4 = £620$$

$$\text{var}(X) = (500 - 620)^2 \times 0.6 + (800 - 620)^2 \times 0.4 = £^2\, 21,600$$

$$\text{skew}(X) = (500 - 620)^3 \times 0.6 + (800 - 620)^3 \times 0.4 = £^3\, 1,296,000$$

and hence the coefficient of skewness of X is:

$$\frac{£^3\, 1,296,000}{(£^2\, 21,600)^{3/2}} = 0.40825 \qquad\qquad\qquad ♦♦$$

15.10 Population moments

In Chapter 11 we defined moments of data sets, *ie* of observations. Now we will define moments of random variables. These are sometimes called *population moments*.

> ### Non-central moments
>
> The k th non-central moment of the random variable X is:
>
> $$E(X^k)$$
>
> The k th non-central moment is also sometimes called the k th moment about 0 or sometimes just the k th moment.

So $E(X)$ is the first non-central moment of the random variable X.

Central moments

The k th central moment of the random variable X is:

$$E\left[(X-\mu)^k\right]$$

where $\mu = E(X)$.

The k th central moment is also sometimes called the k th moment about the mean.

So var(X) is the second central moment of X and skew(X) is the third central moment of X.

Moments about the point *c*

The k th moment of the random variable X about the point c is:

$$E\left[(X-c)^k\right]$$

Example 15.20

The random variable V has the following probability distribution:

v	−1	2
$P(V = v)$	0.4	0.6

Calculate the second moment of V about the point 1.

Solution

The second moment of V about the point 1 is:

$$E\left[(V-1)^2\right] = \left[(-1-1)^2 \times 0.4\right] + \left[(2-1)^2 \times 0.6\right] = 1.6 + 0.6 = 2.2$$

◆◆

Chapter 15 Practice Questions

◆ *Probability functions*

Question 15.1   (IFoA Past Examination Question)

The discrete random variable X has the following probability function:

$$P(X = i) = 0.2 + ai \ : \ i = -2, -1, 0, 1, 2$$

State the possible values that a can take.

Question 15.2   (IFoA Past Examination Question)

The discrete variable X takes 4 distinct values with probabilities:

$$(1+3\theta)/4, \ (1-\theta)/4, \ (1+2\theta)/4, \ (1-4\theta)/4$$

This defines a probability distribution if:

A $-\frac{1}{2} \leq \theta \leq \frac{3}{2}$

B $-\frac{1}{2} \leq \theta \leq \frac{1}{8}$

C $-\frac{3}{4} \leq \theta \leq \frac{1}{4}$

D $-\frac{1}{3} \leq \theta \leq \frac{1}{4}$

Question 15.3

The discrete random variable W has the following probability function:

$$P(W = w) = \frac{2^w}{w!} e^{-2} \qquad w = 0, 1, 2, \ldots$$

Calculate:

(i) $P(W = 3)$

(ii) $P(W > 1)$

◆ *Cumulative distribution functions*

Question 15.4

The random variable X has the following probability function:

$$P(X = x) = \frac{1}{12}(8 - x) \qquad\qquad x = 2, 4 \text{ or } 6$$

(i)   Sketch the graph of the cumulative distribution function

(ii)   State the cumulative distribution function of X.

◆ Measures of location and spread

Question 15.5

The random variable Y has probability function:

$$P(Y = y) = \frac{k}{y} \qquad y = 1, 2, 3, 4$$

Find the mean, mode and median of Y.

Question 15.6   (IFoA Past Examination Question)

A private investor has capital of £16,000. He divides this into eight units of £2,000, each of which he invests in a separate one-year investment. Each of these investments has three possible outcomes at the end of the year:

1.	total loss of capital	probability 0.1
2.	capital payment of £2,000	probability 0.7
3.	capital payment of £5,000	probability 0.2

The investments behave independently of one another, and there is no other return from them.

Calculate the expected payment received by the investor at the end of the year.

Question 15.7

The number of deaths among three life assurance policyholders is given by the random variable X:

$$P(X = x) = {}^{3}C_{x} \times 0.1^{x} \times 0.9^{3-x} \quad x = 0, 1, 2, 3$$

Calculate the mean and standard deviation of the number of deaths.

Question 15.8   (IFoA Past Examination Question)

Consider two independent lives A and B. The probabilities that A and B die within a specified period are 0.1 and 0.2 respectively. If A dies you lose £50,000, whether or not B dies. If B dies you lose £30,000, whether or not A dies.

(i)   Calculate the mean and standard deviation of your total losses in the period.

◆ Functions of random variables

Question 15.9   (IFoA Past Examination Question)

Customer electricity charges C are calculated according to the formula

$$C = 7.00 + 0.0742N$$

where N denotes the number of units used.

In a particular area, N is modelled as a random variable with mean 600 and variance 250.

Calculate the mean and variance of the charges C in their respective units.

Question 15.10

The mean and standard deviation of the random variable U are 8 and 3, respectively. Calculate:

(i) $E(3 + 6U)$

(ii)   the standard deviation of $8 - 2U$

(iii) $\text{var}\left(\dfrac{U-8}{3}\right)$

(iv) $E(U^2 - 4U + 7)$

◆ Measures of skewness

Question 15.11   (IFoA Past Examination Question)

Calculate the coefficient of skewness for the following discrete probability distribution:

x	−2	−1	0	1
$P(X = x)$	0.1	0.1	0.5	0.3

16

Continuous random variables

Learning Objectives

The following learning objectives are covered in this chapter:

- Explain what is meant by a continuous random variable, define the distribution function and the probability density function of such a variable, and use these functions to calculate probabilities.

- Define the expected value of a function of a continuous random variable, the mean, the variance, the standard deviation, the coefficient of skewness and the moments of a continuous random variable, and calculate such quantities.

16.1 Introduction

In Chapter 15 we defined a random variable to be a quantity whose value is uncertain and is subject to variations that are due to chance. In that chapter we restricted our attention to discrete random variables. Now we consider continuous random variables.

Continuous random variables

A random variable is said to be continuous if it can take *any* value within a particular interval, eg $(0,1)$ or $(-\infty, \infty)$.

16.2 Probability density functions

Recall that every discrete random variable has a probability function associated with it. Similarly, every continuous random variable has its own *probability density function* (or PDF). We use the notation $f_X(x)$, or sometimes just $f(x)$, to denote the PDF of the random variable X.

Probability functions must always take non-negative values and must sum to 1. PDFs have similar properties.

Properties of PDFs

$f_X(x)$ is a PDF if the following two conditions hold:

(i) $f_X(x) \geq 0$

(ii) $\int_x f_X(x)\,dx = 1$

The notation $\int_x$ means that we are integrating over all possible values of x.

Technically, a PDF is defined for *all* values of x, with $f_X(x) = 0$ for the values of x that are impossible. For convenience, we tend to state the PDF only for values of x for which it is non-zero.

It is important to realise that the values of $f_X(x)$ are not probabilities, but the function $f_X(x)$ can be used to calculate probabilities.

Calculating probabilities from a PDF

If X is a continuous random variable with PDF $f_X(x)$, then:

$$P(a \leq X \leq b) = \int_a^b f_X(x)\,dx$$

So $P(a \leq X \leq b)$ is equal to the area under the PDF between the values of $x = a$ and $x = b$. This is illustrated in the diagram below.

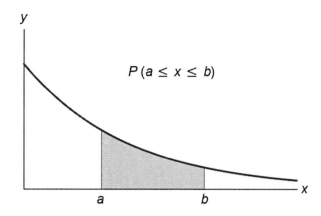

The second property of PDFs says that when the PDF is integrated over all possible values of the random variable, the result is 1. So the total area under any PDF is 1.

From Chapter 9 we know that the values for continuous data are always grouped in some way, and that a histogram of a data set shows the frequency density for each group. The areas of the bars of a histogram represent the frequencies. Remember that a data set gives a snapshot of the past, whereas a random variable provides a model of the future. When we move from the past to the future, we replace the observed frequency densities with the PDF. As we will see later in this chapter, the PDF is also used in the calculation of the mean and variance of a continuous random variable.

Example 16.1

The PDF of the random variable X is given by:

$$f_X(x) = c(1-x) \quad \text{for } 0 < x < 1$$

Calculate the value of the constant c.

Solution

Using the fact that $\int_x f_X(x)\,dx = 1$, we have:

$$\int_0^1 c(1-x)\,dx = c\int_0^1 (1-x)\,dx = c\left[x - \tfrac{1}{2}x^2\right]_0^1 = c\left[(1-\tfrac{1}{2})-0\right] = \tfrac{1}{2}c = 1$$

So $c = 2$.   ♦♦

Example 16.2

The random variable Y has PDF:

$$f_Y(y) = \tfrac{1}{8}y \quad \text{for } 0 \leq y \leq 4$$

Calculate:

(i) $P(2 \leq Y \leq 3)$

(ii) $P(Y \geq 2.8)$

Solution

(i)   To calculate $P(2 \leq Y \leq 3)$, we integrate $f_Y(y)$ between the limits of $y = 2$ and $y = 3$:

$$P(2 \leq Y \leq 3) = \int_2^3 \tfrac{1}{8} y \, dy = \left[\tfrac{1}{16} y^2 \right]_2^3 = \tfrac{9}{16} - \tfrac{4}{16} = \tfrac{5}{16} = 0.3125$$

(ii)   To calculate $P(Y \geq 2.8)$, we integrate $f_Y(y)$ between the limits of $y = 2.8$ and $y = 4$ (the maximum possible value of Y):

$$P(Y \geq 2.8) = \int_{2.8}^4 \tfrac{1}{8} y \, dy = \left[\tfrac{1}{16} y^2 \right]_{2.8}^4 = 1 - 0.49 = 0.51 \qquad \blacklozenge\blacklozenge$$

Let's now consider probabilities of the form $P(X = a)$ where X is a continuous random variable and a is a constant. Integrating the PDF of X, we see that:

$$P(X = a) = \int_a^a f_X(x) \, dx = 0$$

This means that the probability of obtaining any specified value is zero. As a result, with continuous random variables, we don't need to distinguish between strict and weak inequalities. So for any continuous random variable X and any constants a and b:

$$P(a \leq X \leq b) = P(a < X < b)$$

16.3 Cumulative distribution functions

In Chapter 15, we introduced the *cumulative distribution function* (or CDF). Recall that the CDF of the random variable X is denoted by $F_X(x)$ and is defined for all x as follows:

$$F_X(x) = P(X \leq x)$$

We have just seen that we can calculate probabilities involving a continuous random variable by integrating the PDF over an appropriate range. We can also obtain the CDF from the PDF by integration.

> ### CDF of a continuous random variable
>
> If X is a continuous random variable, its CDF is given by:
>
> $$F_X(x) = \int_{-\infty}^x f_X(t) \, dt \quad \text{for all } x$$

In general, the lower limit of this integral is $-\infty$. However, if the smallest possible value of X is a, then $f_X(x) = 0$ for $x < a$, and:

$$F_X(x) = \int_a^x f_X(t) \, dt$$

Since x is the upper limit of this integral, the letter x cannot be used inside the integral itself. Here we have chosen to use the letter t instead.

Example 16.3

The random variable Y has PDF:

$$f_Y(y) = \tfrac{1}{8}y \quad \text{for } 0 \le y \le 4$$

Obtain a formula for $F_Y(y)$ for $0 \le y \le 4$.

Solution

For $0 \le y \le 4$:

$$F_Y(y) = \int_{-\infty}^{y} f_Y(t)\,dt = \int_{0}^{y} \tfrac{1}{8}t\,dt$$

The lower limit on the second integral is 0 since $f_Y(t) = 0$ for $t < 0$. Integrating gives:

$$F_Y(y) = \left[\tfrac{1}{16}t^2 \right]_0^y = \tfrac{1}{16}y^2 - 0 = \tfrac{1}{16}y^2 \qquad\qquad \blacklozenge\blacklozenge$$

Recall that the CDF of a random variable is defined for *all* values. So to specify fully the CDF of the random variable Y in Example 16.3 above, we also need to state the values of $F_Y(y)$ for $y < 0$ and $y > 4$. Since the smallest possible value of Y is 0, we have:

$$F_Y(y) = P(Y \le y) = 0 \quad \text{for } y < 0$$

Also, since the biggest possible value of Y is 4, we have:

$$F_Y(y) = P(Y \le y) = 1 \quad \text{for } y > 4$$

Putting all of this together, we see that the CDF of Y is:

$$F_Y(y) = \begin{cases} 0 & \text{for } y < 0 \\ \tfrac{1}{16}y^2 & \text{for } 0 \le y \le 4 \\ 1 & \text{for } y > 4 \end{cases}$$

However, the usual convention is to state the formula for CDF only over the range of values the variable can actually take. So the CDF of Y may be given as:

$$F_Y(y) = \tfrac{1}{16}y^2 \quad \text{for } 0 \le y \le 4$$

As we have just seen, we can obtain the CDF of a continuous random variable by integrating its PDF. If we know the CDF and we want to obtain the PDF, we can do this by differentiation.

Obtaining a PDF from a CDF

$$f_X(x) = \frac{d}{dx}F_X(x)$$

Example 16.4

The random variable X has CDF:

$$F_X(x) = \frac{x^3}{27} \quad \text{for } 0 \le x \le 3$$

Determine the PDF of X.

Solution

The PDF is:

$$f_X(x) = \frac{d}{dx}\left(\frac{x^3}{27}\right) = \frac{3x^2}{27} = \frac{x^2}{9} \quad \text{for } 0 \le x \le 3$$

(and $f_X(x) = 0$ for all other values of x). ♦♦

◆▶ Calculating probabilities using a CDF

We have already seen that:

$$P(a < X < b) = P(a \le X \le b) = \int_a^b f_X(x)\,dx$$

Now since:

$$\int_a^b f_X(x)\,dx = \int_{-\infty}^b f_X(x)\,dx - \int_{-\infty}^a f_X(x)\,dx$$

we have:

$$P(a < X < b) = P(a \le X \le b) = F_X(b) - F_X(a)$$

So, if we know the CDF, we can use it to calculate probabilities directly. We do not need to obtain the PDF first.

Example 16.5

A random variable V has CDF:

$$F_V(v) = 1 - e^{-0.5v} \quad \text{for } v \ge 0$$

Calculate:

(i) $P(0.5 < V < 1)$

(ii) $P(V > 2)$

Solution

(i) $P(0.5 < V < 1) = F_V(1) - F_V(0.5) = (1 - e^{-0.5}) - (1 - e^{-0.5 \times 0.5}) = e^{-0.25} - e^{-0.5} = 0.17227$

(ii) $P(V > 2) = 1 - P(V \le 2) = 1 - F_V(2) = 1 - (1 - e^{-0.5 \times 2}) = e^{-1} = 0.36788$ ♦♦

16.4 Measures of location

In this section we will describe how to obtain the mean, median and mode of a continuous random variable.

◆ Mean

In Chapter 15 we saw that the *mean* (or *expected value*) of a discrete random variable X is given by:

$$\mu = E(X) = \sum_x x\, P(X = x)$$

To obtain the mean of a continuous random variable, we replace $P(X = x)$ by $f_X(x)$ and, instead of summing, we integrate over all possible values of x.

Mean of a continuous random variable

If X is a continuous random variable, then the mean (or expected value) of X is given by:

$$\mu = E(X) = \int_x x\, f_X(x)\, dx$$

Example 16.6

The random variable X has PDF:

$$f(x) = \frac{2}{x^3} \quad \text{for } x > 1$$

Calculate the expected value of X.

Solution

The expected value of X is:

$$\int_x x\, f_X(x)\, dx = \int_1^\infty x\, \frac{2}{x^3}\, dx = \int_1^\infty 2x^{-2}\, dx = \left[\frac{2}{(-1)} x^{-1} \right]_1^\infty = 0 - (-2) = 2$$

As a reasonableness check, we can see that the expected value lies within the range of values permitted for x, *ie* $(1, \infty)$.   ◆◆

◆ Median

The *median* of a continuous random variable is its middle value. 50% of the total probability lies to the left of this value and the other 50% lies to the right.

Median of a continuous random variable

The median of a continuous random variable X is the value of m such that:

$$F_X(m) = P(X \leq m) = P(X < m) = \int_{-\infty}^{m} f_X(x)\,dx = 0.5$$

Example 16.7

The random variable X has CDF:

$$F_X(x) = \frac{x^3}{27} \quad \text{for } 0 \leq x \leq 3$$

Calculate the median value of X.

Solution

The median is the value of m such that:

$$F_X(m) = \frac{m^3}{27} = 0.5$$

Hence:

$$m = (0.5 \times 27)^{1/3} = 2.38110$$

Again we can see that this lies within the range of values permitted for x, ie $[0,3]$.   ♦♦

In this next example, we are given the PDF rather than the CDF, which means that we need to use integration to determine the median.

Example 16.8

The random variable Y has PDF:

$$f_Y(y) = 0.25\,e^{-0.25y}, \quad y > 0$$

Calculate the median value of Y.

Solution

The median is the value of m such that:

$$\int_{-\infty}^{m} f_Y(y)\,dy = 0.5$$

In this example, $f_Y(y) = 0$ for $y \leq 0$, but m will be greater than 0, so:

$$\int_{-\infty}^{m} f_Y(y)\,dy = \int_{0}^{m} 0.25\,e^{-0.25y}\,dy = \left[-e^{-0.25y}\right]_0^m = 1 - e^{-0.25m}$$

Setting this equal to 0.5, we see that:

$$e^{-0.25m} = 0.5$$

So:

$$m = \frac{\ln 0.5}{-0.25} = 2.77259$$ ◆◆

The diagram below shows the graph of the PDF $f_Y(y) = 0.25\,e^{-0.25y}$, $y > 0$. It also shows how the median divides the total probability into two parts with equal area.

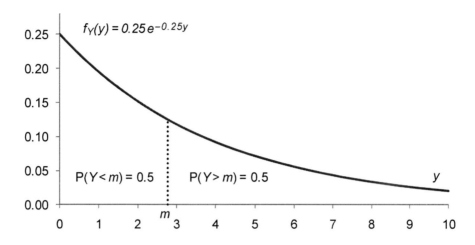

◆ Mode

We saw in Chapter 15 that the *mode* of a discrete random variable is the value with the highest probability. The mode of a continuous random variable is defined in a similar way.

Mode of a continuous random variable

The mode of a continuous random variable is the value that maximises its PDF.

Example 16.9

The random variable X has PDF:

$$f_X(x) = 6\,x\,(1-x), \quad 0 < x < 1$$

Determine its mode.

Solution

To identify the value of x that maximises the PDF, we need to find the stationary points of the function $f_X(x)$. To make the differentiation easier, let's first write the PDF in the form:

$$f_X(x) = 6\,x - 6x^2$$

Differentiating with respect to x gives:

$$f_X'(x) = 6 - 12x$$

This is equal to 0 when $x = 0.5$. So there is a stationary point when $x = 0.5$.

Differentiating again gives:

$$f_X''(x) = -12$$

Since $f_X''(0.5) < 0$, the PDF is maximised when $x = 0.5$. So the mode of X is 0.5. ♦♦

The diagram below shows the graph of the PDF $f_X(x) = 6x(1-x)$, $0 < x < 1$:

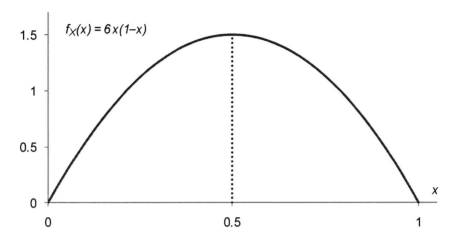

We can see from the graph that the mode of X is 0.5 since the graph reaches its maximum at this point.

Example 16.10

The random variable W has the following PDF:

$$f_W(w) = 1 - 0.5w, \quad 0 \le w \le 2$$

Determine the mode of W.

Solution

Differentiating the PDF with respect to w, we obtain:

$$f_W'(w) = -0.5$$

This is never equal to 0, so there are no stationary points. However, the mode of W can be identified from the graph of the PDF:

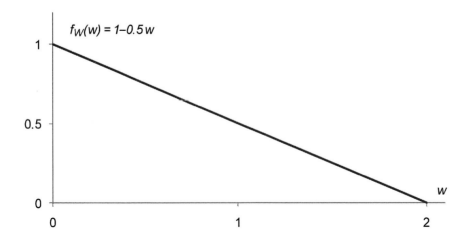

From this graph, we see that the PDF is maximised when $w = 0$. So the mode of W is 0.   ♦♦

16.5   Expected value of a function of a random variable

In Chapter 15 we saw that if X is a discrete random variable and $g(X)$ is a function of X, then:

$$E[g(X)] = \sum_x g(x) P(X = x)$$

We have a corresponding formula for continuous random variables.

Expected value of a function of a continuous random variable

If X is a continuous random variable with PDF $f_X(x)$, and $g(X)$ is a function of X, then:

$$E[g(X)] = \int_x g(x) f_X(x) dx$$

Example 16.11

The random variable Y has PDF:

$$f_Y(y) = \frac{3}{y^4}, \quad y \geq 1$$

Calculate:

(i) $E(Y)$

(ii) $E(5Y - 2)$

(iii) $E\left(\frac{1}{Y}\right)$

Solution

(i) $E(Y) = \int_y y f_Y(y) dy = \int_1^\infty 3y^{-3}\, dy = \left[\frac{3}{-2}y^{-2}\right]_1^\infty = 0 - \left(-\frac{3}{2} \times 1^{-2}\right) = 1.5$

(ii) $E(5Y - 2) = \int_y (5y - 2) f_Y(y) dy = \int_1^\infty (5y - 2) \times 3y^{-4}\, dy$

$$= \int_1^\infty (15y^{-3} - 6y^{-4}) dy$$

$$= \left[\frac{15}{-2}y^{-2} - \left(\frac{6}{-3}y^{-3}\right)\right]_1^\infty$$

$$= 0 - \left(-\frac{15}{2} + 2\right)$$

$$= 5.5$$

(iii) $E\left(\frac{1}{Y}\right) = \int_y \frac{1}{y} f_Y(y)\,dy = \int_1^\infty 3y^{-5}\,dy = \left[\frac{3}{-4}y^{-4}\right]_1^\infty = 0 - \left(-\frac{3}{4} \times 1^{-4}\right) = 0.75$ ♦♦

◆ Linear functions

In the example above, we found that:

$$E(5Y - 2) = 5\,E(Y) - 2 = 5.5$$

In this case, the function $g(Y) = 5Y - 2$ is a linear function of Y. In Chapter 15, we showed that if X is a discrete random variable and a and b are constants, then:

$$E(aX + b) = aE(X) + b$$

Now suppose that X is a continuous random variable. Using the general result for functions of continuous random variables, we have:

$$E(aX + b) = \int_x (ax + b) f_X(x)\,dx = a\int_x x\,f_X(x)\,dx + b\int_x f_X(x)\,dx$$

But $\int_x x\,f_X(x)\,dx = E(X)$ and $\int_x f_X(x)\,dx = 1$. So the result $E(aX + b) = aE(X) + b$ holds for both discrete and continuous random variables.

Expected value of a linear function of a random variable

For *any* random variable X and any constants a and b:

$$E(aX + b) = aE(X) + b$$

Example 16.12

Given that $E(Z) = 4$, calculate:

(i) $E(6 - 2Z)$

(ii) $E\left(\dfrac{5Z + 1}{6}\right)$

Solution

(i) $E(6 - 2Z) = 6 - 2E(Z) = 6 - (2 \times 4) = -2$

(ii) $E\left(\dfrac{5Z + 1}{6}\right) = \dfrac{5}{6}E(Z) + \dfrac{1}{6} = \left(\dfrac{5}{6} \times 4\right) + \dfrac{1}{6} = \dfrac{21}{6} = 3.5$ ♦♦

◆ Linear combinations

Let's now consider combinations of random variables such as $3X^2 - 4X + 9$. We saw in Chapter 15 that if X is a discrete random variable, then:

$$E(3X^2 - 4X + 9) = 3E(X^2) - 4E(X) + 9$$

Now suppose that X is a continuous random variable with PDF $f_X(x)$. In that case:

$$E(3X^2 - 4X + 9) = \int_x (3x^2 - 4x + 9)\, f_X(x)\, dx$$

$$= \int_x 3x^2 f_X(x)\, dx + \int_x (-4x) f_X(x)\, dx + \int_x 9 f_X(x)\, dx$$

$$= 3\int_x x^2 f_X(x)\, dx - 4\int_x x f_X(x)\, dx + 9\int_x f_X(x)\, dx$$

From the definition of expected values, we know that:

$$\int_x x^2 f_X(x)\, dx = E(X^2)$$

$$\int_x x f_X(x)\, dx = E(X)$$

and we know that the PDF integrates to 1, *ie*:

$$\int_x f_X(x)\, dx = 1$$

So the result $E(3X^2 - 4X + 9) = 3E(X^2) - 4E(X) + 9$ also holds if X is a continuous random variable.

Example 16.13

Given that $E(Z) = 6$ and $E(Z^2) = 100$, calculate $E\left[(2 - 3Z)^2\right]$.

Solution

$$E\left[(2 - 3Z)^2\right] = E(4 - 12Z + 9Z^2) = 4 - 12E(Z) + 9E(Z^2) = 4 - (12 \times 6) + (9 \times 100) = 832 \qquad \blacklozenge\blacklozenge$$

16.6 *Variance and standard deviation*

In Chapter 15 we defined the variance and standard deviation of a random variable. Recall that:

$$\sigma^2 = \text{var}(X) = E[(X - \mu)^2] = E(X^2) - [E(X)]^2$$

and that the standard deviation of X is the square root of its variance. These definitions hold for *all* random variables. Earlier in this chapter we explained how to calculate the expected value of a function of a continuous random variable. In particular:

$$E[(X - \mu)^2] = \int_x (x - \mu)^2 f_X(x)\, dx$$

However, it is generally easier to calculate $\text{var}(X)$ using the $E(X^2) - [E(X)]^2$ approach rather than using the integral expression above.

Example 16.14

The random variable Y has PDF:

$$f_Y(y) = \frac{3}{y^4}, \quad y \geq 1$$

Calculate the standard deviation of Y.

Solution

From Example 16.11, we know that $E(Y) = 1.5$. In addition:

$$E(Y^2) = \int_y y^2 f_Y(y)dy = \int_1^\infty 3y^{-2}\,dy = \left[\frac{3}{-1}y^{-1}\right]_1^\infty = 0 - \left(-3 \times 1^{-1}\right) = 3$$

So:

$$\text{var}(Y) = 3 - 1.5^2 = 0.75$$

and the standard deviation of Y is:

$$\sqrt{0.75} = 0.86603$$

◆◆

 ## *Linear functions of a random variable*

In Chapter 15 we proved the result below.

Variance of a linear function of a random variable

For any random variable X and any constants a and b:

$$\text{var}(aX + b) = a^2\,\text{var}(X)$$

This result is derived in the same way for both discrete and continuous random variables. Taking the square root of both sides of the equation above, we see that the standard deviation of $aX + b$ is equal to a times the standard deviation of X.

16.7 *Skewness*

Recall that the skewness of the random variable X is given by:

$$skew(X) = E[(X - \mu)^3] = E(X^3) - 3\mu E(X^2) + 2\mu^3$$

and the coefficient of skewness of the random variable X is given by:

$$\frac{skew(X)}{[\text{var}(X)]^{3/2}}$$

These formulae hold for all random variables. However, in the case of a continuous random variable, it is usually easier to calculate the skewness using the $E(X^3) - 3\mu E(X^2) + 2\mu^3$ approach.

Recall that there are no restrictions on the value of $skew(X)$ – it could be positive, negative or zero. Likewise there are no restrictions on the coefficient of skewness. The skewness of a continuous random variable is:

- positive if the PDF has a tail to the right (*ie* the positive side)

- negative if the PDF has a tail to the left (*ie* the negative side)

- zero if the PDF is symmetric.

Example 16.15

The random variable X has PDF:

$$f_X(x) = 1 - \tfrac{1}{2}x \qquad\qquad 0 \le x \le 2$$

Calculate the coefficient of skewness of X.

Solution

We have:

$$\mu = \int_X x\, f_X(x)\,dx = \int_0^2 x\left(1 - \tfrac{1}{2}x\right)dx = \int_0^2 \left(x - \tfrac{1}{2}x^2\right)dx = \left[\tfrac{1}{2}x^2 - \tfrac{1}{6}x^3\right]_0^2 = (2 - \tfrac{4}{3}) - 0 = \tfrac{2}{3}$$

$$E(X^2) = \int_X x^2\, f_X(x)\,dx = \int_0^2 \left(x^2 - \tfrac{1}{2}x^3\right)dx = \left[\tfrac{1}{3}x^3 - \tfrac{1}{8}x^4\right]_0^2 = (\tfrac{8}{3} - 2) - 0 = \tfrac{2}{3}$$

and:

$$E(X^3) = \int_X x^3\, f_X(x)\,dx = \int_0^2 \left(x^3 - \tfrac{1}{2}x^4\right)dx = \left[\tfrac{1}{4}x^4 - \tfrac{1}{10}x^5\right]_0^2 = (4 - \tfrac{16}{5}) - 0 = \tfrac{4}{5}$$

So:

$$skew(X) = E(X^3) - 3\mu E(X^2) + 2\mu^3 = \tfrac{4}{5} - \left(3 \times \tfrac{2}{3} \times \tfrac{2}{3}\right) + \left(2 \times (\tfrac{2}{3})^3\right) = \tfrac{8}{135}$$

To calculate the coefficient of skewness, we also need the variance:

$$var(X) = E(X^2) - [E(X)]^2 = \tfrac{2}{3} - \left(\tfrac{2}{3}\right)^2 = \tfrac{2}{9}$$

Hence the coefficient of skewness is:

$$\frac{\tfrac{8}{135}}{(\tfrac{2}{9})^{1.5}} = 0.56569 \qquad\qquad\qquad\qquad\qquad\qquad ♦♦$$

In fact, this is the same distribution as the random variable W in Example 16.10 and we can see from the graph of the PDF that it has a tail on the right, and is therefore positively skewed.

16.8   Population moments

Recall that:

- the k th moment (or k th non-central moment) of the random variable X is $E(X^k)$

- the k th central moment of the random variable X is $E\left[(X-\mu)^k\right]$

- the k th moment of the random variable X about the point c is $E\left[(X-c)^k\right]$.

If X is a discrete random variable, we can calculate these moments using the formula for the expected value of a function of a discrete random variable, *ie*:

$$E[g(X)] = \sum_x g(x)P(X = x)$$

If X is a continuous random variable, we can use the formula:

$$E[g(X)] = \int_x g(x)f_X(x)\,dx$$

 ### Example 16.16

The random variable V has PDF:

$$f_V(v) = \tfrac{1}{2}v, \text{ for } 0 \le v \le 2$$

Calculate:

(i)   the fourth moment of V

(ii)   the second moment of V about the point 1.

Solution

(i)   The fourth moment of V is:

$$E(V^4) = \int_v v^4 f_V(v)\,dv = \int_0^2 \tfrac{1}{2}v^5\,dv = \left[\tfrac{1}{12}v^6\right]_0^2 = \tfrac{16}{3} - 0 = 5\tfrac{1}{3}$$

(ii)   The second moment of V about the point 1 is:

$$E[(V-1)^2] = \int_v (v-1)^2 f_V(v)\,dv = \int_0^2 (v-1)^2 \tfrac{1}{2}v\,dv$$

Multiplying out the expression inside the integral, we see that:

$$E[(V-1)^2] = \int_0^2 (v^2 - 2v + 1) \times \tfrac{1}{2}v\,dv = \tfrac{1}{2}\int_0^2 (v^3 - 2v^2 + v)\,dv$$

Integrating then gives:

$$E[(V-1)^2] = \tfrac{1}{2}\left[\tfrac{1}{4}v^4 - \tfrac{2}{3}v^3 + \tfrac{1}{2}v^2\right]_0^2 = \tfrac{1}{2}\left[\left(4 - \tfrac{16}{3} + 2\right) - 0\right] = \tfrac{1}{3} \qquad \blacklozenge\blacklozenge$$

Chapter 16 Practice Questions

◆❯ Probability density functions

Question 16.1   (IFoA Past Examination Question)

Consider the family of distributions with probability density functions:

$$f(x) = \frac{1}{2}\left[1 + kx(1 - x^2)\right], \qquad -1 < x < 1$$

where $-1 < k < 1$.

(i)   Verify that the area under the density curve is 1.

(ii)   Find the mean of the distributions in terms of k.

Question 16.2   (IFoA Past Examination Question)

The random variable X has probability density function:

$$f(x) = \begin{cases} k(1 - x^2) & -1 \le x \le 1 \\ 0 & \text{otherwise} \end{cases}$$

Evaluate the constant k and hence calculate $\operatorname{var}(X)$.

Question 16.3   (IFoA Past Examination Question)

The probability density function of a random variable X is given by:

$$f(x) = \begin{cases} kx(1 - ax^2) & 0 \le x \le 1 \\ 0 & \text{otherwise} \end{cases}$$

where k and a are positive constants.

(i)   Show that $a \le 1$, and determine the value of k in terms of a.

(ii)   For the case $a = 1$, determine the mean of X.

Question 16.4   (IFoA Past Examination Question)

In an investigation into the proportion (θ) of lapses in the first year of a certain type of policy, the uncertainty about θ is modelled by assuming that θ is a continuous random variable with PDF:

$$f(\theta) = 9(1 - \theta)^8 \quad 0 < \theta < 1$$

Using this model, calculate the probability that θ exceeds 0.2.

◆ *Cumulative distribution functions*

Question 16.5   (IFoA Past Examination Question)

A random variable X, which can be used in certain circumstances as a model for claim sizes, has cumulative distribution function:

$$F(x) = \begin{cases} 0 & \text{for } x \leq 0 \\ 1-\left(\dfrac{2}{2+x}\right)^3 & \text{for } x > 0 \end{cases}$$

Calculate the value of the conditional probability $P(X > 3 \mid X > 1)$.

◆ *Measures of location and spread*

Question 16.6

A continuous random variable Y has probability density function:

$$f_Y(y) = \tfrac{1}{4}(4-y), \quad \text{for } 1 \leq y \leq 3$$

Calculate the mean, median, mode and variance of Y.

Question 16.7   (IFoA Past Examination Question)

A plumber has a call-out charge of £20 and in addition he charges £30 per hour for all his jobs. In a particular week the mean and standard deviation of the lengths of his jobs are 3.5 hours and 0.5 hours respectively.

Calculate the mean and standard deviation of the invoice values for this particular week.

◆ *Skewness*

Question 16.8

The random variable W has PDF:

$$f_W(w) = \tfrac{2}{3}w, \quad \text{for } 1 \leq w \leq 2$$

Calculate the coefficient of skewness of W.

Solutions to Practice Questions

Chapter 1

1.1		1, 2, 3, 4
1.2		1, 3, 6, 8, 10
1.3	**(i)**	False
	(ii)	False
	(iii)	True
1.4		D
1.5		Σ and Π
1.6		T^2
1.7		(i) and (iii)
1.8	**(i)**	$£^{-1}$
	(ii)	$£, £^2, £^3$
	(iii)	$c = 1.5$
1.9		2.4%
1.10		1 March 2018

Chapter 2

2.1	0.068, 15.349, 10.000
2.2	2.900
2.3	14.4, 5.99, 0.0801
2.4	4,720
2.5	£1,500,000,000
2.6	0.021
2.7	0.295729
2.8	0.100
2.9	0.693
2.10	7.743
2.11	214.734
2.12	243.9
2.13	360
2.14	0.380
2.15	29.04
2.16	10.42
2.17	29.2
2.18	−153.614
2.19	2.351 or −0.851.

2.20	(i)	£541.75
	(ii)	£83,132
2.21		12.2%

Chapter 3

3.1		B
3.2	(i)	4.481689
	(ii)	−11.512925
3.3		B
3.4	(i)	Odd function
	(ii)	Neither
	(iii)	Even function
3.6		$\frac{1}{3}$
3.8		A
3.9	(i)	$-1.5 < x < 1$

3.9 (ii) $x < \dfrac{\mu - 2}{3}$ or $x > \dfrac{\mu + 2}{3}$

3.10		55
3.11		x^2 if $0 \le x < 3.87$ or 15 if $3.87 \le x \le 6$
3.12		0.443
3.13	(i)	250
	(ii)	450

Chapter 4

4.1 $2x^{3b} + 2x^{b+3}$

4.2 $2\log_a x - \log_a y$ or $\log_a\left(\dfrac{x^2}{y}\right)$

4.3 $\dfrac{7x^2 - 11x - 8}{(3x + 1)(x - 1)}$

4.4 $\dfrac{(x + 1)}{(x - 2)^2}$

4.5 $(2x + 1)(x - 3)$

Roots are −0.5 and 3

4.6 $x = 1.10102$ or $x = 10.89898$

4.7 $\alpha = \dfrac{11}{2}$, $\beta = \dfrac{11}{6}$

4.8 $\mu = 0.69438$, $\sigma = \pm 0.89914$

4.9 $\alpha = 4$, $\lambda = 27$

4.10 $-2 < x < 5$

4.11 $-3 < x < 4$

4.12   £676

4.13	70
4.14	6,648.5
4.15	295,425
4.16	D
4.17	420
4.18	3,584

4.19 $\frac{1}{4} - \frac{3}{4}x + \frac{27}{16}x^2 - \frac{27}{8}x^3 + \cdots$

Valid for $-\frac{2}{3} < x < \frac{2}{3}$

Chapter 5

5.1	(i)	15
	(ii)	60,000,000
5.2		21.8‰
5.3		$45
5.4		£467, 0.0321, 3.21%
5.5		0.1667
5.6		0.048685%
5.7		0.0123
5.8		13.9%
5.9		−0.778 , 2.333 or 3.4
5.10		0.88628

5.11 (i) $y_t = (-1 + 1.75t) \times 4^t$

(ii) $y_t = (A + Bt)2^t$

5.12 $y_t = 12.5(-2)^t - 7.5(-4)^t$

Chapter 6

6.1	5
6.2	$4x + 3$

6.3 (i) $\frac{8\sqrt[3]{x}}{3}$

(ii) $\frac{4}{x}$

(iii) $3e^x$

(iv) $-\frac{12}{5x^{8/5}}$

6.4	$5(4^t)\ln 4$
6.5	20
6.6	8,034
6.7	−772.17
6.8	$36r(3r^2 - 4)^5$

6.9   **(i)** μ

       (ii) $\dfrac{\alpha}{\lambda}$

6.10   **(i)** $90x\left(5x^2-7\right)^8$

       (ii) $-6xe^{-3x^2}$

       (iii) $\dfrac{2\left(12x^2-5\right)}{4x^3-5x+1}$

       (iv) $4\lambda xe^{2x^2}\exp\left\{\lambda(e^{2x^2}-1)\right\}$

       (v) $(x+1)(x+3)e^x$

       (vi) $\dfrac{e^{2x}\left(1-4x\ln x\right)+1}{x\left(e^{2x}+1\right)^3}$

       (vii) $8(2x+7)^3\left\{\dfrac{2x+7}{4x+3}+2\ln(4x+3)\right\}$

       (viii) $\left(x^2-2x+1\right)^4\left(-33x^2+76x-43\right)$

6.11   **(i)** $4\left(27x^2+18x+11\right)$

       (ii) $-\dfrac{x+4}{4(x+1)^{\frac{5}{2}}}$

       (iii) $-\dfrac{1}{x^2}+\dfrac{1}{x}$

       (iv) $64\left(1-8x+8x^2\right)e^{-4x}$

6.12 -1.1036

6.13 $2^x(\log 2)^3-6x^{-4}$

6.14   D

6.15 $\frac{16}{3}$

6.16   maximum at $\left(-\frac{1}{3},\frac{194}{27}\right)$ and minimum at $(1,6)$

6.17   maximum at $(-2.5,149.75)$ and minimum at $(3,-183)$

6.18 $\frac{4}{3}$

6.20 $\dfrac{1.0652}{\lambda^{1/4}}$

6.21   29 years and 10 months; a minimum

6.22 $ay+2bxy^2+3cx^2y^3$

6.23 $\dfrac{\partial f}{\partial x} = 12(3x + y)^3 - 4xy^2 - 21(4 - 7x)^2$

$\dfrac{\partial^2 f}{\partial x^2} = 108(3x + y)^2 - 4y^2 + 294(4 - 7x)$

$\dfrac{\partial f}{\partial y} = 4(3x + y)^3 - 4x^2 y$

$\dfrac{\partial^2 f}{\partial y^2} = 12(3x + y)^2 - 4x^2$

$\dfrac{\partial^2 f}{\partial x \partial y} = 36(3x + y)^2 - 8xy$

6.24 $16x^2 y^3 z^3$

6.25   saddle point at $(0,0)$, local minimum at $\left(\dfrac{4}{3}, 0\right)$

6.26   6.333

6.27 $a = 1,\ b = -1$

Chapter 7

7.1   D

7.2   26

7.3   (i) $2x^3 + 3x^2 + 6x + c$

(ii) $-\dfrac{2}{x} + \dfrac{12}{5} x^{\frac{5}{3}} + c$

(iii) $\tfrac{1}{4} e^{2x} + c$

(iv) $2 \times \dfrac{6^{\frac{1}{2}x}}{\ln 6} + c$

(v) $\ln\left|x^2 + 5x + 7\right| + c$

7.4   (i)   1.3506

(ii)   372.8010

(iii) $1 - e^{-3\lambda}$

(iv)   11.9895

7.5 $\dfrac{343}{24}$

7.6   (i) $-\dfrac{1}{2\left(x^2 + 3x + 4\right)^4} + c$

(ii) $\tfrac{7}{6} e^{3x^2 - 4} + c$

(iii) $\tfrac{1}{2} e^{x^2} + c$

7.7 $\ln\left|\dfrac{(x+1)^4}{(x-1)^3}\right| + c$

7.8   **(i)** $\dfrac{40}{3}$

              (ii) $\dfrac{4}{3}\ln\left(\dfrac{3e^3}{2e^3+1}\right)$

7.9   **(i)** $\frac{1}{56}(x+1)^7(7x-1)+c$

              (ii) $\frac{1}{4}x^2(2\ln x -1)+c$

7.10 $\ln\left(\dfrac{7}{6}\right)-\dfrac{5}{42}$

7.11   **(i)**   0.000145

              (ii) $\dfrac{1}{2}\ln\left(\dfrac{29}{9}\right)$

              (iii) $\ln 6 - \dfrac{1}{2}\ln 2$

              (iv) $\dfrac{1}{4}\left(e^2+1\right)$

7.12   B

7.13   0.05

7.14   0.25

Chapter 8

8.1 $\begin{pmatrix} 3 \\ -8 \\ -5 \end{pmatrix}$

8.2   **(i)** $\begin{pmatrix} -3 \\ 22 \\ -22 \end{pmatrix}$

              (ii) $p = 4$ and $q = -7$

8.3 $\mathbf{e} = \begin{pmatrix} -31 \\ -20 \end{pmatrix}$

8.4 $\sqrt{38}$

8.5 $\dfrac{1}{\sqrt{29}}(3\mathbf{i}-2\mathbf{j}+4\mathbf{k})$

8.6   **(i)** $137.7°$

              (ii) $105.2°$

8.7 $x = -4$

8.8 $x = 0,\ y = 2$

8.9   **(i)** $\dfrac{3}{\sqrt{913}}\mathbf{i}+\dfrac{2}{\sqrt{913}}\mathbf{j}-\dfrac{30}{\sqrt{913}}\mathbf{k}$

  (ii) $-\dfrac{3}{\sqrt{913}}\mathbf{i}-\dfrac{2}{\sqrt{913}}\mathbf{j}+\dfrac{30}{\sqrt{913}}\mathbf{k}$

8.10   **(i)** $\begin{pmatrix} 6 & 7 \\ 2 & 3 \end{pmatrix}$

  (ii) $\begin{pmatrix} 3 & 6 & 2 & 11 \\ 14 & -2 & -4 & 18 \end{pmatrix}$

  (iii) $\begin{pmatrix} 18 & 4 \\ -9 & -7 \\ -8 & -4 \\ 16 & -2 \end{pmatrix}$

8.11 $\begin{pmatrix} -8 & 14 \\ 18 & -32 \end{pmatrix}$

8.12 -1

8.13 $\mathbf{A}^2 = \begin{pmatrix} 15 & 42 & 21 \\ 9 & 33 & 27 \\ -9 & -25 & 10 \end{pmatrix}$ and $\mathbf{A}^3 = \begin{pmatrix} 78 & 273 & 210 \\ 48 & 174 & 207 \\ -69 & -208 & -35 \end{pmatrix}$

8.14   **(i)** -11
   (ii) 5

8.15   **(i)** $\begin{pmatrix} 0 & 0.25 \\ 1 & -0.5 \end{pmatrix}$

  (ii) $\begin{pmatrix} 1 & 1 \\ 2 & 3 \end{pmatrix}$

  (iii) $\begin{pmatrix} 4 & -1 \\ 12 & -4 \end{pmatrix}$

  (iv) $\begin{pmatrix} 16 & -5 \\ 44 & -14 \end{pmatrix}$

  (v) $\begin{pmatrix} 2 & 1 \\ 4 & 0 \end{pmatrix}$

Chapter 9

9.1   0.89   3.5   7.5   5.75   1.83
9.2   **(i)**   The frequency densities are:
          0.2   2   2.7   6.3   13.4   23.2   40.8
  (ii)   Male mortality is higher than female mortality at younger ages and lower than female mortality at older ages. The graphs are negatively skew for both sexes.
  (iii)   The frequencies are:
          5   7   15   38   78   131   226
9.3   The data set is roughly symmetric about the point 5.5.

9.4   **(i)**   The cumulative frequencies are:

                2   7   14   26   30

        (ii)(a)   18

        (ii)(b)   2¼ minutes

9.5   The frequency densities are:

                0.2   0.4   2   3.2   4.4   4   3   1.4

9.6   **(i)**   862   1,470   2,723   3,789   4,347   5,637

        (ii)   37%

9.7   Personnel has a higher average age, larger spread, and is negatively skewed. The data set for Marketing is fairly symmetric.

9.8   **(ii)**   The results for Group A are slightly lower on average than Group B. Group A is slightly more spread out than Group B. Both data sets are positively skewed. The differences between the data sets appear to be small, and there does not appear to be any significant difference between them.

Chapter 10

10.1   5

10.2 $£1,000 < c \le £1,500$

10.3   7.667

10.4   864

10.5   4.4

10.6   £23,800

10.7   £42,000

10.8   34 minutes

10.9   1.165

10.10   £26,087

10.11   **(i)**   2

         (ii)   2.5

10.12   172.27cm

10.13   £121

10.14   2

10.15   £218.33

10.16   £1,855.60   £1,735

Chapter 11

11.1   £208, £212, £220, £12

11.2   2

11.3   £98

11.4   min = £55 Q_1 = £136 Q_2 = £176 Q_3 = £253   max = £336

11.5   7.04

11.6   8.49 years

11.7   1.46

11.8   19.87 minutes

11.9   £34,667, £34,039

11.10   £26,087, £5,126

11.11   −2.92
                   The data set is negatively skewed.
11.12   7.8%

Chapter 12

12.1   (i) $\frac{4}{9}$

             (ii) $\frac{1}{3}$

12.2   (i)   0.2
             (ii)   0.5
12.3   (i)   0.85
             (ii)   0.6
12.5   10%
12.6   (i)   0.36
             (ii)   0.06
12.7   (i)   0.0429
             (ii)   0.179
             (iii)   0.0181
12.8   (i)   0.42
             (ii)   0.36
12.9   (i) $\frac{4}{15}$

             (ii) $\frac{1}{5}$

12.10 $\frac{14}{55} = 0.255$

12.11   6
12.12   0.46

Chapter 13

13.1   (i)   0.0975
             (ii)   0.7905
13.2   (i)   0.2
             (ii)   0.8
13.3   (i)   0.64
             (ii)   0.16
             (iii)   0.2
13.4   (i) $\frac{7}{15}$

             (ii) $\frac{3}{5}$

13.5   (i)   0.475
             (ii)   0.6857
13.6   0.5396
13.7   0.3538
13.8 $\frac{5}{9}$

13.9   0.6597

13.10 **(i)**   0.06075

   (ii)   0.7037

Chapter 14

14.1 **(i)**   36

   (ii) $\frac{1}{6}$

14.2 **(i)**   3,628,800

   (ii) $\frac{1}{3,628,800}$

14.3 **(i)**   90

   (ii) $\frac{1}{90}$

   (iii) $\frac{1}{10}$

14.4   364

14.5   10,500

14.6   0.14023

14.7   0.075852

14.8   0.21304

14.9 $\frac{7}{10}$

14.10   0.040091

14.11 $\frac{3}{5}$

Chapter 15

15.1 $-0.1 \le a \le 0.1$

15.2   D

15.3 **(i)**   0.18045

   (ii)   0.59399

15.4 **(ii)** $F_X(x) = \begin{cases} 0 & x < 2 \\ \frac{1}{2} & 2 \le x < 4 \\ \frac{5}{6} & 4 \le x < 6 \\ 1 & 6 \le x \end{cases}$

15.5   mean = 1.92   mode = 1   median = 2

15.6   £19,200

15.7   mean = 0.3   standard deviation = 0.5196

15.8   mean = £11,000   standard deviation = £19,209

15.9   mean = 51.52   variance = 1.37641

15.10 **(i)**   51

   (ii)   6

   (iii)   1

   (iv)   48

15.11   −0.83853

Chapter 16

16.1 (ii) $\frac{2}{15}k$

16.2 $k = \frac{3}{4}$ $\text{var}(X) = \frac{1}{5}$

16.3 (i) $k = \dfrac{4}{2-a}$

(ii) $\frac{8}{15}$

16.4 0.13422

16.5 0.216

16.6 mean $= \frac{11}{6}$ median $= 1.76$ mode $= 1$ variance $= \frac{11}{36}$

16.7 mean $= £125$ standard deviation $= £15$

16.8 -0.22931

Index